EFFECTIVE SMALL BUSINESS MANAGEMENT
An Entrpreneurial Approach

Sixth Edition

Norman M. Scarborough
Thomas W. Zimmerer

Prentice Hall, Upper Saddle River, New Jersey 07458

Acquisitions editor: *Stephanie K. Johnson*
Managing editor: *Melissa Steffens*
Assistant editor: *Hersch Doby*
Project editor: *Joseph F. Tomasso*
Manufacturer: *Technical Communication Services*

Printed in the United States of America

10   9   8   7   6   5   4

ISBN 0-13-017285-5

Prentice-Hall International (UK) Limited, *London*
Prentice-Hall of Australia Pty. Limited, *Sydney*
Prentice-Hall Canada Inc., *Toronto*
Prentice-Hall Hispanoamericana, S.A., *Mexico*
Prentice-Hall of India Private Limited, *New Delhi*
Prentice-Hall of Japan, Inc., *Tokyo*
Prentice-Hall (Singapore) Pte Ltd
Editora Prentice-Hall do Brasil, Ltda., *Rio de Janeiro*

TABLE OF CONTENTS

CHAPTER		PAGES
1	Entrepreneurs: The Driving Force Behind Small Business	1
2	Strategic Management and the Entrepreneur	17
3	Choosing a Form of Ownership	34
4	Franchising and the Entrepreneur	52
5	Buying an Existing Business	68
6	Creating the Market Plan	86
7	Creating the Financial Plan	103
8	Cash Flow Management	122
9	Crafting a Winning Business Plan	138
10	Pricing for Profit	154
11	Creative Use of Advertising and Promotion	171
12	International Opportunities for Small Business	188
13	Sources of Equality Financing	205
14	Sources of Debt Financing	221
15	Location, Layout and Physical Facilities	237
16	Purchasing, Quality Control and Vendor Analysis	258
17	Managing Inventory	274
18	Using Technology to Gain a Competitive Edge	290
19	Staffing and Leading a Growing Company	306
20	Managing Succession and Risk Management in the Family Business	323
21	Ethics, Social Responsibility and the Entrepreneur	339
22	Business Law and Government Regulation	356

Chapter 1 –
Entrepreneurs: The Driving Force Behind Small Businesses

Multiple Choice Questions

1. Research on entrepreneurship in the United States shows that:
   a) about 5 million Americans are involved in starting a new business each year.
   b) between 30–40% of all households have some involvement in a new or small business.
   c) the number of start-ups has been in decline since the 1980s.
   d) more men than women are starting new businesses as a result of corporate downsizing.

   Answer b   Page 2

2. The age of the entrepreneur is marked by a number of characteristics, such as:
   a) a surge in entrepreneurship in Eastern Europe and other countries.
   b) a significant improvement in the survivability of new business.
   c) new businesses starting when large companies sell off subsidiaries.
   d) a concentration of entrepreneurial activity in the United States.

   Answer a   Page 2

3. Which of the following corporate trends have contributed to the growth of entrepreneurship?
   a) The acquisition and merging of megacorporations
   b) The idea that "small is beautiful" in large companies, resulting in less hierarchy and layers of management
   c) The flood of venture capital being made available to small businesses
   d) The downturn in international markets forcing a focus on the domestic market

   Answer b   Page 3

4. Research on the career choices of college seniors shows that:
   a) prior to graduation 30% have started or are planning to start their own companies.
   b) 1 in 10 male college graduates goes directly into his/her own businesses.
   c) nearly half of all minority college seniors plan to start their own companies.
   d) nearly a third of women college seniors are interested in starting their own companies.

   Answer d   Page 3

5. Researchers who study entrepreneurs have discovered that:
   a) successful entrepreneurs start with an idea, resources, and a small management team.
   b) there is one key set of traits that mark a successful entrepreneur.
   c) entrepreneurs desire responsibility and are willing to take moderate risks.
   d) the most successful entrepreneurs are willing to take extreme risks and bet the farm in order to succeed.

   Answer c   Page 4

6. Research by KRC Research and Consulting shows that:
   a) nearly half of all entrepreneurs end up returning to corporate jobs.
   b) 55% of Americans want to be their own boss.
   c) while nearly half of all startups fail, 25% of the remaining half turn owners into millionaries.
   d) an equal number of women and minorities are starting their own businesses.

   Answer b   Page 4

7. In starting Pickled Trees, Dennis Gabrick's biggest problem was:
   a) raising funds to expand the business.
   b) finding good executive talent to help him grow the business.
   c) explaining his product.
   d) developing a method of distribution for his international clients.

Answer c   Page 5

8. Dirk wants to be in control. He's tired of taking orders from others and wants to feel a   sense of accountability for the outcome of his work. Dirk displays the entrepreneurial characteristic of:
   a) the desire for immediate feedback.
   b) a desire for responsibility.
   c) confidence in his ability to succeed.
   d) a high energy level.

Answer a   Page 6

9. Entrepreneurs seem to be characterized by:
   a) a desire for money.
   b) an inability to organize but strong conceptual skills.
   c) a desire to work alone because of weak management skills and a need for control.
   d) a high energy level.

Answer d   Page 6

10. According to the Hayberg Consulting Groups study, which of the following is a characteristic of a typical entrepreneur?
   a) A preference for high risk
   b) A desire for immediate profit
   c) A strong present orientation
   d) A high degree of commitment

Answer d   Page 7

11. Juan is able to work well in a constantly changing atmosphere and has little concern for what tomorrow will bring. Juan demonstrates which of the following characteristics of a typical entrepreneur?
   a) The willingness to take extreme risks
   b) A desire for immediate feedback
   c) A tolerance for ambiguity
   d) A future orientation

Answer c   Page 7

12. Entrepreneurs start businesses for a number of reasons including:
   a) an opportunity to make a difference.
   b) having to deal with less government regulation than as an executive of a large company.
   c) a much lower risk of career failure due to layoff or acquisition than working for a large company.
   d) the opportunity to get rich much quicker than if they work for a large company.

Answer a   Page 8

13. Surveys show that owners of small businesses believe that:
    a) they work harder on their own than if they worked for someone else.
    b) they earn less than if they worked for someone else.
    c) they are less satisfied than if they worked for someone else.
    d) venture capital is relatively easy to raise.

Answer a   Page 8

14. A significant benefit of starting your own company is:
    a) more leisure time because there is less of a need to punch a time clock.
    b) contributing to society and being recognized for your efforts.
    c) to be able to choose who you work with or don't work with.
    d) more job security than working for a large corporation.

Answer b   Page 9

15. Kyoto has started an interior decoration business. Everything about the business, from its name to the color schemes used in the corporate letterhead, is an expression of her personality. She sees this business as her greatest personal achievement. Kyoto is experiencing the opportunity _____ of small business ownership.
    a) to reap unlimited profits
    b) to contribute to society
    c) to make a difference
    d) to reach her full potential

Answer d   Page 9

16. Joanne is thinking about running her own business. What risks does she face?
    a) She could get stuck in a job she hates.
    b) Having to deal with more government regulation than if she were a manager in a larger company.
    c) Less status in society, as most people do not respect small business owners.
    d) The risk of losing all her money

Answer b   Page 10

17. Mary and Ted are discussing starting a new business and are asking themselves a series of questions like; "What is the worst that could happen if we fail?" "How likely is that to happen?" They are assessing which potential drawback of small business ownership?
    a) The long hours and hard work involved
    b) The risk of losing their entire investment
    c) The lower quality of life they'll experience
    d) The uncertainty of their income

Answer b   Page 10

18. Margaret Ellen Pender's wedding planning business arose out of:
    a) a business planning exercise she did for her MBA.
    b) her failure to succeed as a middle manager in a retail woman's clothing business.
    c) managing the wedding of a friend.
    d) a lifelong dream of working for herself, helping people plan beautiful weddings.

Answer c   Page 11

19. Potential drawbacks of small business ownership include:
    a) a relatively low guaranteed income.
    b) a significantly freer personal schedule but less personal income and assets with which to enjoy the more relaxed schedule.
    c) a high likelihood of a lower quality of life while starting and establishing the small business.
    d) relatively limited potential for further personal development.
Answer c   Page 12

20. More businesses are started by individuals between ____ than at any other age.
    a) 30–34
    b) 40–44
    c) 50–54
    d) 20–24
Answer a   Page 12

21. Which of the following trends is feeding the growth of entrepreneurial activity?
    a) A greater focus on professional advancement combined with the "flattening" of large corporations' management hierarchies
    b) The rapid growth of the need for low-technology products
    c) A favorable attitude toward entrepreneurs in American society
    d) Diminished wage increases in corporations and the desire for a better standard of living
Answer c   Page 13

22. The growth of entrepreneurship is being fed by:
    a) the return to a manufacturing-based economy.
    b) technological advancements.
    c) diminished opportunities in overseas markets for larger corporations.
    d) the vilifying of large corporations in society.
Answer b   Page 14

23. The service sector of American business accounts for ___ percent of all jobs and ___ percent of the gross domestic product.
    a) 50, 65
    b) 30, 45
    c) 70, 80
    d) 90, 85
Answer d   Page 14

24. Online commerce between 1997 and 2001 will:
    a) double.
    b) triple.
    c) increase five-fold.
    d) increase seven-fold.
Answer d   Page 15

25. The international market:
    a) has proven to be a tremendous opportunity for small business.
    b) is being dominated by large corporations based in Europe and Japan.
    c) is largely closed to small U.S.-based businesses because of the growth of international entrepreneurship.
    d) provides greater opportunities for women and minority entrepreneurs than U.S. domestic markets do.

Answer a   Page 15

26. About ___ percent of U.S. small businesses export, and they account for nearly ___ percent of all U.S. exports.
    a) 15, 50
    b) 6, 30
    c) 12, 35
    d) 4, 22

Answer b   Page 16

27. Women entrepreneurs:
    a) are starting businesses at twice the rate of men.
    b) own 28% of all U.S. businesses.
    c) will own about 50% of all U.S. businesses by the year 2000.
    d) find it much easier to find start-up capital than men.

Answer a   Page 16

28. Companies started by women differ from companies started by men in that:
    a) men's start-ups tend to be smaller and less well-financed than women's.
    b) women's companies tend to be labor-intensive businesses and therefore employ more people, even though they have smaller revenues.
    c) women's companies start smaller and more slowly.
    d) men tend to start their businesses with their own capital, women with others' capital.

Answer c   Page 16

29. Women entrepreneurs seem to face barriers that men generally don't, such as:
    a) a psychological inability to face risk.
    b) a lack of education and professional experience.
    c) their companies tend to be less stable, and therefore it is more difficult to hire talent to help them run their businesses.
    d) skepticism by the business world in general.

Answer d   Page 17

30. The biggest barrier women face when starting a business is:
    a) access to capital.
    b) social pressure to stay home and raise a family.
    c) skepticism by the business world.
    d) an inability to attract talent to help them grow the business.

Answer a   Page 17

31. Small companies in Russia:
    a) are largely started and managed by women.
    b) account for 12 percent of all goods produced.
    c) are largely in manufacturing, accounting for 50% of all production.
    d) account for nearly 37% of their gross domestic product.

Answer b   Page 18

32. Minorities cite which of the following as the primary barrier to their entreprenuership?
    a) skepticism
    b) access to capital
    c) discrimination
    d) social pressure

Answer c   Page 18

33. Most of today's immigrant entrepreneurs come into the U.S. with:
    a) significant educational and financial resources.
    b) few skills, little education, and no financial resources.
    c) few resources but lots of dedication and desire.
    d) little education but significant financial backing from their families in their home countries.

Answer c   Page 19

34. Part-time entrepreneurship has an additional advantage over starting up a company full-time in that:
    a) it is a much lower risk for the entrepreneur.
    b) it doesn't require having a business plan.
    c) the entrepreneur can change products and markets more easily.
    d) the entrepreneur doesn't need to know the industry as well.

Answer a   Page 19

35. Currently, nearly _____ entrepreneurs operate their businesses from home.
    a) 10.3 million
    b) 17.6 million
    c) 23.5 million
    d) 30.7 million

Answer d   Page 20

36. Home-based business for full-time, primary self-employed workers has grown _____ in the last 8 years.
    a) about 25%
    b) over 55%
    c) less than 20%
    d) at twice the rate of corporate job creation

Answer b   Page 20, Fig. 1.6

37. Which of the following is true about home-based businesses?
    a) Over 2/3 of all home-based businesses are owned by minority males.
    b) Home-based businesses tend to focus on blue-collar, lower skill industries.
    c) The growth of technology has significantly slowed the growth of home-based businesses.

  d) The average home-based business earns over $50,000 a year.

Answer d   Page 21

38. Family-owned businesses:
  a) comprise 70 percent of all U.S. businesses.
  b) generate less than 20 of the nation's Gross National Product (GNP).
  c) employ more than 50 million people.
  d) are largely headed by women.

Answer c   Page 21

39. Approximately ____ % of family businesses survive the transition of the leadership to the <u>second</u> generation.
  a) 90
  b) 57
  c) 30
  d) 10

Answer c   Page 21

40. When building a home-based business, it is important that the entrepreneur:
  a) keep friends and neighbors from disturbing him/her while working at home.
  b) not discuss it with the family to avoid raising expectations and creating undue pressure.
  c) have all business mail sent to the home address.
  d) not take the home office deduction to avoid IRS scrutiny of his/her tax return.

Answer a   Page 22

41. When running a home-based business:
  a) you generally don't need a separate business line, especially during the day.
  b) you still need to dress for work and for client meetings.
  c) zoning laws do not apply.
  d) you can have up to six employees in your home without informing the local zoning commission.

Answer b   Page 22

42. "Copreneurs" are marked by:
  a) a division of labor by expertise.
  b) their similarity to the traditional mom and pop operation.
  c) a decline in the number of businesses.
  d) a greater success at raising venture capital than sole proprietorship-type businesses.

Answer a   Page 23

43. Successful copreneurs are marked by which of the following characteristics?
  a) distinct and different business and life goals
  b) a clear delineation of who is the superior partner and who is the subordinate partner
  c) a blending of responsibilities, roles, and authority
  d) mutual respect for each other's talents

Answer d   Page 23

44. The number of corporate castoffs who have become entrepreneurs in the early 1990s:
  a) has declined 50% over the 1980s.

> b) has doubled since 1994.
> c) has only risen a total of 25% in the last decade.
> d) hit the 2 million mark in 1996.

Answer b   Page 24

45. Approximately ____ or ___ of businesses in the United States are considered small today.
    a) 10.5 million, 37%
    b) 22.4 million, 98%
    c) 2.5 million, 9.8%
    d) 15 million, 46%

Answer b   Page 24

46. Bill and Sally have tired of the corporate rat race. They leave their investment banking positions in New York, move to Colorado and start a business raising Mohair sheep. This couple is an example of the entrepreneurial phenomenon of:
    a) corporate dropouts.
    b) corporate downsizing.
    c) corporate raiders.
    d) corporate castoffs.

Answer d   Page 24

47. Small businesses thrive in every industry, but the majority of them are in the:
    a) general construction industry.
    b) retail businesses.
    c) mining and manufacturing.
    d) service industries.

Answer d   Page 25

48. More businesses fail because of _____ than for any other reason.
    a) incompetent management
    b) theft by employees
    c) insufficient capital
    d) poor choice of location

Answer a   Page 25

49. The technology that has spurred the growth of entrepreneurship by young entrepreneurs is:
    a) cellular phones.
    b) the fax.
    c) the world wide web.
    d) direct mail databases.

Answer c   Page 26

50. A recent study of entrepreneurs between age 18 and 25 showed that:
    a) they tend to fail at twice the rate of older entrepreneurs because they take greater risks.
    b) they have more difficulty getting financial backing due to their age.
    c) women entrepreneurs outnumber men entrepreneurs 3 to 1 in this age bracket.
    d) they start an average of 2.3 companies.

Answer d   Page 26

51. Tom was a financial consultant who liked to work with his hands, especially in making furniture. He quit his rat race financial job to start a small custom furniture business. After struggling for several years he closed it and went back to financial services. Tom discovered that there was a big difference between making furniture for himself and running a customer furniture manufacturing business. Tom's business failed because of:
    a) uncontrolled growth.
    b) poor financial control.
    c) his lack of experience.
    d) an inability to access start-up capital.

Answer c   Page 27

52. Entrepreneurial businesses fall victim to this circumstance because they think it only benefits large companies. Without it, a firm has no sustainable basis for survival.
    a) A lack of strategic planning
    b) Poor financial controls
    c) Uncontrolled growth
    d) Lack of inventory control

Answer a   Page 27

53. Startup companies will tend to outgrow their capital base each time their sales increase:
    a) 100%.
    b) 40–50%.
    c) 70–80%.
    d) 25–40%.

Answer b   Page 28

54. The location of the business is especially important for what type of start-up businesses?
    a) manufacturing.
    b) service.
    c) computer-based service.
    d) retail.

Answer d   Page 29

55. A key characteristic of a successful entrepreneur is:
    a) never having failed.
    b) expert technical knowledge of the product.
    c) learning to fail intelligently.
    d) earning at least a 25% return for investors.

Answer c   Page 30

56. John is running a new company. Currently his business is in rapid growth, his focus is on sales, he sees all kinds of opportunities and is trying to capture them all. John is most likely at what stage in the corporate life cycle?
    a) Stage 1 - courtship.
    b) Stage 3 - Go-Go.

    c) Stage 4 - Adolescence.
    d) Stage 5 - Prime.
Answer b   Page 31

57. In the corporate life cycle, the stage where the company has its first brush with death, where the focus is on what went wrong and how do we fix it, is:
    a) Stage 9 - bureaucracy.
    b) Stage 8 - recrimination.
    c) Stage 7 - aristocracy.
    d) Stage 6 - stability.
Answer b   Page 31

58. The key ingredient-the crucial element-to avoiding the failure of a new business is:
    a) the business plan.
    b) knowing the business.
    c) technical expertise regarding the product.
    d) differentiating the business and product from the competition.
Answer a   Page 32

59. The key to effective financial management in a start-up is:
    a) excellent controls.
    b) the use of ABC accounting processes.
    c) having sufficient start-up capital.
    d) having an adequate inventory on hand.
Answer c   Page 32

60. Which of the following is true about avoiding business failure?
    a) You must understand financial statements.
    b) You need to learn how to manage others.
    c) You must differentiate your product from the competition.
    d) You must do all of these.
Answer d   Page 33

True or False Questions

61. There were more new incorporations in the United States in 1996 than in any previous year.
Answer T   Page 2, Figure 1.1

62. There has been a significant change in the U.S. economic structure, one that favors small business.
Answer T   Page 3

63. Entrepreneurs are people who grow existing businesses by careful management of existing resources.
Answer F   Page 4

64. Entrepreneurs are noted for their ability to bounce back after a business failure.
Answer T   Page 5

65. The start-ups of Pickled Trees, A Song of Love, and Fluke Farms are examples of the entrepreneurial characteristics of persistence and the ability to recover from failure.

Answer F   Page 5

66. Typically, entrepreneurs are very good conceptually but are <u>not</u> able to organize and manage people and jobs.

Answer F   Page 6

67. To many entrepreneurs, the opportunity for future earnings is more important than the immediate earning potential of the business.

Answer F   Page 7

68. One hallmark of true entrepreneurs is their ability to adapt to the changing demands of their customers and businesses.

Answer T   Page 7

69. Research has isolated a set of characteristics that can predict who will succeed as an entrepreneur.

Answer F   Page 8

70. Studies indicate that the opportunity to make a difference is a significant benefit in the eyes of most entrepreneurs.

Answer T   Page 8

71. The opportunity to reap unlimited profits is the primary motivator for most entrepreneurs.

Answer F   Page 9

72. While entrepreneurs have high professional ethics, the general distrust of business people tends to carry over to them as well.

Answer F   Page 9

73. It is common for entrepreneurs to feel their work isn't really work because they enjoy it so much.

Answer T   Page 10

74. Entrepreneurs usually experience greater income stability running their own businesses than they did in their corporate careers.

Answer F   Page 10

75. Margaret Ellen Pender's start-up of the wedding planning business demonstrates the importance of the entrepreneur's ability to see an opportunity and to organize a work process.

Answer T   Page 11

76. Many entrepreneurs discover they work fewer hours (less than 45 hours a week) as new business owners than they did as middle managers in large corporations.

Answer F   Page 12

77. It is common to experience a lower quality of life during a business start-up than after the business is established.

Answer T   Page 12

78. Most entrepreneurs start their businesses when they are in their late 30s or early 40s.

Answer T   Page 12, Figure 1.3

79. In today's economy, entrepreneurs are seen as heroes.
Answer T   Page 13

80. Over 1,500 colleges and universities offer courses on entrepreneurship.
Answer T   Page 13

81. With all the talk about a service economy, only 45% of all jobs are actually in services in the United States
Answer F   Page 14

82. Advances in technology available to entrepreneurs permit them to move into manufacturing and compete directly with Fortune 500 companies.
Answer F   Page 14

83. For the most part, small businesses are unable to compete internationally.
Answer F   Page 15

84. Companies started by women tend to grow more rapidly than those started by men.
Answer T   Page 16

85. Women entrepreneurs take as many and as large risks as men do in starting businesses.
Answer F   Page 16

86. The biggest barrier facing women entrepreneurs is the skepticism of the business community that they can make their businesses succeed.
Answer F   Page 17

87. Since 1977, the number of businesses owned and run by women has doubled.
Answer F   Page 17, Figure 1.5

88. Women entrepreneurs have a higher success/survival rate than do men.
Answer T   Page 17

89. In Russia, few start-up companies fail due to the intense drive of Russian entrepreneurs and the wide open market opportunities that exist in Russia today.
Answer F   Page 18

90. Minorities own approximately 12.7% of all U.S. small businesses.
Answer F   Page 18

91. African-Americans, while continuing to grow as entrepreneurs, are starting businesses at a significantly slower rate than either women or traditional male entrepreneurs.
Answer F   Page 18

92. Hispanic-owned businesses grew faster than any other minority and are expanding at almost three times the rate of other businesses.
Answer T   Page 18

93. Immigrant entrepreneurs tend to arrive in the United States with less education and experience but more drive and access to capital through their "ethnic" connections.

Answer F   Page 19

94. Although it is a lower risk way to start, very few entrepreneurs start part-time. Most prefer to cut all ties and "dive" into their business full-time, right from the start.
Answer F   Page 19

95. Home-based businesses generate nearly $383 billion in revenues every year and create over 8,000 jobs a day.
Answer T   Page 20

96. Home-based businesses are more likely to involve white-collar work than blue-collar work.
Answer T   Page 21

97. Studies show that <u>unlike</u> most small business start-ups, home-based businesses have a very high success rate with about 85% still in business after 3 years.
Answer T   Page 21

98. Despite their popularity, family-owned businesses are actually a small portion of the economy and contribute less than 25% of the GNP to the economy of the United States.
Answer F   Page 21

99. One-third of the Fortune 500 companies are family businesses.
Answer T   Page 21

100. Family-owned businesses have a significant advantage over other forms of small business, in that they have a very high survival rate when transitioning between generations of leadership.
Answer F   Page 21

101. When an entrepreneur develops a relationship with a manager in a large established company in order to draw on the corporate manager's experience , it is called "Copreneurship."
Answer F   Page 21

102. Research shows that for "Copreneurship" to work, responsibilities must be divided by gender.
Answer F   Page 23

103. One important characteristic of successful "copreneurs" is their ability to separate their business life from their personal life, so that one doesn't consume the other.
Answer T   Page 23

104. "Corporate dropouts" are middle managers who are laid off from large corporations and decide to start their own businesses rather than return to a corporate job.
Answer F   Page 24

105. The trend in corporate downsizing and the resulting trust gap have spawned both the "corporate castoff" and the "corporate dropout."
Answer T   Page 24

106. Approximately 4% of all small companies create about 70% of all the new jobs in the 1990s.
Answer T   Page 25

107. Small businesses create more jobs than either medium or large businesses.
Answer T   Page 25

108. Small businesses produce over 50% of the country's Gross National Product (GNP) on less than half of all business sales.
Answer T   Page 25

109. Studies by the SBA show that 63% of small businesses fail with six years.
Answer T   Page 25

110. The primary cause of small business failures is lack of capital.
Answer F   Page 25

111. Research shows that companies started by entrepreneurs under the age of 25 tend to grow rapidly and then fail, at a rate of 4 out of 5.
Answer F   Page 26

112. The growth of the service industry and especially fast-food has opened the door for younger entrepreneurs to get started due to the low start-up costs.
Answer F   Page 26

113. Lack of experience is the number one cause of small business failures.
Answer F   Page 27

114. The two common pitfalls of poor financial control are undercapitalization and lax customer credit policies.
Answer T   Page 27

115. When a small company's sales increase by 40-50%, the company will have outgrown its current capital base.
Answer T   Page 28

116. The choice of location has two important features: adequate parking and ease of access by customers.
Answer F   Page 29

117. Most successful entrepreneurs accept failure as part of what they do, and they use it to learn for the "next time."
Answer T   Page 30

118. It is in Stage 5: The Prime, where the entrepreneur needs to refocus the vision. The company is balanced between control and flexibility, and it is disciplined yet still innovating.
Answer T   Page 31, Table 1.3

119. Entrepreneurs tend to create thorough, well thought out business plans prior to implementing new businesses.
Answer F   Page 32

120. In start-ups, it is often safest to be a "me-too" business, follow the leaders in the market until sufficient cash flow develops to permit R & D into new and innovative products.
Answer F   Page 33

Essay Questions

121. Briefly outline the key characteristics of a typical entrepreneur.
Pages 4–7

122. Identify and explain the advantages and the disadvantages of small business ownership.
Pages 8–13

123. Explain at least five of the factors that are feeding the entrepreneurial boom in the United States and abroad.
Pages 13–15

124. Entrepreneurial activity is culturally diverse. Discuss the role of women, minorities, and immigrant entrepreneurs in this activity, profiling their characteristics, their impact, and the specific barriers they need to overcome in their small business start-ups.
Pages 16–19

125. What role do corporate cast-offs and corporate dropouts play in the growth of entrepreneurship in the United States?
Pages 23–24

126. What are the primary causes of small business failure in the United States?
Pages 25–30

127. Outline the ten stages of the corporate life cycle, explaining the primary attributes of each.
Page 31, Table 3.1

128. What can an entrepreneur do to avoid the failure of his/her company? Discuss at least six actions they can take.
Pages 32–33

Mini-Case

Case 1: Bill's Dilemma

Bill Hudson was a real craftsman when it came to being a machinist. Bill had learned almost all that he knew from Hugo Huffman, his first and only employer. Bill Hudson was married and had three young children. He was 33 years old and had worked for Hugo ever since he finished his tour in the army. In 12 years, Bill had polished his skills under the watchful and critical eye of Hugo Huffman. Hugo was quick to recognize Bill's talent for the trade. Bill had a positive attitude about learning and displayed a drive for perfection that Hugo admired.

Hugo's Machine Shop was a successful small business. Its success was based mostly on the reputation for quality that had been established over its 42 years in operation. Hugo had come to this country with his new wife, Hilda, when he was in his late twenties. Now the business was a success, but Hugo remembered the early years when he and Hilda had to struggle. Hugo wanted the business to continue to produce the highest quality craftsman products possible. On a Friday evening, he called Bill into his office at closing time, poured him a cup of half-day-old coffee, and began to talk with him about the future.

"Bill, Hilda and I are getting old and I want to retire. It's been 42 years of fun but these old hands need a rest. In short, Hilda and I would like you to buy the business. We both feel that your heart is in this craft and that you would always retain the quality that we have stood for." Bill was taken aback by the offer. He, of course, knew Hugo was getting older, but had no idea Hugo would retire. Bill and his wife, Anna, had only $4,200 in the bank. Most of Bill's salary went for the normal costs of rearing three children. Hugo knew Bill did not have the money to buy the business in cash, but he was willing to take a portion of the profits for the next 15 years and a modest initial investment from Bill.

Bill had, for the past four years, made most of the technical decisions in the shop. Bill knew the customers and was well respected by the employees. He had never been involved in the business side of the operation. He was a high school graduate but had never taken business-oriented courses. Bill was told by Hugo that even after deducting the percentage of the profits he would owe under the sales agreement, he would be able to almost double his annual earnings. Bill would have to take on all the business functions himself because Anna had no business training either.

Questions

1. Which entrepreneurial/small business owner characteristics does Bill have that may be important to his success? Which characteristics could lead to his failure?

2. What steps should Bill take to avoid the pitfalls common to a small business?

3. If you were Hugo, would you sell Bill the business under the terms discussed in the case?

Chapter 2 –
Strategic Management and the Entrepreneur

Multiple Choice Questions

1. The strategic management process:
   a) is especially difficult for the small business because of its limited resources.
   b) divides mass markets into smaller, less homogeneous units.
   c) provides the small business owner with the tools for managing the uncontrollable elements in the external business environment.
   d) helps a small business develop the game plan that guides it in creating its mission, vision, goals, and objectives.

   Answer d   Page 40

2. The primary output of the strategic management process should be:
   a) a matching of its strengths and weaknesses to the opportunities and threats in the environment.
   b) an enticement to outside investors and lenders to put money into the business.
   c) a complete explanation of the company's product or service.
   d) a description of the company's competitive situation.

   Answer a   Page 40

3. A small business's "aggregation of factors that sets it apart from its competitors" is its:
   a) strategic plan.
   b) competitive advantage.
   c) vision.
   d) competitive strategy.

   Answer b   Page 40

4. The strategic planning process for small businesses is:
   a) market-focused.
   b) the same as it is for a large company.
   c) generally done by top management with little or no participation by employees.
   d) product-focused and similar to that for large companies.

   Answer a   Page 41

5. How is the strategic planning process for small companies different from that for large companies?
   a) The planning horizon should cover at least five years into the future.
   b) The process should begin with setting objectives and conclude with competitive analysis.
   c) The process should be informal and not overly structured—"a shirtsleeve approach."
   d) It should be conducted by top management and provided to lower management.

   Answer c   Page 41

6. _____ focuses everyone's attention and efforts on the same target market. It is an expression of what the owner believes in.
   a) The mission statement
   b) The company vision
   c) The strategic plan
   d) The operational plan

   Answer b   Page 42

7. Which of the following best expresses the relationship of a company vision to its mission?
   a) The company vision comes from the company mission.
   b) The mission statement is the written expression of the company vision.
   c) The company mission statement is the verbal expression of the written vision.
   d) There is no relationship between the two.

Answer b   Page 42

8. Which of the following is true about successful entrepreneurs and their vision?
   a) It is created independently of their market or their customers.
   b) It includes their understanding of the competition and their key market segments.
   c) They are able to communicate it and their enthusiasm for it to all those around them.
   d) They create it in cooperation with their employees.

Answer c   Page 42

9. Answering the question "What business am I in?" defines the company's:
   a) mission.
   b) assessment of its own strengths and weaknesses.
   c) external opportunities and threats.
   d) goals and objectives.

Answer a   Page 42

10. A mission statement should answer which of the following questions?
    a) What are the needs and wants of the target customers?
    b) How will we finance our growth and expansion?
    c) Who are our competitors?
    d) How much money will we make?

Answer a   Page 42

11. The most basic and essential communication tool that comes out of the strategic planning process is:
    a) the company's vision.
    b) the mission statement.
    c) the individual action plans used to implement it.
    d) an analysis of the competition.

Answer b   Page 43

12. Once the vision and mission are established, the entrepreneur needs to:
    a) select the target market.
    b) conduct market research.
    c) choose a competitive strategy.
    d) define the firm's core competencies.

Answer d   Page 43

13. The key to the success of the strategic plan is:
    a) a thorough competitive analysis.
    b) building the core competencies and focusing on them.
    c) an accurate SWOT analysis.
    d) properly segmenting the target market for maximum effectiveness.

Answer b   Page 44

14. When identifying a small business's core competencies, the entrepreneur should seek to answer the question:
    a) why do our target customers buy or use our product/service?
    b) what return on investment do we need to generate?
    c) what are the threats to our business in the external environment?
    d) how do we want to do business?

Answer d   Page 45

15. _____ involves carving the mass market up into smaller, more homogeneous units and then attacking each segment with a specific marketing strategy designed to appeal to its members.
    a) Competitive analysis
    b) Market segmentation
    c) Product differentiation
    d) Strategic management

Answer b   Page 46

16. A company's efforts to influence customers' perceptions regarding its image and that of its products by differentiating them from the competition is called:
    a) visioning.
    b) segmenting.
    c) positioning.
    d) marketing.

Answer c   Page 46

17. _____ are positive internal factors that contribute towards accomplishing the company's objectives.
    a) Strengths
    b) Weaknesses
    c) Opportunities
    d) Threats

Answer a   Page 47

18. _____ are negative internal factors that inhibit the accomplishment of a firm's objectives.
    a) Strengths
    b) Weaknesses
    c) Opportunities
    d) Threats

Answer b   Page 47

19. When the small business owner assesses her company's strengths and weaknesses, she is dealing with the _____ business environment.
    a) macro
    b) external
    c) competitive
    d) internal

Answer d   Page 47

20. _____ are negative external forces that inhibit the firm's ability to achieve its objectives.
    a) Strengths
    b) Weaknesses
    c) Opportunities
    d) Threats

Answer d   Page 48

21. Corey notices a "backlash" against health food among people who eat out. He decides to open a restaurant that stresses "good home cooking," heavy with gravies, breads, oils, etc. Cory has identified and is trying to capitalize on a/an _____ in the market environment.
    a) strength
    b) weakness
    c) threat
    d) opportunity

Answer d   Page 48

22. Every business is characterized by a set of controllable variables called _____ that determines the relative success (or lack of it) of market participants:
    a) distinctive competencies
    b) key success factors
    c) opportunities and threats
    d) competitive edge

Answer b   Page 48

23. These are products of the interaction of various forces, trends, and events that are outside the control of the small business.
    a) distinctive competencies
    b) key success factors
    c) opportunities and threats
    d) strengths and weaknesses

Answer c   Page 48

24. A small firm's ability to identify and manipulate the _____ in its business determines its ability to compete effectively.
    a) key success factors
    b) corporate vision and mission
    c) opportunities and threats
    d) market environment

Answer a   Page 48

25. _____ are relationships between a controllable variable—plant size, quality, packaging— and a critical factor influencing the firm's ability to compete in the marketplace.
    a) Core competencies
    b) The competitive advantages
    c) Key success factors
    d) Goals and objectives

Answer c   Page 48

26. A small business owner would conduct a competitive analysis in order to:
    a) influence customers' perceptions of the company and products' image.
    b) avoid surprises from existing competitors and to identify potential new competitors.
    c) divide the market into smaller, homogeneous units.
    d) scan the environment for weaknesses and strengths on which to capitalize.

Answer b   Page 50

27. Joan is seeking to answer a series of questions such as: How do competitor's cost structures compare to ours, what new competitors are entering the industry, what do our customers say about competitors, etc. By asking these questions, Joan is:
    a) conducting a SWOT analysis.
    b) identifying her company's key success factors.
    c) formulating strategic options for her company.
    d) performing a competitive analysis.

Answer d   Page 50

28. Purchasing rival companies' products, taking them apart, and analyzing them is:
    a) industrial espionage.
    b) illegal due to federal regulation.
    c) benchmarking.
    d) cataloguing.

Answer c   Page 51

29. The information-gathering process in competitive analysis:
    a) is an expensive process which only established small companies can afford.
    b) can be relatively inexpensive and easy for the small business owner to conduct.
    c) is closely regulated by various federal laws.
    d) is a process that requires expert help but is relatively inexpensive.

Answer b   Page 51

30. A competitive profile matrix:
    a) identifies a firm's core competencies.
    b) permits the small business owner to divide a mass market into smaller, more manageable segments.
    c) compares the firm's and its competitors' key success factors.
    d) creates a road map of action for the entrepreneur in order to fulfill his/her company's mission, goals, and objectives.

Answer c   Page 51

31. When Josh and Michael Bracken operated their Nursery and Garden Center, they decided the key to survival against the mega-nursery centers was:
    a) their ability to compete on the basis of price.
    b) to differentiate themselves by offering a local tailored selection of products.
    c) in their moving to a more accessible location.
    d) to merge with another local nursery and compete based on size.

Answer b   Page 52

32. What steps could a small business owner take to track potential competitive strategic actions?
    a) Price his/her product much lower than the competitors.
    b) Develop and communicate to employees a clear and powerful vision and mission statement.
    c) Create appropriate goals and objectives.
    d) Search for unexplored opportunities that are compatible with his/her company's strength.

Answer d   Page 53

33. _____ are the broad, long-range attributes the small business seeks to accomplish; _____ are the specific, measurable milestones the company wants to achieve.
    a) Goals; objectives
    b) Goals; strategies
    c) Objectives; goals
    d) Strategies; goals

Answer a   Page 53

34. _____ are specific measurable targets to be accomplished in a defined time period.
    a) Core competencies
    b) Objectives
    c) Goals
    d) Key success factors

Answer b   Page 53

35. The key to successful goal setting is:
    a) to set goals based on what you can see and expect to achieve.
    b) keep goals conceptual, in your head; once written, they tie you down.
    c) to take one step at a time toward the goal.
    d) to not review your progress until the end, to avoid being sidetracked.

Answer c   Page 54

36. The small firm's "game plan" is its:
    a) objectives.
    b) goals.
    c) competitive edge.
    d) strategy.

Answer d   Page 55

37. The focal point of a firm's strategy is:
    a) the firm's goals and objectives.
    b) the firm's key success factors.
    c) the customer.
    d) the firm's strengths and weaknesses.

Answer b   Page 55

38. If Groupware Inc. is in a high innovation, high risk environment, their most effective strategy is to:
    a) be the first mover in the market.
    b) minimize risk by franchising their business.

    c) defend their present position and accept limited growth.
    d) consider a joint venture.
Answer a   Page 56

39. Malcolm is starting a business in a highly innovative field and the risks are high. His best choice of strategy would be to:
    a) move quickly, be the first mover in the market.
    b) minimize risk by franchising the business.
    c) defend the present position and accept limited growth.
    d) consider a joint venture.
Answer b   Page 56

40. The most common environment for most small businesses is:
    a) high innovation, low risk.
    b) high innovation, high risk.
    c) low innovation, high risk.
    d) low innovation, low risk.
Answer c   Page 57

41. Small firms pursuing a cost leadership strategy have an advantage in reaching customers whose primary purchase criterion is:
    a) quality.
    b) constant innovation.
    c) price.
    d) customer service.
Answer c   Page 58

42. Cost leadership has several inherent dangers such as:
    a) choosing to distinguish the product but that does not boost its performance.
    b) an overfocus on the physical characteristics of the product.
    c) the identified niche is not large enough to be profitable.
    d) an overfocus on costs to the elimination of other strategies.
Answer d   Page 59

43. A small company following a _____ strategy seeks to build customer loyalty by positioning its goods and services in a unique fashion.
    a) differentiation
    b) cost leadership
    c) focus
    d) niche
Answer a   Page 59

44. A differentiation strategy:
    a) seeks to find and defend an identifiable market niche.
    b) is built on a company's distinctive competence.
    c) must create the perception of value in the customer's eyes through the lowest possible price.
    d) focuses solely on making the physical characteristics of the product as unique as possible.
Answer d   Page 59

45. Tyson Foods' practice of adding value to its chicken products by deboning, skinning, bite-sizing, or pre-cooking them is an example of a:
    a) cost leadership strategy.
    b) differentiation strategy.
    c) focus strategy.
    d) concentration strategy.

Answer b   Page 59

46. Which of the following is a danger in choosing a differentiation strategy?
    a) Charging a price so high that the company prices itself out of the market
    b) Choosing a basis for price leadership that is essentially unimportant to the customer
    c) Choosing a market that is not large enough to be profitable
    d) An overfocus on overhead costs

Answer a   Page 59

47. Rather than attempting to serve the total market, the small firm pursuing a _____ strategy specializes in serving a specific target segment.
    a) cost leadership
    b) differentiation
    c) focus
    d) head-to-head

Answer c   Page 60

48. A ___ strategy tends to be ideally suited to the small business.
    a) differentiation
    b) focus
    c) cost leadership
    d) product quality

Answer b   Page 60

49. The principle behind a _____ strategy is to select one or more market segments, identify customers' special needs, and approach them with a good or service designed to excel in meeting these needs.
    a) cost-leadership
    b) differentiation
    c) focus
    d) concentration

Answer c   Page 60

50. An effective strategic plan does which of the following?
    a) Identifies a complete set of success factors—financial, operating, and marketing, that yield a competitive advantage for the company
    b) Focuses on one generic strategy to the exclusion of all other strategies
    c) Always seeks a high profile in the specific markets chosen.
    d) Is always cost based

Answer a   Page 61

51. The most successful strategic plans make the _____ focal.
    a) competitive analysis
    b) customer
    c) product
    d) control process
Answer b   Page 61

52. Small businesses tend to have which of the following competitive advantage(s) due to their size?
    a) Lower operating and manufacturing costs
    b) Quick response to customer needs
    c) The ability to gain significant market share due to a concentration of resources
    d) A depth of management expertise
Answer b   Page 61

53. Small bookstores have a giant killer of a competitive advantage in their:
    a) lower costs.
    b) better locations.
    c) customer service.
    d) large selection.
Answer c   Page 62

54. The operational strategies that a small company uses:
    a) are developed early in the strategic planning process.
    b) are always focused on one generic strategy.
    c) should be indirect and nonaggressive in the chosen markets.
    d) should be directly related to its competitive advantages in the markets it serves.
Answer d   Page 63

55. When translating strategic plans into action plans, the small business owner should:
    a) not delegate authority or responsibility at this point.
    b) not assign priorities to the action plans, but manage the process from the conceptual level.
    c) not adjust or change the plan but commit to implementing as it stands.
    d) remember that no strategic plan is complete until it's put into action.
Answer d   Page 63

56. A small business owner needs to remember that when it comes to employee involvement in the strategic planning process:
    a) involvement is a prerequisite for the achievement of total employee commitment.
    b) his/her employees look to him/her for leadership and do not want to be involved.
    c) the delegation of authority is not as important as communicating a clear vision.
    d) employees do not need to be involved in the strategic process but do need to be involved in the operational process.
Answer a   Page 63

57. The final step of the strategic planning process is:
   a) establishing accurate controls.
   b) translating the strategic plan into operational plans.
   c) evaluating the competitive environment.
   d) choosing a marketing strategy to pursue.
Answer a   Page 63

58. The ____ is a set of measures unique to the company that gives managers a quick and comprehensive view of how the business is doing and includes both financial and operational factors.
   a) core competencies
   b) key success factors
   c) balanced scorecard
   d) action plan
Answer c   Page 63

59. In the creation of the balanced scorecard, the entrepreneur needs to:
   a) assess competitor's strengths and weaknesses and set measures against them.
   b) establish goals for each critical factor of company performance.
   c) think about the resource requirements necessary to implement the action plans.
   d) do all of these.
Answer b   Page 64

60. It is important for the small business owner to remember that the strategic planning process is:
   a) an ongoing process that must be repeated.
   b) a top management process completed only once every two years.
   c) a process which involves all the employees once every five years.
   d) one that should produce a detailed, elaborate plan for running the business over the next 3–5 years.
Answer a   Page 65

True or False Questions
61. While strategic planning is important for large businesses, it is not essential to   managing a small company successfully.
Answer F   Page 39

62. The idea behind strategic planning is to give the business owner a way to match his/her company's strengths and weaknesses to the opportunities and threats in the business environment.
Answer T   Page 40

63. Large companies have a natural advantage over small firms when it comes to preparing a strategic plan.
Answer F   Page 40

64. Their narrower product lines, smaller customer bases and more limited geographic areas give small companies a natural advantage over large businesses when preparing a strategic plan.

Answer T   Page 41

65. The strategic planning process for small companies should cover at least five years into the future.
Answer F   Page 41

66. The strategic planning process for small companies should begin with setting goals and objectives.

Answer F   Page 41

67. A well-conceived and defined vision can be a competitive weapon in the marketplace by helping everyone understand and focus on the same target.
Answer T   Page 41

68. The aggregation of factors that sets a small business apart from its competitors is its mission statement.
Answer F   Page 42

69. What is our competitive advantage? Who are the key stakeholders in our company? are questions the entrepreneur needs to answer when creating the mission statement.
Answer T   Page 43

70. Strategic thinking helps an entrepreneur develop a strategic profile for his/her business.
Answer T   Page 43

71. The typical company has but one or two core competencies and focuses on them.
Answer F   Page 43

72. When Alan Lewis wanted to evaluate his company's mission statement he asked the people who knew best, his customers.
Answer F   Page 44

73. Successful small businesses know both their market segments and their core competencies.
Answer T   Page 45

74. Market segmentation is simply differentiating the company and/or product apart from the competition.
Answer F   Page 45

75. Appropriate market segmentation requires information—knowing who the small firm's customers are and what they are like.
Answer T   Page 46

76. Positioning the company in the market means carving the market up into small, homogeneous units and attacking each segment with a specific strategy.
Answer F   Page 46

77. Proper market positioning provides a small business with a means of developing a competitive advantage.
Answer T   Page 46

78. A successful competitive strategy focuses on eliminating its weaknesses by investing sufficient resources to turn them into strengths.
Answer F   Page 47

79. After a company's strengths and weakness are assessed, the strategic planning   process should identify opportunities and threats facing the company and should isolate the key factors for success in the business.
Answer T   Page 48

80. Key success factors are simply relationships between controllable factors and critical elements that permit a firm to compete in its industry.
Answer T   Page 48

81. Most small business owners believe it is relatively unimportant to monitor their competitors' activities.
Answer F   Page 50

82. One of the goals of competitive analysis is to improve a firm's reaction time to competitor's actions.
Answer T   Page 50

83. It is possible for a small business owner to gather competitive data inexpensively, even data on other companies' financial condition.
Answer T   Page 51

84. The purchasing of rival companies' products, taking them apart, and analyzing them, in order to collect competitive information, is an illegal trade practice under the Clayton Act.
Answer F   Page 51

85. The competitive profile matrix matches the firm's core competencies with those of selected competitors.
Answer F   Page 51

86. Pierce Sears failure of Thomas Wilson and Company's soft drink business is an example of the consequences for a small business when it does not differentiate itself from larger competitors.
Answer T   Page 52

87. Goals and objectives provide the direction for the small firm and are essential to the strategic planning process.
Answer T   Page 53

88. Goals indicate how the small firm's resources will be allocated to specific ventures or activities.
Answer F   Page 53

89. Before a business owner can build any strategies, he/she must have clear goals and objectives in order to have an appropriate target to aim his/her strategies toward.
Answer T   Page 53

90. "We're in the retail clothing business" violates the goal characteristic of specificity.
Answer T   Page 53

91. Specific objectives reduce an entrepreneur's flexibility.
Answer F   Page 53

92. It is important to reward yourself as you achieve each goal on the path to reaching your objectives, rather than wait until the objective is fully achieved.
Answer T   Page 54

93. When striving to accomplish goals, it is best to measure the sacrifices necessary, to enhance the feeling of success when they are achieved.
Answer F   Page 54

94. Setting objectives forces managers to prioritize the goals of the business.
Answer T   Page 55

95. Setting seemingly impossibly high objectives, those outside the likely reach of employees, helps managers to create and maintain a high motivation level.
Answer F   Page 55

96. Sharply focused strategies increase the likelihood that business objectives will be achieved.
Answer T   Page 55

97. A strategy is a road map of action for fulfilling a firm's mission, goals and objectives.
Answer T   Page 55

98. New ventures based on a truly unique idea tend to be high on innovation and low on risk, requiring little start-up capital.
Answer T   Page 55

99. Awana is introducing a new Internet product that requires a large amount of start-up capital to buy equipment and hire people. Awana's start-up would fit into the high innovation, low risk category of the entrepreneurial strategic matrix.
Answer F   Page 56

100. An effective strategy for a high innovation, high risk start-up would be to move quickly in the market and to defend the firm's current position.
Answer F   Page 56

101. Because most entrepreneurs launch conventional businesses in well-established industry that are low on innovation, most entrepreneurs' companies fit into the low innovation, low risk quadrant of the strategic matrix.
Answer F   Page 57

102. Most part-time, home-based business start-ups tend to fit into the low innovation, low risk quadrant of the strategic matrix.
Answer T   Page 58

103. Small firms pursuing a cost leadership strategy have an advantage in reaching customers whose primary purchase criterion is high quality.
Answer F   Page 58

104. The best way to build a cost leadership competitive advantage is to focus entirely on manufacturing costs.
Answer F   Page 59

105. A danger of cost leadership is that a company may misunderstand what processes actually drive its true costs.
Answer T   Page 59

106. One key to building a successful differentiation strategy is to be better than competitors at some characteristic that customers value.
Answer T   Page 59

107. To be successful, a differentiation strategy must create the perception of value in the customer's eyes.
Answer T   Page 59

108. A differentiation strategy carries a risk with it, in that a firm may not adequately segment the market and properly target those special needs.
Answer T   Page 59

109. A focus strategy recognizes that all markets are homogeneous.
Answer F   Page 60

110. A small business following a focus strategy attempts to serve its narrow target markets more effectively and efficiently than competitors trying to appeal to the broad market.
Answer T   Page 60

111. The focus strategy depends on creating value for the customer either by being the low cost producer or by differentiating the product or service in a unique fashion, but doing it in a narrow target segment.
Answer T   Page 60

112. Focus strategies, unlike Porter's other generic strategies, are without risk because they tend to combine elements of all three strategies.
Answer F   Page 61

113. Offering lower prices is the best method for a small business to establish its competitive edge.
Answer F   Page 61

114. The focal point of the entire strategic plan and the competitive strategy chosen is the customer.

Answer T   Page 61

115. Small businesses have some competitive advantages over larger companies—being able to respond quickly, having greater flexibility, being able to build and defend niches, etc.
Answer T   Page 61

116. The best conversion of strategic plans to operational plans is done by top management without the help of the employees.
Answer F   Page 63

117. To be of any real value to the small business owner, strategic plans must be broken down beyond operational plan level into projects with assigned responsibilities.
Answer T   Page 63

118. The secret to good control is the identification and tracking of key performance indicators.
Answer T   Page 63

119. The key to the balanced scorecard is identifying the key single measure for the specific company being evaluated.
Answer F   Page 64

120. The balanced score looks at the small business from the perspectives of the customer, the company itself, innovation, and finances.
Answer T   Page 65

Essay Questions

121. What is the importance of strategic management to small businesses? In your discussion, explain how strategic planning is different for a small business.
Pages 40-41

122. Explain how vision and mission work together, providing direction for the small business. In your discussion, identify at least five key questions a mission statement should answer.
Pages 41–43

123. Describe core competencies and the role they play in helping the company segment its market and develop effective competitive strategies.
Pages 43–46

124. What is the importance of positioning for the small business?
Pages 46–47

125. Discuss the importance of knowing your firm's strengths and weaknesses and what opportunities and threats exist in the external environment.
Pages 47–48

126. What are key success factors and how do they help the small business compete?
Pages 48–50

127. Why is it important for a business owner to monitor the competition? Explain how a business owner could use a competitive profile matrix to do that. Include in the review what its value is, what information it contains, and how a small business owner would create it.
Pages 50–53

128. Create three goals and objectives for the following small company:
An Internet database for small business exporters that offers to match domestic
entrepreneurs to foreign distributors, venture capitalists, and/or joint venture candidates.
The
company takes a percentage fee for its service.
Pages 53–54

129. Explain the entrepreneurial strategic matrix, diagramming the matrix, identifying the characteristics of each quadrant, and naming two effective strategies for each quadrant.
Pages 55–58

130. Michael Porter defines three basic strategies cost leadership, differentiation, and focus. Describe each, explain under what conditions each works, and what the pitfalls are of each one.
Pages 58–61

131. Explain the "balanced scorecard," reviewing its strengths and the four perspectives it takes in evaluating a business.
Pages 64–65

Mini-Case

Case 2-1: "Meeting the Competition?"

Thelma and Louise have been running a "Sub and Chicken" shop for about two years. They cater to the employees of a local foundry as well as the office staffs of numerous small white-collar businesses in a five-mile radius. They offer ready-made food served in 90 seconds from the placement of the order, and custom-made subs, created at the direction of the customer. They do not offer a delivery service and their prices are a bit high. Their seating capacity is overflowing at meal time, their decor hasn't been updated since before they moved into the building, and the dining area tends to be a bit run down and not too clean. But customers love the food and the service, and Thelma and Louise have fashioned friendships with many of their regulars.

A franchise of a national chain of sandwich shops opens a store about five blocks from Thelma and Louise's shop. They have lower prices and delivery service. They don't pre-make meals, nor do they customize the sandwiches. The franchise offers a variety of standardized subs made fresh and some other pre-packaged items. Their service is about 3-6 minutes. The employees earn minimum wage, and while they are efficient at their jobs and polite, they aren't concerned with the individual customers. The franchise is new, brightly decorated, very clean, and spacious. The franchise had been looking for a location for about six months before they opened and had even approached Thelma and Louise about selling out.

Questions

1. List the strengths and weaknesses of both Thelma and Louise's store and the franchise store.

2. What should Thelma and Louise have been doing, and what can they now do to assess the threat that this new franchise is to them?

3. Which of Porter's generic strategies would give Thelma and Louise a competitive advantage? Why? Which generic strategy is the franchise most likely following? Explain your reasoning.

4. How could Thelma and Louise "fight" this threat? What would you recommend they do?

Chapter 3 –
Choosing a Form of Ownership

Multiple Choice Questions

1. The key to choosing the "right" form of ownership is:
   a) knowing the cost factor in time and money.
   b) understanding how each form affects both business and personal circumstances.
   c) having an experienced attorney and accountant to advise you in the choice.
   d) the fact you can not change the form of ownership once your company is established.

Answer b   Page 70

2. Which of the following questions influence an entrepreneur's choice of a business form of ownership?
   a) Do I understand the advantages and disadvantages of each type of ownership?
   b) What are my succession and retirement plans?
   c) To what extent am I willing to be personally responsible for the debts of the business?
   d) How much of my business can I outsource to make up for my lack of expertise?

Answer c   Page 71

3. When choosing a form of ownership, the entrepreneur should realize that:
   a) it is difficult if not impossible to change forms of ownership once the company is established.
   b) the expense of changing forms of ownership makes it prohibitively expensive to change.
   c) the most common form of ownership is the partnership and is the least expensive to establish.
   d) he/she will most likely change the form of ownership as the company grows in size and revenues.

Answer d   Page 72

4. The most common form of business ownership is the:
   a) sole proprietorship.
   b) partnership.
   c) corporation.
   d) S-corporation.

Answer a   Page 73

5. Juan is starting a software writing company. He is the owner and has only 3 employees. He wants a simple inexpensive form of ownership that leaves him in control and that he can quickly dissolve if he decides to change to another business. His best choice of form of ownership would be:
   a) S-corporation.
   b) partnership.
   c) corporation.
   d) sole proprietorship.

Answer d   Page 73

6. Sole proprietorships characteristically are:
   a) fairly complex to create.
   b) subject to special legal restrictions.
   c) expensive to create.
   d) easy to discontinue.

Answer d   Page 73

7. The name chosen for a small business is very important because:
   a) it reflects on the owner's personality because the owner is the business.
   b) it can attract the attention of potential customers and encourage people to think about the business.
   c) names are expensive to create and copyright.
   d) it determines where the business will be listed in the classified pages of the telephone directory.

Answer b   Page 74

8. A small business's name should have which of the following characteristics?
   a) Complex and sophisticated to fit the business as it grows
   b) Similar to what other businesses in the same product line use
   c) Sufficiently long to completely describe what the company does
   d) Short and easy to remember

Answer d   Page 74

9. The most critical disadvantage of the sole proprietorship is:
   a) unlimited personal liability.
   b) limited access to capital.
   c) lack of continuity.
   d) limited skills and capacities of the owner.

Answer a   Page 75

10. Which form of ownership generally has the least ability to accumulate capital?
    a) Partnership
    b) Sole proprietorship
    c) Corporation
    d) S-corporation

Answer b   Page 75

11. While a sole proprietorship gives the owner maximum flexibility in running the business, it also:
    a) makes the company a prime target for an acquisition or merger.
    b) creates a sense of isolation.
    c) makes it difficult to hire management talent to help grow the business.
    d) makes it difficult to sell.

Answer b   Page 76

12. Common ownership interest in a business, sharing profits (or losses) of a business, and the right to participate in managing the operations of the business are characteristics of a/an:
    a) corporation.
    b) sole proprietorship.
    c) partnership.
    d) S-corporation.
Answer c   Page 77

13. If a partnership is formed without an agreement, the partnership is automatically subject to the:
    a) Certification of Incorporation laws.
    b) Uniform Partnership Act.
    c) Limited Liability Company Act.
    d) Revised Uniform Limited Partnership Act.
Answer b   Page 77

14. Probably the most important feature of a partnership agreement is:
    a) that it identifies the name of the partnership.
    b) that it states the purpose and location of the business.
    c) that determines how the partnership will pay taxes and fees.
    d) that it resolves potential sources of conflict.
Answer d   Page 77

15. Which of the following is true about the content of a standard partnership agreement?
    a) It does not specify how profits and losses will be distributed.
    b) It includes the Certificate of Incorporation.
    c) It specifies how the partnership may be dissolved and assets divided.
    d) While it specifies the location of the business and its purpose, it does not name the partners or their legal addresses in order to maintain privacy for the partners.
Answer c   Page 77

16. A partnership agreement sets how the partners will be compensated. Normally:
    a) partners are not entitled to salaries or wages, but are compensated by a share of the profits of the business.
    b) the general partner's salary is set at 2 times the salaries of the limited partners.
    c) both general and limited partners are permitted salaries, but all silent or dormant partners are compensated only by sharing in the profits.
    d) while the agreement establishes payout schedules, it does not spell out what constitutes profit.
Answer a   Page 78

17. The three key elements of any partnership are:
    a) common ownership in the business, sharing the business' profits or losses, and the right to participate in managing the business.
    b) equal ownership in the business, sharing its profits and losses, and the right to participate in managing the business.

c) equal ownership in the business, sharing its profits and losses, and the right to limited liability for all partners.

d) common ownership in the business, sharing its profits and losses, and the right to limited liability for all partners.

Answer a   Page 78

18. The Uniform Partnership Act outlines a number of general obligations that partners have such as the obligation to:

a) give other partners complete information about all business affairs.

b) share in the management and operation of the business.

c) be compensated for personal expenses incurred.

d) have access to the business's books and records.

Answer a   Page 79

19. All partnerships must have:

a) at least three limited partners.

b) no dormant partners.

c) at least one general partner.

d) at least one silent or money partner.

Answer c   Page 79

20. In her partnership, Ana has unlimited liability for the partnership's debts. She would be the ____ partner.

a) limited

b) dormant

c) nominal

d) general

Answer d   Page 79

21. A partnership is like a _____ in the ease and expense of establishment.

a) corporation

b) limited liability company

c) professional corporation

d) sole proprietorship

Answer d   Page 79

22. Partnerships have a number of advantages over other forms of ownership, such as:

a) a larger pool of capital and little government regulation.

b) very easy liquidation of owners' investment.

c) limited liability for all partners.

d) they may be easily formed by an individual.

Answer a   Page 79

23. A partnership is:

a) taxed like a corporation.

b) not subject to the double taxation of some other forms of business.

c) taxed at the lowest rate for an individual.

d) taxed under capital gains laws as all profits are considered to come from appreciated assets.

Answer b   Page 80

24. Antonio is a limited partner and is neither active nor generally openly associated with the firm. He is the _____ partner.
    a) limited
    b) secret
    c) honorary
    d) dormant
Answer d   Page 80

25. Thelma is active in the management of the business, but does not disclose her participation to the public for personal reasons. Thelma represents a ___ partner in this partnership.
    a) limited
    b) secret
    c) honorary
    d) dormant
Answer b   Page 80

26. A significant disadvantage of a partnership is:
    a) the unlimited personal liability for all partners.
    b) the inability to attract either additional capital or new partners due to the complexity of rewriting the agreement.
    c) the difficulty of disposing a partnership interest without dissolving the partnership.
    d) the regulatory complexity under which a partnership must be formed and operated.
Answer c   Page 80

27. Like a sole proprietorship, a partnership suffers from the disadvantage of:
    a) poor capital accumulation.
    b) unlimited liability for all owners.
    c) double taxation of profits.
    d) the complexity of regulations under which it must operate.
Answer a   Page 80

28. In a general partnership:
    a) each partner is held responsible for an agreement or a decision made by any one of the partners.
    b) partners can be held responsible only for decisions they make personally.
    c) no partner can be held legally responsible for decisions since the partnership itself is a legal entity.
    d) no decision is binding unless all partners agree to it in writing.
Answer a   Page 81

29. According to your authors, partnership battles most frequently occur over issues of:
    a) the name and location of the business, i.e., the state within which it is licensed.
    b) the purpose and market of the business.
    c) the product line and its development.
    d) unbalanced work loads, unfair distribution of profits, etc.

Answer d   Page 81

30. Leroy and Tom are co-owners of Detailers Like Us, a car cleaning and restoration business. Sometimes they get into arguments about their business decisions. What could they do to lessen conflict and avoid a potential "business divorce"?
    a) Hire a good small business attorney to "break" any tie votes in a decision conflict.
    b) Divide business responsibilities based on their interests and stick to that division.
    c) Develop their own separate set of goals for the business and focus on accomplishing them.
    d) Keep every agreement oral for maximum flexibility.
Answer b   Page 82

31. _____ occurs when a general partner ceases to be associated with the business; _____ is the final act of winding up the business.
    a) Dissolution; termination
    b) Expulsion; dissolution
    c) Termination; dissolution
    d) Agency; dissolution
Answer a   Page 83

32. A limited partnership is a modification of a/an _____ form of ownership.
    a) sole proprietorship
    b) general partnership
    c) corporation
    d) S-corporation
Answer b   Page 83

33. In a limited partnership, the limited partners are treated like ____ by the law.
    a) investors
    b) general partners
    c) sole proprietors
    d) honorary partners
Answer a   Page 83

34. A/an _____ operates like a regular partnership except its shares of ownership are traded on stock exchanges.
    a) joint venture
    b) master limited partnership
    c) professional corporation
    d) S-corporation
Answer b   Page 84

35. A _____ is a relatively new form of ownership that resembles a corporation without many of the restrictions.
    a) joint venture
    b) master limited partnership
    c) limited liability company
    d) limited partnership
Answer c   Page 84

36. The _____ is the most complex form of ownership and is a separate legal entity in the eyes of the law.
    a) sole proprietorship
    b) partnership
    c) corporation
    d) joint venture

Answer c   Page 84

37. The _____ is a separate legal entity apart from its owners and may engage in business, make contracts, sue and be sued, and pay taxes.
    a) sole proprietorship
    b) corporation
    c) partnership
    d) joint venture

Answer b   Page 84

38. A corporation receives its authority to operate from:
    a) the federal government.
    b) the state.
    c) the board of certification.
    d) the stockholders.

Answer b   Page 85

39. A corporation doing business in the state in which it is incorporated is considered to be a/an _____ corporation.
    a) alien
    b) domestic
    c) foreign
    d) local

Answer b   Page 85

40. The "Das Spelunker" corporation, formed in Germany and conducting business in the United States, is considered to be a/an _____ corporation.
    a) alien
    b) domestic
    c) foreign
    d) local

Answer a   Page 85

41. Acme Corporation is chartered in Delaware, but its primary area of operation is in South Carolina. In South Carolina, Acme would be considered a/an _____ corporation.
    a) alien
    b) domestic
    c) foreign
    d) local

Answer c   Page 85

42. Which of the following generally is <u>not</u> required by a Certificate of Incorporation?
    a) The names and the addresses of the incorporators
    b) A statement of the corporation's purpose
    c) A statement of how stock proceeds will be used
    d) The corporation's bylaws
Answer c   Page 86

43. The primary reason entrepreneurs choose to incorporate is because of:
    a) the corporation's ability to attract capital.
    b) the need to attract top quality management talent to grow the business.
    c) the lower tax rates inherent in the corporate form of ownership.
    d) the limited liability of stockholders.
Answer d   Page 86

44. The form of ownership with the <u>greatest</u> ability to accumulate capital is the:
    a) sole proprietorship.
    b) partnership.
    c) joint venture.
    d) corporation.
Answer d   Page 87

45. The <u>corporate</u> form of ownership has a significant advantage in that:
    a) it is easy to transfer ownership.
    b) it has a lower tax rate than either partnerships or sole proprietorships.
    c) there is little cost to its formation.
    d) there is little regulatory oversight by the government.
Answer a   Page 87

46. Which of the following is a disadvantage of the corporation form of ownership?
    a) An inability to accumulate capital
    b) The unlimited liability to the members of the board
    c) Double taxation on profits and individuals
    d) The lack of continuity
Answer c   Page 87

47. Corporate officers can still face liability if they fail to:
    a) conduct an annual audit of corporate accounts.
    b) maintain certain standards of behavior.
    c) properly register their stock offerings with the SEC.
    d) declare their conflicts of interest due to holdings in competitive companies.
Answer b   Page 88

48. Carlos founded the "Taco Factory" 20 years ago as a family-oriented restaurant business. Over the years as he grew the business, he incorporated and sold stock. Recently the stockholders voted to seek liquor licenses and sell beer and hard liquor in the restaurants. Carlos opposed this, citing the history of the restaurant's "family" environment, but was voted down. Carlos experienced which drawback of the corporate form of ownership?
    a) The inability to accumulate capital
    b) The potential for diminished managerial incentives
    c) Legal requirements and red tape
    d) The potential loss of control
Answer d   Page 89

49. This form of ownership is the same as a corporation in terms of legal characteristics even though Congress is considering legislation that would further simplify its formation and running. Its distinction from a corporation is made for federal income tax purposes only.
    a) S-corporation
    b) master limited partnership
    c) sole proprietorship
    d) limited liability company
Answer a   Page 89

50. Jeff is forming a company. If he chooses a/an _____ form of ownership, he can have no more than 35 stockholders and must have only one class of stock.
    a) partnership
    b) corporation
    c) S-corporation
    d) master limited partnership
Answer c   Page 90

51. An S-corporation form of ownership overcomes which disadvantage of the regular or "C" corporation form of ownership?
    a) The double taxation issue
    b) The expense and difficulty of formation
    c) The amount of regulation and red tape involved in its operation
    d) The potential loss of control by the founder
Answer a   Page 90

52. One of the unfortunate disadvantages of an S-corporation is that:
    a) ownership may not be easily transferred by the sale of stock.
    b) it is subject to double taxation as is a normal corporation.
    c) it is unable to attract and accumulate capital.
    d) the costs of many fringe benefits cannot be deducted as business expenses.
Answer d   Page 91

53. An owner should choose an S-corporation form of ownership when he/she:
    a) has an established company that is suffering losses due to double taxation.
    b) is starting up a company and anticipating either net losses or high profits with large dividends.
    c) owns a company in which net profits before any compensation to shareholders are less than $100,000 per year.
    d) has an existing sole proprietorship and wants to lower the tax bill through deducting fringe benefits as business expenses.

Answer b   Page 92

54. The limited liability company is most like a/an:
    a) general partnership.
    b) master partnership.
    c) sole proprietorship.
    d) S-corporation.

Answer d   Page 92

55. A limited liability company differs from an S-corporation in:
    a) that it is not subject to the same amount of restrictions.
    b) its ability to attract and accumulate capital.
    c) that ownership is not transferable through the sale of stock.
    d) that it is limited to only one class of stock.

Answer a   Page 93

56. A limited liability company is formed under:
    a) a Certificate of Incorporation.
    b) a Partnership Agreement.
    c) Articles of Organization.
    d) the Revised Uniform Partnership Act.

Answer c   Page 93

57. Which of the following is true about choosing a limited liability company form of ownership?
    a) It has no disadvantages except its newness.
    b) It is ideal for a new company but difficult to convert to with an existing company.
    c) It is inexpensive, easy to form, and covered by little regulation due to its newness.
    d) It's an excellent conversion vehicle for existing businesses that are suffering from double taxation but problematic for sole proprietorships.

Answer b   Page 94

58. In a joint venture, individuals join together in co-ownership for:
    a) continuous operation.
    b) six to twelve months.
    c) a given limited purpose.
    d) perpetuity.

Answer c   Page 94

59. A joint venture is different from a partnership in that the joint venture:

    a) can be formed only by two individuals.
    b) is formed for a specific purpose.
    c) continues indefinitely.
    d) requires that profits be shared equally.
Answer b   Page 94

60. Income from a joint venture is taxed exactly like income from a/an:
    a) sole proprietorship.
    b) partnership.
    c) corporation.
    d) S-corporation.
Answer b   Page 94

True or False Questions

61. One of the first and most fundamental decisions an entrepreneur faces is choosing a form of ownership.
Answer T   Page 70

62. For entrepreneurs launching their first business, the sole proprietorship is the best form of ownership.
Answer F   Page 71

63. Factors an entrepreneur should consider when choosing a form of ownership should include but not be limited to: tax considerations, liability exposure, business goals, managerial ability, etc.
Answer T   Page 71

64. While there are many forms of ownership, the three major forms are: proprietorship, partnership, and S-corporation.
Answer F   Page 72

65. Of all U.S. business firms, sole proprietorships are the most common, accounting for nearly 74% of all businesses in the United States.
Answer T   Page 73

66. The sole proprietorship is the simplest and least expensive form of ownership to begin.
Answer T   Page 73

67. While the sole proprietorship is the easiest type of business to get into, it is the most heavily regulated.
Answer F   Page 73

68. The name an entrepreneur chooses for her/his business is relatively unimportant as people buy the product not the company name.
Answer F   Page 74

69. In a sole proprietorship, the owner has limited liability.
Answer F   Page 75

70. If a sole proprietorship fails, the owner is not liable for its debts since the business is a separate legal entity.
Answer F   Page 75

71. One of the advantages of a sole proprietorship is that skills and capabilities are unlimited because you, as sole proprietor, are able to assume all of these responsibilities.
Answer F   Page 75

72. The sole proprietorship has the least ability to accumulate capital.
Answer T   Page 75

73. When the owner of a sole proprietorship dies, the business automatically terminates.
Answer T   Page 76

74. The most common form of ownership in the United States is the partnership.
Answer F   Page 77

75. Perhaps the most important feature of a partnership agreement is its ability to resolve potential sources of conflict among partners.
Answer T   Page 77

76. State law requires that persons creating a partnership file the articles of partnership with the Secretary of State.
Answer F   Page 77

77. If a partnership agreement does not exist, the partnership will be governed by the Uniform Partnership Act.
Answer T   Page 77

78. The terms of a partnership agreement are legally binding even if some of the items are illegal.
Answer F   Page 78

79. In a partnership, profits (and losses) are shared according to any ratio stated in the articles of partnership.
Answer T   Page 78

80. Partnership agreements do not cover how to dissolve a partnership or sell a partnership interest.
Answer F   Page 78

81. The Uniform Partnership Act covers three elements of a partnership; the common ownership interest, sharing profits or losses, and management participation rights.
Answer T   Page 78

82. Under the UPA, each partner has the following rights: to work for the partnership without salary, to give a formal accounting of the business affairs, to submit to majority vote or arbitration differences that may arise, etc.
Answer F   Page 78

83. There is no legal limit to the number of general partners a partnership must have, but it must have one.
Answer T   Page 79

84. A limited partner is liable only for the amount he has invested in the business.
Answer T   Page 79

85. A limited partner does not have the right to manage the business in any way and still maintain limited status.
Answer T   Page 79

86. One of the advantages of a partnership over a proprietorship is the increased sources of capital and credit it offers.
Answer T   Page 79

87. The partnership, like the proprietorship, avoids the disadvantage of double taxation.
Answer T   Page 80

88. In a partnership, the general partner(s) share their unlimited liability for the business debts with both silent and dormant partners.
Answer F   Page 80

89. A partnership agreement cannot restrict the disposal of any partner's share of the business.
Answer F   Page 80

90. Each partner is an agent for the business and can legally bind other partners to business agreements.
Answer T   Page 81

91. A common denominator in many partnership disputes is the lack of a written agreement clearly spelling out the roles, rights and responsibilities of each partner.
Answer T   Page 81

92. In most good partnerships there is little, if any, conflict.
Answer F   Page 82

93. A key to minimizing conflict and protecting against "business divorce" is to get any agreements about responsibilities, duties, expectations, etc., in writing.
Answer T   Page 82

94. Limited partners may withdraw, die, or sell their ownership in the partnership without forcing its dissolution.
Answer T   Page 83

95. A partnership cannot be dissolved <u>except</u> in the case of the general partner's expressed wish that the partnership cease.
Answer F   Page 83

96. In a limited partnership, the "limited partner" is primarily an investor and can   lose only the amount invested in the business.
Answer T   Page 84

97. Master Limited Partnerships are relatively new business structures that are just like corporations, including being able to trade their stock on stock exchanges.
Answer F   Page 84

98. A corporation exists separately from the lives of its owners.
Answer T   Page 84

99. A foreign corporation is one chartered in a foreign country.
Answer F   Page 85

100. A corporation formed and chartered in Kansas is considered a domestic corporation when doing business in Kansas.
Answer T   Page 85

101. Most states <u>do not</u> require a Certificate of Incorporation or a charter to be filed.
Answer F   Page 85

102. Stockholders in the corporation have the same kind of liability as do general partners in a partnership.
Answer F   Page 86

103. Ownership of a corporation can easily be transferred through the sale of stock.
Answer T   Page 87

104. To avoid becoming liable for corporate actions, officers should ensure that they hold annual meetings, keep minutes of those meetings, make sure the board of directors makes all decisions, etc.
Answer T   Page 88

105. "Double taxation" refers to the fact that the corporation itself must pay taxes on its net profits, and the stockholders must also pay taxes on the portion of those same profits distributed to them as dividends.
Answer T   Page 87 88

106. Owners/founders can be minority stockholders in a corporation but never lose their final authority or control over business decisions because they are the owners.
Answer F   Page 89

107. An S-corporation maintains the advantages of the corporate form of ownership while having the ability to be taxed as a partnership.
Answer T   Page 89

108. A professional corporation is created in the same way as a regular corporation, and exists to provided limited liability to doctors, lawyers, etc.
Answer T   Page 89

109. An S-corporation can issue both voting and non-voting common stock to its shareholders.
Answer T   Page 90

110. Like "C" corporations, S-corporations must pay taxes on any assets that have appreciated in value and are sold.
Answer F   Page 91

111. In an S-corporation, the costs of many fringe benefits paid to stockholders with 2% or more stock cannot be deducted as business expenses.
Answer T   Page 92

112. S-corporation status usually benefits start-up companies anticipating losses, and highly profitable firms with substantial dividends to pay out to shareholders.
Answer T   Page 92

113. Small companies with net profits of less than $100,000 per year before any compensation to shareholders are ideally suited for S-corporation status.
Answer T   Page 92

114. A "limited liability company" is legally treated just like a limited partnership.
Answer F   Page 92

115. An LLC form of ownership is ideal for small companies in almost any industry.
Answer T   Page 93

116. It is relatively easy and inexpensive to convert existing businesses into LLCs.
Answer F   Page 94

117. The biggest disadvantage of an LLC is its newness.
Answer T   Page 94

118. A joint venture is very similar to a corporation, but is only formed for a specific event or occasion.
Answer F   Page 94

119. The income derived from a joint venture is taxed if it arises from a partnership.
Answer T   Page 94

120. If Kirk and his dad formed a partnership and if Kirk's father provides the money and lets Kirk manage the by himself, then Kirk's father would be a limited partner and Kirk would be the general partner.
Answer T   Page 95

Essay Questions

121. What are the nine general factors an entrepreneur should consider when choosing the form of small business ownership? List and explain at least six of them.
Page 71

122. Why would an entrepreneur choose a sole proprietorship? What drawbacks should be considered?
Pages 73–76

123. Identify what items are included in a standard partnership agreement.
Pages 77–78

124. What advantages does a partnership offer the entrepreneur over forming a sole proprietorship?
Pages 79–80

125. Explain 1) a limited partnership and 2) a master limited partnership, identifying what other types of ownership they are similar to as well as their advantages and disadvantages.
Pages 83–84

126. What are the pluses and minuses for the owners of a company in choosing to incorporate their business?
Pages 86–89

127. Why would someone choose an S-corporation? Discuss who can, how it is done, how it is different from or similar to other types of corporations, and its advantages and disadvantages.
Pages 89–92

128. What is a limited liability company (LLC) and why would an entrepreneur choose it as a form of ownership?
Pages 92–94

129. What is a joint venture and when is it appropriate to use this form of a company?
Page 94

Mini-Cases

Case 3-1: "Today, You Gotta Be a Corporation"

Duke has been a successful used car dealer for 25 years in the same location, operating as a proprietorship. In those 25 years, he's expanded his operation and become the largest independent used car dealer in a city of 85,000 people. Few people in town can boast of a business reputation better than Duke's. As he says, "I've always done business in a fair and honest fashion, and I've tried to give my customers an honest deal. The public has responded well, and last year the business revenue increased to an all-time high of $830,000."

As the business has grown, so have Duke's liabilities. On a given day, Duke will have cars worth from $350,000 to $450,000 as inventory on the lot. "Twenty years ago, if I'd asked the bank for a line of credit of $200,000, they'd have tossed me out the front door. There's no question, today business is different."

Duke's only daughter recently married a garage mechanic who has worked in the area for the past three years. Though Duke thinks the boy is certainly nice enough, he doesn't believe he is very smart. "The kid sure knows how to fix a car, but that's as far as it goes," says Duke. "On my last visit to the accountant, he suggested I consider incorporating. I guess he knows what he's talking about. That's all you hear today—'you gotta be a corporation.' I guess he's right. But, to tell you the truth, I don't know."

Questions
1. Should Duke incorporate or should he remain a proprietorship? Why or why not?

2. Would you recommend Duke establish an S-corporation? What conditions would he have to meet?

3. Would a limited liability corporation be any better for Duke? Why or why not?

4. Duke is considering forming a partnership with his son-in-law, the mechanic. What would you advise Duke to do if he decides to form a partnership?

Case 3-2: Problems in Paradise
Paradise was founded six years ago by Miguel and Mary Alice. In the past few years, Paradise has become the most fashionable women's clothing store in a medium-sized college town in the Midwest. The town houses two institutions of higher education—the state university with an enrollment of 28,000 and a private women's college with an enrollment of 1,100. Miguel and Mary Alice met in college in a retail management class. In fact, the store was created as part of a semester project the two collaborated on.

From its initial opening in a small, downtown, side street location, Paradise was a success. Miguel and Mary Alice had a magic touch in working together in choosing, displaying, and selling merchandise that college women wanted. Last year Paradise moved to a new regional shopping mall, which was built one-half mile from campus. The new store is five times larger than the old one. The business borrowed extensively to cover inventory and operating costs. Operating expenses are nearly five times what they were in the old location, but sales revenues are projected to increase five-fold.

Miguel and Mary Alice have never felt the need for a written partnership agreement. They simply shook hands and started the business. For both of them, Paradise was a dream come true. Neither of them drew much more than their personal living expenses. Every spare dollar was reinvested in the growing business. Their close friends joke about how each is married to the same spouse—the business.

Questions
1. What form of ownership do Miguel and Mary Alice have?

2. Explain why they should draw up an agreement at this point. What impact, if any, might the Uniform Partnership Act have on them and their business if they do not write up a formal agreement of ownership?

Case 3-2: Continued

Had it not been for Ramona, Miguel's fiancee, there might never have been a problem in Paradise. Ramona had been working as a very successful model for a clothing manufacturer in New York City for four years when Miguel went to New York on a buying trip. If there is such a thing as "love at first sight," Miguel and Ramona experienced it. Ramona was taken with Miguel's Midwest freshness and flair for style, as well as his in-depth knowledge of the fashion industry. Miguel was struck by Ramona's beauty and intelligence.

When he returned to Paradise after the buying trip, Miguel informed Mary Alice that he planned to move to New York and marry Ramona. Because of Ramona's modeling career, the couple would live in New York. Miguel offered to sell his share of the partnership to Mary Alice. Mary Alice was shocked. When they began the business, both thought Paradise would last forever.

Mary Alice offered an alternative. She would run the business, the day-to-day operations. Miguel would become a limited partner, telecommuting as much as possible from New York. They would write in Ramona as a partner as well, but she would have no operating or other responsibilities and would be "invisible" to the public. Mary Alice offered this alternative as she could not raise the money to buy Miguel out and did not want to sell Paradise.

Questions - continued

3. What form of ownership is Mary Alice suggesting? What would her role be in this form and what are her subsequent responsibilities and liabilities?

4. What type of partnership is Mary Alice offering Miguel? What would be his responsibilities and liabilities under this form of ownership?

5. What type of partnership is Mary Alice offering Ramona?

Chapter 4 –
Franchising and the Entrepreneur

Multiple Choice Questions

1. Franchising is growing at a rate of about _____ times the rate of the economy.
   a) 2.5
   b) 10
   c) 25
   d) 100

Answer b   Page 101

2. Franchises account for about _____% of all retail sales.
   a) 74
   b) 34
   c) 63
   d) 43

Answer d   Page 102

3. By the year 2004, franchises will:
   a) account for 100% of all retail sales.
   b) have sales of nearly $2.5 trillion dollars worldwide.
   c) employ more than 1 million people.
   d) have largely ceased to function in their current form.

Answer b   Page 102

4. Franchising is currently dominated by:
   a) auto dealers.
   b) service-oriented franchises.
   c) retail outlets.
   d) fast food restaurants.

Answer c   Page 102

5. _____ franchising exists when a franchisee is licensed to sell specific products under the franchisor's brand name through a selective distribution system.
   a) Trade name
   b) Pure
   c) Conversion
   d) Product distribution

Answer d   Page 103

6. In _____ franchising, a franchisee purchases only the right to become identified with the franchisor's trade name.
   a) trade name
   b) pure
   c) conversion
   d) product distribution

Answer a   Page 103

7. _____ franchising involves providing the franchisee with a complete business system--the established name, the building layout and design, accounting systems, etc.
   a) Product distribution
   b) Trade name
   c) Pure
   d) Conversion

Answer c   Page 103

8. Most gasoline products are sold through the _____ system of franchising.
   a) product distribution
   b) trade name
   c) pure
   d) conversion

Answer a   Page 103

9. McDonald's is an example of a _____ franchise.
   a) conversion
   b) trade name
   c) product distribution
   d) pure

Answer d   Page 103

10. Which of the following factors has contributed to franchising's popularity?
    a) The overseas expansion of large companies, leaving domestic markets unattended
    b) The rekindling of the entrepreneurial spirit
    c) The changes in the financial markets, making it easier to find financing
    d) The decrease in males looking to be their own boss

Answer b   Page 103

11. What is the relationship between women entrepreneurs and franchising?
    a) They are entering franchising in greater numbers due to frustration with the glass ceiling.
    b) Nearly 22% of all franchises are owned by women.
    c) Women tend to enter product-related rather than service-related franchises.
    d) Women are buying franchises at the same rate as men.

Answer a   Page 103

12. The success of franchising is largely due to:
    a) the economic growth of the United States and other developed nations, economies.
    b) more college students choosing to go to work for themselves rather than for corporations.
    c) the mutual benefits it provides to the franchisor and franchisee.
    d) all of these factors.

Answer c   Page 104

13. Franchising provides the <u>franchisor</u> with the benefit of:
    a) a lower tax rate on corporate profits.
    b) a nationally recognized brand name and purchasing power.
    c) minimal capital requirements to finance business growth.

   d) a largely unregulated industry in which to build a company.
Answer c   Page 104

14. McDonald's worldwide success as a franchise can be attributed to a few simple strategies, including:
    a) complete customization of the menu to fit local tastes.
    b) meeting with employees often and providing rigorous training.
    c) using U.S. managers and employees whenever possible.
    d) standardizing processes and closely managing workers.
Answer b   Page 105

15. McDonald's attributes the success of their international franchises to several factors including:
    a) understanding the country's culture.
    b) hiring expatriate managers.
    c) extensively revising the menu to fit each country.
    d) minimizing worker autonomy by closely supervising workers.
Answer a   Page 105

16. The typical franchise company averages sales of less than ____ outlets in the first year.
    a) three
    b) seven
    c) ten
    d) one
Answer a   Page 106

17. In view of the cause of most new business failures, probably the most valuable service provided franchisees by the franchisor is:
    a) management training and experience.
    b) national advertising.
    c) financial assistance.
    d) territorial protection.
Answer a   Page 106

18. While franchising lets the entrepreneur own and start a business quickly:
    a) franchises are still beyond the reach of 80% of Americans.
    b) it still takes 6 to 18 months to break even.
    c) franchises still fail at the same rate as other types of business start-ups.
    d) most franchisees are dissatisfied with their franchise arrangement.
Answer b   Page 106

19. At the most basic level, when a franchisee purchases a franchise, he/she essentially is buying:
    a) the franchisor's experience.
    b) management training.
    c) prime locations.
    d) a brand name.
Answer a   Page 107

20. In franchising, the reputation of the franchisor is dependent on:
    a) their locations and popularity with the local customer.
    b) the brand name recognition and appeal.
    c) the rate of growth and the number of national outlets.
    d) the quality of the goods and services provided.
Answer d   Page 107

21. Franchise advertising programs:
    a) are organized by the franchisor but controlled locally by the franchisee.
    b) are an expense borne by the franchisor.
    c) require franchisees to spend a minimum amount on local advertising.
    d) allow voluntary participation.
Answer c   Page 108

22. When it comes to financial assistance for franchisees, the franchisor often:
    a) provides direct financing.
    b) assists in finding financing and occasionally provides direct assistance in a specific area.
    c) waives royalty fees for franchisees not making an adequate profit.
    d) generally does nothing, as finding financing is a requirement for qualifying for a franchise.
Answer b   Page 108

23. The primary advantage of buying a franchise over starting your own company is:
    a) in the purchase of the franchisor's experience, expertise, and products.
    b) the fact it is much less expensive than doing your own business start-up.
    c) the extensive assistance offered in finding start-up capital.
    d) the absolute territory protection offered by all franchisors.
Answer a   Page 109

24. Most franchise experts consider the most important factor in the success of a franchise to be:
    a) the simplicity of the idea.
    b) location.
    c) territorial protection.
    d) financing.
Answer b   Page 109

25. Territorial protection in franchising:
    a) varies according to industry.
    b) is basically every franchisee for him/herself.
    c) is absolute and uniform across industries.
    d) is no longer an issue for most franchisees.
Answer a   Page 109

26. The failure rate for franchises is:
    a) higher than the rate for all new businesses.
    b) no different from the rate for all new businesses.
    c) lower than the rate for all new businesses.
    d) indeterminable because of the Right to Privacy Act.
Answer c   Page 110

27. Approximately ____% of new businesses fail by the second year of operation, while ____% of all franchises fail in any given year.
    a) 2; 17
    b) 12; 15
    c) 14; 22
    d) 24; 7
Answer d   Page 110

28. There are two main risks in purchasing a franchise. First, that of the franchisor's experience and business system, and second:
    a) the brand name recognition of the franchise.
    b) the entrepreneur's managerial skills and motivation.
    c) the franchisor's financing.
    d) the economy trends in the country at the time the franchisee begins operation.
Answer b   Page   110

29. Wayne Flesjer's failure in his Subway franchise effort was largely due to:
    a) poor location.
    b) not understanding the business.
    c) undercapitalization.
    d) the lack of support from the franchisor.
Answer b   Page 111

30. Despite all the benefits, there are a number of disadvantages to franchises, such as:
    a) the time consumed by the management training and support the franchisor provides.
    b) the cost of national advertising.
    c) strict adherence to standardized operations.
    d) territory limitations.
Answer c   Page 112

31. The commerce department reports that the most expensive franchises in terms of total investment are:
    a) retail franchises.
    b) business service franchises.
    c) McDonald's franchises.
    d) hotel and motel franchises.
Answer d   Page 112

32. The payment the franchisee makes to the franchisor based on gross sales is:
    a) a royalty.
    b) the start-up fee.
    c) a technical assistance fee.
    d) a national advertising fee.
Answer a   Page 112

33. Franchise royalty fees typically average ____ of a franchisee's gross sales.
    a) 1% to 3%
    b) 5% to 7%

c) 1% to 15%

d) 7% to 12%

Answer b   Page 112

34. When it comes to purchasing products, equipment, etc., the franchisor:

   a) cannot require the franchisees buy from the franchise company.

   b) can set prices paid for the products, etc., but cannot set the retail price the franchisee charges.

   c) is permitted to set the retail price for the franchisee.

   d) cannot require franchisees to buy from an "approved" supplier.

Answer b   Page 113

35. Typically, the franchisor controls are very tight on what the franchisee:

   a) does in terms of who they hire as employees.

   b) sets in terms of retail pricing and hours of operation.

   c) does with his/her net profits after fees and taxes are paid.

   d) sells in terms of the product or service they offer.

Answer d   Page 113

36. The biggest challenge facing the growth of new franchises is:

   a) the lack of capital.

   b) competition from independent entrepreneurs.

   c) market saturation.

   d) the recent downturn in the economy.

Answer c   Page 113

37. The best way to describe the typical franchisee is as:

   a) a happy prisoner.

   b) an independent entrepreneur.

   c) a small cog in a corporate wheel.

   d) a member of a large but sometimes conflicted family.

Answer a   Page 114

38. The typical franchisee is:

   a) 40 years old, has a net worth of over $300,000, and is probably college educated.

   b) 25-35, has a net worth over $100,000, and is high school educated.

   c) a women 35-45, with net worth of about $250,000, and is probably college educated.

   d) 40 years old, minority male, with a net worth of $350,000, high school educated and experienced in the field the franchise is in.

Answer a   Page 115

39. A "good franchisee" is characteristized as _____ according to franchisors.

   a) being highly independent

   b) being experienced in the line of business of the franchise

   c) having strong technical skills and being highly risk adverse

   d) having excellent leadership and management skills

Answer d   Page 115

40. To protect investors from unscrupulous franchisors, the Trade Regulation Rule
    a) FCC.
    b) Justice Department.
    c) FDA.
    d) FTC.

Answer d   Page 116

41. The Uniform Franchise Offering Circular:
    a) was developed in 1946 in the State of California.
    b) includes 23 major topics in its disclosure statement.
    c) requires the release of a detailed earnings projection.
    d) is only necessary in the 33 states that do not have their own franchise disclosure laws.

Answer b   Page 116

42. The FTC's philosophy focuses on:
    a) catching and prosecuting abusers of franchise laws.
    b) verifying the accuracy of UFOC information.
    c) providing information to prospective franchisees and helping them make good decisions.
    d) licensing prospective franchisors.

Answer c   Page 116

43. Recent changes the FTC has made to the UFOC requirements include:
    a) revealing detailed earnings information.
    b) only a three-day waiting period from getting the UFOC to signing a contract.
    c) a statement as to the accuracy of the information in the document.
    d) how franchisors advertise and the impact of any regulations on their industry.

Answer d   Page 116

44. Which of the following should make a potential franchisee suspicious about a franchisor's honesty?
    a) Claims that the franchise contract is a standard one and that there's no need to read it
    b) An offer of direct financing of a specific element of the franchise package
    c) Not providing detailed operational information until 10 days before signing the contract
    d) Requiring franchisees to spend a certain percentage of profits on advertising

Answer a   Page 118

45. Which of the following is an indication of a dishonest franchisor?
    a) Very thorough and complete operations and training manuals
    b) Recommending retail prices and providing a list of "approved" suppliers of products and materials needed for running the franchise
    c) Attempts to discourage you from allowing an attorney to evaluate the franchise contract
    d) Not providing a set of detailed earnings projections for each potential franchisee

Answer c   Page 118

46. When buying a franchise, the potential franchisee should first:
    a) search for start-up capital for local banks.
    b) evaluate him/herself as to the fit with the franchise.
    c) work in a similar business or industry for a year.
    d) contact the local chamber of commerce for information on the local economy.

Answer b   Page 119

47. When studying the franchise's UFOC, the potential franchisee should look for a turnover rate under:
    a) 20%.
    b) 15%.
    c) 10%.
    d) 5%.

Answer d   Page 120

48. When evaluating a franchise, the potential franchisee should:
    a) interview both current and former franchisees.
    b) only interview franchise employees as franchisees vary greatly in their opinions.
    c) ask about what oral promises the franchisor will give regarding future earnings.
    d) look at the local labor market to see if there is a pool of appropriate candidates for employment.

Answer a   Page 122

49. A recent FTC study suggests that ___% of new franchisees sign franchise contracts without reading them.
    a) 40
    b) 25
    c) 60
    d) 10

Answer a   Page 123

50. Typically, franchise contracts:
    a) are short-term, for 10 years or less.
    b) are heavily weighted in favor of the franchisee due to federal regulation.
    c) do not cover transfer and buyback provisions.
    d) are not negotiated by established franchisors.

Answer d   Page 123

51. The most litigated subject of the franchisee agreement is:
    a) franchisee fees.
    b) advertising expenditures.
    c) termination of contract.
    d) resale price maintenance clauses.

Answer c   Page 123

52. Under what circumstances would a typical franchisor have the right to cancel a franchise contract?
    a) The franchisee declares bankruptcy.
    b) The franchise fails to following retail pricing guidelines set by the franchisor.
    c) Within five days of the initial signing of the contract
    d) If the franchisor decides he/she wants to buy back the franchise

Answer a   Page 123

53. When franchise contracts are renewed:

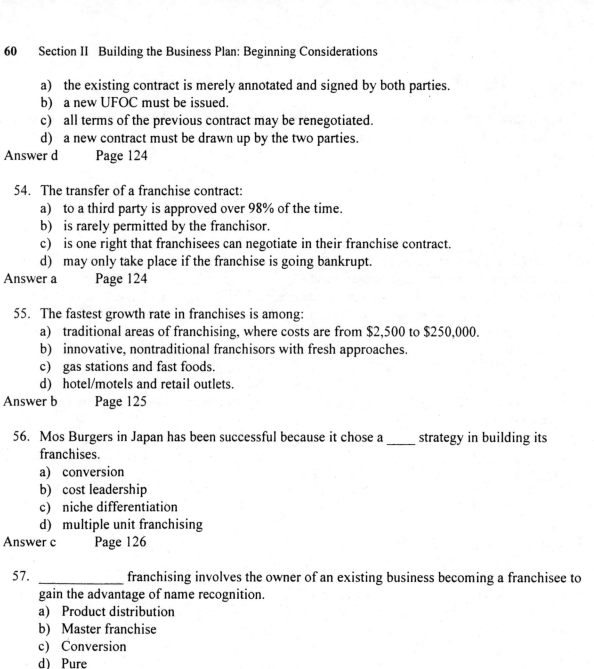

a) the existing contract is merely annotated and signed by both parties.
b) a new UFOC must be issued.
c) all terms of the previous contract may be renegotiated.
d) a new contract must be drawn up by the two parties.

Answer d   Page 124

54. The transfer of a franchise contract:
a) to a third party is approved over 98% of the time.
b) is rarely permitted by the franchisor.
c) is one right that franchisees can negotiate in their franchise contract.
d) may only take place if the franchise is going bankrupt.

Answer a   Page 124

55. The fastest growth rate in franchises is among:
a) traditional areas of franchising, where costs are from $2,500 to $250,000.
b) innovative, nontraditional franchisors with fresh approaches.
c) gas stations and fast foods.
d) hotel/motels and retail outlets.

Answer b   Page 125

56. Mos Burgers in Japan has been successful because it chose a ____ strategy in building its franchises.
a) conversion
b) cost leadership
c) niche differentiation
d) multiple unit franchising

Answer c   Page 126

57. _____ franchising involves the owner of an existing business becoming a franchisee to gain the advantage of name recognition.
a) Product distribution
b) Master franchise
c) Conversion
d) Pure

Answer c   Page 127

58. The most efficient method of franchising, from the franchisor's point-of-view, which has become popular in the 1990s and permits one franchisee to hold several franchises from the same franchise company, is called:
a) multi-unit franchising.
b) master franchising.
c) conversion franchising.
d) piggybacking.

Answer a   Page 127

59. Establishing a Mrs. Fields Cookies franchise inside a Hardees fast-food franchise is an example of _____ franchising.
    a) multi-unit
    b) master
    c) piggyback
    d) conversion
Answer c   Page 128

60. When the franchisor has the right to establish a semi-independent organization in a particular territory to recruit, sell, and support other franchises, it is called a _____ franchise.
    a) multi-unit
    b) piggyback
    c) conversion
    d) master
Answer d   Page 128

61. What impact is the world wide web having on franchising?
    a) At this point, no impact because e-commerce is too new
    b) Little impact since most e-commerce is being done by large established corporations
    c) It is significantly reshaping it, improving communication, increasing sales opportunities, etc.
    d) No one knows because no data is being gathered and the FTC is looking into regulating it.
Answer c   Page 129

True or False Questions

62. A popular way to start a business, franchising has grown at a rate 2^2 times that of the economy.
Answer F   Page 101

63. Franchising is big business with more than 4,500 franchisors in the United States today with 600,000 outlets.
Answer T   Page 102

64. Franchises account for 43% of all retail sales, almost $810 billion dollars.
Answer T   Page 102

65. Franchising is a modern creation—a form of ownership started by McDonald's in the mid-1950s.
Answer F   Page 102

66. Isaac M. Singer invented the franchise system with his Singer Sewing Machines during the time of the Civil War.
Answer T   Page 102

67. By definition, a franchise is owned by a semi-independent franchisee who pays a fee to a franchisor in return for the right to sell the franchised goods or services.
Answer T   Page 102

68. In a franchise arrangement, the franchisor controls the distribution methods of the business venture.
Answer T   Page 102

69. Trade name franchising involves licensing the rights to sell specific products under the manufacturer's brand name.
Answer F   Page 103

70. The type of franchising growing fastest is product distribution franchising.
Answer F   Page 103

71. Pure franchising occurs when the franchisee purchases only the right to become identified with the franchisor's trade name.
Answer F   Page 103

72. Pure franchising involves the right to use all the elements of a fully integrated business operation.
Answer T   Page 103

73. Over α of franchises are owned by women, either outright or as part of a male-female team.
Answer T   Page 103

74. Franchising benefits the <u>franchisor</u> by providing a quick way to expand the distribution system and a way to grow without the cost and effort to develop managers internally.
Answer T   Page 104

75. As with most franchises, the key to McDonald's success is the standardization of their product, processes, etc.
Answer T   Page 105

76. McDonald's relies almost exclusively on the trade name type of franchising.
Answer F   Page 105

77. Over 70% of all franchisors have more than 60 locations.
Answer F   Page 106

78. When a franchisee buys a franchise, he/she is purchasing the expertise and the business experience of the franchisor.
Answer T   Page 106

79. The basic and first question an entrepreneur should ask him/herself before jumping into a franchise is, "How much is this going to cost me?"
Answer F   Page 106

80. Quality is so important in franchising that most franchisors retain the right to terminate the franchise contract and to repurchase the outlet if a franchisee fails to maintain quality standards.
Answer T   Page 107

81. Most franchisors provide extensive financial help like loans and low-rate financing for their franchises.
Answer F   Page 108

82. Buying a franchise prevents an entrepreneur from making many mistakes and avoids the most inefficient type of learning—trial and error.
Answer T   Page 109

83. According to experts, the most important factor in franchising is location.
Answer T   Page 109

84. Most franchisors do <u>not</u> offer franchisees territorial protection, denying them the right to exclusive distribution of the brand name in a particular geographic area.
Answer F   Page 109

85. The failure rate for franchises is well below that for other types of new businesses.
Answer T   Page 110

86. By signing the franchise contract, a franchisee typically surrenders some freedom and autonomy in operating his/her business.
Answer T   Page 110

87. The primary thing that Manuel Morales did before buying an HQ Business Center franchise was talk with a number of franchisees and visit over 20 HQ Centers.
Answer T   Page 111

88. The only fee that franchisors can collect from franchisees is a one-time franchise fee   paid at the outset of the relationship.
Answer F   Page 112

89. In addition to other fees, franchisees must also pay royalties but only on net profits—no profits, no royalties.
Answer F   Page 112

90. In many franchises, strict uniformity is the rule rather than the exception.
Answer T   Page 112

91. Franchisors can require franchisees to purchase materials and supplies only from approved suppliers.
Answer T   Page 113

92. Franchisees generally sell only those products or services that the franchisor has approved but may sell complimentary products as long as they aren't a second competing franchise.
Answer F   Page 113

93. Territorial encroachment is becoming a hotly contested issue as franchisors have nearly exhausted prime locations for franchises.
Answer T   Page 113

94. Independent entrepreneurs with a "go-my-own-way" attitude are ideally suited for becoming franchisees.
Answer F   Page 114

95. The ideal franchisee is 25-35, female, risk adverse, and an experienced creative, outgoing person who's eager to succeed, but not so independent that she resents other people's advice.
Answer F   Page 115

96. It is important for potential entrepreneurs to have extensive experience in the business in which they are buying a franchise.
Answer F   Page 115

97. The typical franchisor does not require a franchisee to have high levels of formal education, but the potential franchisee must be motivated to succeed and be financially stable.
Answer T   Page 115

98. The FTC Trade Regulation Rule applies to all franchisors in all states regardless of state disclosure laws.
Answer T   Page 116

99. If a franchisor encourages you to sign without reading the agreement, or discourages you from "spending the money on an attorney," this is a warning sign that the franchisor might be dishonest.
Answer T   Page 116

100. New York was the first state to enact the Franchise Investment Law, which has since been adopted by numerous other states.
Answer F   Page 116

101. According to the Trade Regulation Rule, every franchisor must provide detailed information on their operations at the first personal contact, or at least 10 days before a franchise contract is signed.
Answer T   Page 116

102. The FTC verifies the accuracy of the franchise disclosure information required by the Trade Regulation Rule.
Answer F   Page 118

103. One expert, the president of a franchise consulting firm, estimates that 5–10% of franchises are dishonest.
Answer T   Page 118

104. One of the best ways for an entrepreneur to evaluate a potential franchisor is to interview several franchise owners who have been in business at least one year.
Answer T   Page 120

105. Do not heed any information gathered from past franchisees, because they will distort the reasons why they left the franchise.
Answer F   Page 120

106. Most often, disputes over a franchise contract arise after the agreement is in force.
Answer T   Page 123

107. The franchise contract defines the rights and the obligations of both parties and sets the guidelines which govern the franchise relationship.
Answer T   Page 123

108. Having an attorney review and evaluate a franchise contract really is unnecessary since the FTC requires all franchisors to offer a "standard" franchise contract.
Answer F   Page 123

109. The most litigated subject of a franchise agreement is the termination of the contract by either party.
Answer T   Page 123

110. Franchisors are obligated to renew a franchisees' contract unless there has been malfeasance on the part of the franchise.
Answer F   Page 123

111. In most cases, a franchisee does not have to get the franchisor's approval to sell the franchise to a third party.
Answer F   Page 124

112. Franchising, as a method of conducting business, has declined in importance in the past five years in international markets.
Answer F   Page 125

113. The primary market for U.S. franchisors is Canada, with Japan and Europe next.
Answer T   Page 125

114. Mos Burgers in Japan have competed with McDonald's by carefully copying what McDonald's has done and then undercutting McDonald's prices.
Answer F   Page 126

115. Nancy has owned her own hair salon for ten years. She's recently signed an agreement with Budget Cutters to become one of their outlets. This is an example of conversion franchising.
Answer T   Page 127

116. A multi-unit franchise gives the franchisee the right to open more than one franchise outlet in a territory within a specific time frame.
Answer T   Page 127

117. A master franchise gives the franchisee the right to combine two distinct franchises under one roof.
Answer F   Page 128

118. When Wal-Mart began having McDonald's restaurants share their retail space they were exercising master franchising.
Answer F   Page 128

119. A significant growth area in franchising is providing time-saving services to baby boomers.
Answer T   Page 128

120. Molly Maid is primarily using the Internet to provide better support and to stay in close contact with their franchisees.

Answer T   Page 129

Essay Questions

121. Franchising is an important part of the U.S. economy. Briefly explain its importance, define franchising, and identify the three basic types of franchises.

Pages 102–103

122. Explain the benefits of franchising to the franchisee.

Pages 106–110

123. Although franchising is the fastest growing segment of small business, it has drawbacks. Name and explain at least five drawbacks to franchising from the franchisee's perspective.

Pages 110–114

124. What characteristics do franchisors look for in a "good franchisee."

Pages 115–116

125. What is the Uniform Franchise Offering Circular? Offer several examples of what type of information is required in the UFOC.

Pages 116–118

126. What clues should you look for that should arouse your suspicions regarding the honesty and legitimacy of a franchise? Identify at least eight.

Page 118

127. Outline the process of buying a franchise naming and briefly explaining each step you should go through.

Pages 119–122

128. Discuss franchise contracts covering their current state, factors in their termination, renewal, and transfer, and what the most common dispute tends to be.

Pages 123–124

129. Describe the key trends that will affect franchising over the next decade.

Pages 125–128

Mini-Case

Case 4.1 - Pipe Dreams

Ralph Emerson thought he'd been a librarian long enough, and when the opportunity to open a small tobacco, pipe, and cigar shop in the newly renovated downtown business district arose, he was ready to act. Pipe Dreams is a franchisor of smoke shops, and was founded eight years ago by a noted tobacconist in New York City. The concept for the shops is simple, yet sophisticated. It is simple in the sense that the shops sell only tobacco-related products, but sophisticated in the breadth and quality of the inventory they carry. Each franchise, depending on size, is stocked with inventory selected by the company's founder. The franchisor finances the shop's initial inventory. The franchisee is expected to create a decor within predetermined standards that Pipe Dreams establishes. Each franchisee must attend a three-day workshop, outlining the fundamentals of tobacco blending, the merchandising of pipes and cigars, and the techniques of successful business operation.

The franchise contract requires the franchisee to contribute 1.5% of gross revenue to a national advertising campaign. According to the contract, Pipe Dreams will finance the required fixtures for the store for ten years. Also, the franchisor supplies all inventory at very favorable prices because it purchases in large quantities.

Ralph knows he can buy tobacco products from a variety of wholesalers. He also has some ideas on what would make a tobacco shop successful in this town. Ralph knows that Pipe Dreams franchisees have had a high success rate in the past.

Questions

1. Help Ralph make a decision by outlining the advantages and the disadvantages of a franchise agreement.

2. Assuming that Ralph has adequate capital, would you recommend that he invest in the franchise or open his own tobacco shop? Why?

Chapter 5 –
Buying an Existing Business

Multiple Choice

1. It is estimated that more than ____ companies are sold each year and the average value is less than:
   a) 1 million, $10 million.
   b) 500,000, $5 million.
   c) 250,000, $3.5 million.
   d) 175,000, $2.5 million.

Answer b   Page 134

2. When buying an existing business, the potential buyer should remember that:
   a) it is a long process and the buyer should be patient.
   b) existing businesses often do not continue to be successful after a change in ownership.
   c) it is often more difficult to find capital for an existing business than it is for a start-up.
   d) he/she will likely have to make significant changes in the work force.

Answer a   Page 135

3. One of buying an existing business is:
   a) you always get the best location.
   b) the opportunity to participate in a national advertising campaign.
   c) equipment is installed and production capacity is known.
   d) easy implementation of innovations and changes from past policies

Answer c   Page 135

4. One significant similarity between starting a company and buying a franchise is:
   a) getting a motivated and trained work force.
   b) the opportunity to get management assistance in running the company.
   c) the current profit potential of the business.
   d) having inventory in place.

Answer b   Page 136

5. When it comes to buying an existing business, it is not uncommon to find it:
   a) overpriced.
   b) difficult to finance.
   c) with accounts receivable worth more than face value.
   d) bargain priced.

Answer d   Page 136

6. When buying an existing business, one should remember that:
   a) it is generally not important to independently evaluate the inventory.
   b) you are always buying goodwill with the tangible assets of the business.
   c) it is as easy to make change in an existing business as it is in a start-up.
   d) the real reason for selling is seldom stated honestly.

Answer d   Page 137

7. The inventory in an existing business:
    a) is always current and salable.
    b) usually appreciate over time, making the business a bargain.
    c) needs to be checked for age and salability.
    d) is usually stated honestly and does not need independent auditing.

Answer c   Page 138

8. Accounts receivable in an existing business:
    a) are rarely worth their face value.
    b) unlike inventory, are often worth their face value.
    c) appreciate over time due to interest and penalties.
    d) are not a significant consideration when buying an existing business.

Answer a   Page 138

9. Research shows that nearly ___ of all business acquisitions fail to meet the buyer's expectations.
    a) 25%
    b) 33%
    c) 50%
    d) 67%

Answer c   Page 139

10. The first step an entrepreneur should take when acquiring an existing business is to:
    a) explore financing options.
    b) prepare a list of potential candidates.
    c) analyze his/her skills, abilities, and interests in an honest self-audit.
    d) contact existing business owners in the area and ask if their companies are for sale.

Answer c   Page 139

11. Once an entrepreneur has evaluated him/herself, the next step in the acquisition process would be to:
    a) explore financing options.
    b) prepare a list of potential candidates and investigate them.
    c) work on a smooth transition.
    d) evaluate the physical condition of the business.

Answer b   Page 139

12. When conducting a self-evaluation, it is important to consider:
    a) what kind of business you want to have and want to avoid.
    b) how much money you have to invest.
    c) what kind of people you like to work with.
    d) how good are your sales and negotiating skills.

Answer a   Page 139

. 13. The biggest source for the best companies to buy is:
    a) business brokers.
    b) commercial bankers.
    c) trade associations.

    d) the hidden market.

Answer d   Page 140

14. The process of gathering information about the company, valuing the company, and performing a detailed review of all records, agreements, and compliance is called:
    a) a letter of intent.
    b) nondisclosure.
    c) valuation.
    d) due diligence.

Answer d   Page 141

15. When negotiating the deal, the most important thing to remember is:
    a) terms are more important than the price paid.
    b) to negotiate the lowest possible price.
    c) often the difference in available funds can be made up by collecting accounts payable.
    d) the owner of the business always asks 14–22% more than he/she is willing to take.

Answer a   Page 141

16. Perhaps the ideal source of financing the purchase of an existing business is:
    a) the seller.
    b) the Small Business Administration.
    c) a venture banker.
    d) your local bank.

Answer a   Page 142

17. Which of the following statements concerning the financing of a business purchase is true?
    a) Often, the business seller is a poor source of financing.
    b) The buyer should be able to make the payments on the loans out of the company's cash flow.
    c) The buyer should begin arranging financing late in the purchasing process, to avoid the processing expenses if the deal falls through.
    d) Traditional lenders tend to be more eager to lend on an existing business than they are with a start-up.

Answer b   Page 142

18. Which of the following is a way to smooth the transition of leadership/management from the seller of a business to the buyer?
    a) Focus on the customer, offer new incentives, improve customer service.
    b) Focus on the employees, listen to them, keep them informed.
    c) Concentrate on operations, updating equipment and changing processes.
    d) Visit your competitors and introduce yourself and get to know them.

Answer b   Page 142

19. When approaching a candidate company, the buyer should:
    a) immediately sign a "no compete" covenant agreement with the seller to show good faith.
    b) always use a business broker to smooth the purchase process.
    c) request both personal and business financial statements from the owner.
    d) bring a letter of intent with him/her.

Answer c   Page 143

20. During the acquisition process, the potential buyer must sign a _____ which is an agreement to keep all conversations and information secret and legally binds the buyer from telling anyone any information the seller shares with him/her.
    a) no compete covenant
    b) nondisclosure statement
    c) letter of intent
    d) purchase agreement

Answer b   Page 143

21. In evaluating an existing business, entrepreneurs should seek to answer several questions, including:
    a) can financing be arranged?
    b) what business broker should I use?
    c) what industries will be "hot" in the future and is this business in one of them?
    d) what legal aspects should be considered?

Answer d   Page 144

22. The most common reasons owners of small- and medium-sized businesses give for selling their businesses are:
    a) need for money and low return on investment.
    b) boredom and burnout.
    c) low return on investment and burnout.
    d) poor location and low return on investment.

Answer b   Page 144

23. When a buyer is reviewing a candidate company's lease arrangements, location and appearance, intangible assets, etc., he is answering what basic acquisition question?
    a) Is the business financially sound?
    b) Why does the owner want to sell?
    c) What is the physical condition of the business?
    d) What legal aspects should be considered?

Answer c   Page 145

24. If the firm owns any trademarks, patents, or copyrights, or has built up a positive reputation with customers and suppliers, the business has what is/are called:
    a) capital.
    b) goodwill.
    c) intangible assets.
    d) market potential.

Answer c   Page 145

25. Before buying an existing business, the buyer should analyze two external elements of the business:
    a) its capital and market potential.
    b) its customer characteristics and direct competitors.
    c) its intangible assets and financial status.
    d) the market potential of the products and the existing inventory.

Answer b   Page 145–146

26. The biggest factor that moved Hendrix Neimann to buying Automatic Door Specialists was:
    a) time.
    b) money.
    c) the owner's expertise.
    d) the viability of the market.
Answer a   Page 147

27. When Hendrix Neimann visited ADS and talked to the employees, he discovered:
    a) the company was as the owner had represented it.
    b) the company was a potential goldmine and was in much better shape than he anticipated.
    c) fraud; the owner had liens against the company and was not in a position to sell it.
    d) the employees' perspective was much different and more negative than the owners.
Answer d   Page 147

28. Which of the following is a criterion for a bulk transfer?
    a) The buyer must take physical possession of all assets within 10 days of sale.
    b) The buyer must have rights to all intangible assets.
    c) Letters from the seller's attorney must attest to the fact that there are no liens or suits against the company.
    d) The buyer must give notice of the sale to each creditor at least 10 days before he takes possession of the goods or pays them for the goods.
Answer d   Page 148

29. Normally, when buying a business, the seller:
    a) does not sign a restrictive covenant.
    b) notifies creditors 10 days prior to the sale of the business.
    c) cannot assign his credit arrangements with suppliers to the buyer.
    d) has little formal role or obligation in preparing documents and information necessary to the sale.
Answer c   Page 148

30. An agreement between a business seller and the buyer, in which the seller agrees not to open a competing business within a specific time period and geographic area, is called a:
    a) nondisclosure statement.
    b) restrictive covenant.
    c) bulk transfer.
    d) letter of intent.
Answer b   Page 148

31. To be enforceable, a covenant not to compete must be:
    a) for the life of the business.
    b) approved by a court of law.
    c) for both direct and indirect competitive businesses.
    d) reasonable in scope.
Answer d   Page 149

32. When the buyer is examining the income statements, tax returns, and balance sheets of the business, he/she is seeking an answer to the basic question:
    a) Is the business financially sound?
    b) Why does the owner want to sell?
    c) What is the physical condition of the business?
    d) What legal aspects should be considered?

Answer a   Page 149

33. When seeking to evaluate the financial soundness of the company prior to purchase, the buyer needs to examine several specific financial elements including:
    a) the company's lease agreement for its facilities.
    b) any current product liability suits.
    c) the current owner's (and relatives') compensation.
    d) the physical plant and existing inventory.

Answer c   Page 150

34. It is important to remember when assessing the financial soundness of a company that:
    a) if profits are adequate, there will be sufficient funds to pay salaries and fund cash flow.
    b) cash flow is the key financial element in determining financial soundness.
    c) revenues need to equal twice the debt load in order for the company to be viable.
    d) the buyer is buying the past revenues and profits of the company.

Answer b   Page 150

35. Which of the following statements about valuing a business is true?
    a) The balance sheet technique is the best way to value a business.
    b) Business valuation is partly art and partly science.
    c) Buyers should rely on established "rules of thumb" to decide what a company is worth.
    d) The primary reason buyers purchase existing businesses is to get their current earning potential.

Answer b   Page 151

36. When valuing a business:
    a) no surprise is the best surprise.
    b) only the owner/seller has access to business records.
    c) it is wisest to use one method of valuing for the sake of consistency.
    d) the potential buyer should remember that this is an important process because he/she is buying the current earning potential of the company.

Answer a   Page 151

37. The valuation method that is commonly used, but tends to oversimplify the valuation process, is called:
    a) the excess-earnings method.
    b) the balance sheet method.
    c) the capitalization method.
    d) the market approach.

Answer b   Page 153

38. A valuation method that is more realistic than the balance sheet because it adjusts book value to reflect actual market value is the:
    a) excess-earnings method.
    b) market approach.
    c) capitalization method.
    d) adjusted balance sheet method.

Answer d   Page 153

39. Which of the following valuation methods does <u>not</u> consider the future income-earning potential of a business?
    a) Balance sheet technique
    b) Excess-earnings method
    c) Discounted future earnings approach
    d) Market approach

Answer a   Page 153

40. The valuation approach that considers the value of goodwill is the:
    a) balance sheet technique.
    b) excess-earnings method.
    c) discounted future earnings approach.
    d) market approach.

Answer b   Page 155

41. A normal-risk business typically has a rate of return of:
    a) 15%.
    b) 25%.
    c) 35%.
    d) 50%.

Answer b   Page 155

42. In the excess earnings approach to business valuation, a stable, well-established business would use a years-of-profit figure of:
    a) 1.
    b) 3.
    c) 7.
    d) 10.

Answer c   Page 157

43. In the earnings method of business valuation, the "years of profit" figure associated with a "normal risk" business is:
    a) 1–2.
    b) 3–4.
    c) 5–6.
    d) 8–10.

Answer b   Page 157

44. When it comes to transferring goodwill in a business valuation, goodwill:

a) is considered an intangible asset and therefore not taxed.
b) can be used as a deduction by the seller.
c) is taxed for the seller as capital gains.
d) cannot be used as a deduction by the buyer because it is a capital asset.
Answer d   Page 157

45. The capitalized earnings approach determines the value of a business by capitalizing its expected profits using:
a) the rate of return reflecting the risk level.
b) the prime interest rate.
c) the normal rate of return.
d) the prevailing rate of inflation.
Answer a   Page 157

46. The _____ approach to valuing a business assumes that a dollar earned in the future is worth less than that same dollar is today.
a) balance sheet
b) capitalized earnings
c) excess earnings
d) discounted future earnings
Answer d   Page 158

47. Which method of business valuation relies on three forecasts of future earnings—optimistic, pessimistic, and most likely?
a) Balance sheet technique
b) Excess-earnings method
c) Discounted future earnings
d) Market approach
Answer c   Page 158

48. The _____ approach to valuing a business uses the price-earnings ratios of similar businesses to establish the value of a company.
a) balance sheet
b) capitalized earnings
c) discounted future earnings
d) market
Answer d   Page 159

49. A company's P/E ratio is:
a) the price of one share of its common stock divided by its earnings per share.
b) its profits per share divided by its equity per share.
c) its profits per share divided by its excess cash flow per share.
d) the price of one share of its common stock divided by external capitalization.
Answer a   Page 159

50. Which of the following is a drawback of the market approach of valuation?
a) It does not consider current earnings.

b) It may underrepresent earnings.
c) Its reliability depends on the forecasts of future earnings.
d) It over emphasizes the value of goodwill.
Answer b   Page 160

Use the following facts to answer questions 51 through 54.
Baubles and Bells, a small business, is up for sale. The book value of its assets is $397,650, and its liabilities have a book value of $148,500. After adjusting for market value, total assets are worth $386,475, and total liabilities are $153,600. The business is considered to be a "normal risk" venture. The new owner (if he buys) plans to draw a salary of $28,000. Estimated earnings for the upcoming year are $88,400. Complete net earnings estimates for the next five years are:

	Pessimistic	Most Likely	Optimistic
Year 1	$82,000	$88,400	90,500
Year 2	85,000	90,000	93,000
Year 3	88,000	92,500	95,500
Year 4	91,000	95,000	97,000
Year 5	94,000	97,000	98,500

51. Using the balance sheet technique, what is the business worth?
     a) $397,650
     b) $386,475
     c) $249,150
     d) $232,875
Answer c   Page 153

52. Using the adjusted balance sheet technique, what is the business worth?
     a) $397,650
     b) $386,475
     c) $249,150
     d) $232,875
Answer d   Page 153

53. Under the excess earnings method, what is the "extra earning power" of the business?
     a) $86,219
     b) $ 2,181
     c) $11,175
     d) It cannot be determined from the information given.
Answer b   Page 155

54. Using the excess earnings approach, what is the value of the business?
     a) $241,600
     b) $255,693
     c) $239,418
     d) $333,525
Answer c   Page 155–156

55. The majority of small business sales:

    a) are asset sales.
    b) involve the sale of stock, not assets.
    c) involve a stock swap.
    d) involve bank financing with a balloon payment at the end of five years.
Answer a   Page 162

56. About ____ of business sales include covenants to not compete.
    a) 10%
    b) 40%
    c) 5%
    d) 50%
Answer b   Page 162

57. The mechanics of most small business sales involve:
    a) a cash buyout with no financing.
    b) a down payment with a note carried by the seller.
    c) no down payment with a note carried by the seller.
    d) an exchange of one company's stock for another, and stock options for senior managers.
Answer b   Page 162

58. A survey found that ____ of small business owners would sell to an international buyer.
    a) 29%
    b) 98%
    c) 35%
    d) 69%
Answer d   Page 163

59. _____ gives owners the security of a sales contract but permits them to stay at the "helm" for several years.
    a) A controlled sale
    b) Company restructuring
    c) The two-step sale
    d) An ESOP
Answer c   Page 164

60. ESOPs:
    a) allow owners to transfer all or part of their companies to their employees as gradually or as quickly as they choose.
    b) work best in companies where pre-tax profits exceed $50,000.
    c) are beneficial for companies with fewer than 15 to 20 employees.
    d) are one way to sell to an international buyer.
Answer a   Page 164

True or False Questions

61. An important advantage of buying an existing business is the greater likelihood that it will continue to survive and thrive in the marketplace.
Answer T   Page 135

62. With an existing business, the new owner can depend on employees to help him/her make money while he/she is learning the business.
Answer T   Page 135

63. For a new owner of an existing business, physical facilities and equipment costs are very similar to what would have been spent on a start-up with all new facilities and equipment.
Answer F   Page 135

64. When trying to buy an existing business that is more specialized, the buyer will probably pay a premium price.
Answer F   Page 136

65. While there are numerous advantages to buying an existing business, there are also some disadvantages, like the previous owner having created ill-will rather than goodwill with customers and suppliers.
Answer T   Page 137

66. A new owner of an existing business can generally introduce change and innovation almost as easily as if the company was a new business start-up.
Answer F   Page 137

67. Generally speaking, current employees will prove flexible and able to meet whatever changes the new owner desires to make once the business is acquired.
Answer F   Page 137

68. A buyer should never trust the firm's balance sheet evaluation of inventory but should conduct an independent assessment of inventory age and salability.
Answer T   Page 138

69. Accounts receivable are rarely worth face value, and should be "aged" when evaluating a company's assets.
Answer T   Page 138

70. Failing to age accounts receivable could lead a buyer into paying more for a business than it is worth.
Answer T   Page 138

71. Buying businesses is generally a positive experience, with nearly 75% of buyers saying the business acquisition more than met their expectations.
Answer F   Page 239

72. The business acquisition process should begin with creating a list of criteria for selecting the business to buy.
Answer F   Page 139

73. Part of a "self-audit" when buying a business is to ask yourself "what do I expect to get out of the business" and "how much can I put into the business?"

Answer T   Page 139

74. "Knocking on the doors" of businesses an entreprenuer would like to buy—although they are not advertised "for sale"—is a waste time.
Answer F   Page 140

75. In most business sales, the buyer bears the responsibility of determining whether or not the business is a good value.
Answer T   Page 141

76. The final price a buyer pays for a business depends, in part, on the buyer's skills as a negotiator.
Answer T   Page 141

77. Traditional lenders of capital often shy away from deals involving the purchase of an existing business.
Answer T   Page 142

78. The most likely cause of obstacles to a smooth transition from the seller of a business to the buyer is people dynamics—the stress of the anxiety created by the sale that leads to resistance to change.
Answer T   Page 142

79. The most common reasons that owners of small businesses give for selling are the intensity of competition and an inability to raise sufficient cash to continue to grow.
Answer F   Page 144

80. The entrepreneur who buys an existing business must recognize that accounts receivable rarely are worth their "face value."
Answer T   Page 145

81. Most business buyers can expect to find detailed, accurate, and audited financial records in the companies they are looking at buying.
Answer F   Page 145

82. Before purchasing an existing business, an entrepreneur should analyze closely both direct and indirect competitors.
Answer F   Page 147

83. Any liens against a business must be satisfied by the current owner before the sale can be consumated.
Answer F   Page 147

84. If a banker requires the current loan on a business to be paid at the time of the sale to the new owner, the banker will require a due-on-sale clause in the agreement.
Answer T   Page 148

85. A bulk transfer prevents creditors of the seller of a business from laying claim to the assets the buyer purchases to satisfy the seller's debts.

Answer T   Page 148

86. To be enforceable, a restrictive covenant must be comprehensive, have a term of 3–5 years, and must contain a total-prohibition clause.
Answer F   Page 148

87. Ralph buys a software business from Waldo in Columbus, Ohio. As part of the deal, Waldo signs a covenant not to compete by opening another software business anywhere in Ohio for the rest of his life. Such a covenant would be enforceable.
Answer F   Page 148–149

88. If the corporation, rather than the business seller, signs a restrictive covenant, the seller may not be bound by its terms.
Answer T   Page 149

89. When a buyer purchases an existing business, she may "inherit" liability for damages and injuries caused by products the company has manufactured or sold in the past.
Answer T   Page 149

90. When an entrepreneur purchases an existing business, he or she essentially is purchasing its future profit potential.
Answer T   Page 149

91. A business owner who buys a company whose financial statements show a pattern of short-term profitability is guaranteed of getting a good deal.
Answer F   Page 150

92. The best method for valuing a business is to use established rules of thumb.
Answer F   Page 151

93. Hendrix Neimann faced several problems with ADS once he bought it but the problem that eventually caused him to close his doors was a weak cash flow.
Answer T   Page 152

94. The balance sheet technique of determining a business's value uses the company's net worth or owner's equity as the firm's value, but it oversimplifies the valuation process.
Answer T   Page 153

95. The adjusted balance sheet method of valuing a business changes the book value of net worth to reflect actual market value.
Answer T   Page 153

96. Business evaluations based on balance sheet methods offer one key advantage: they consider the future earning potential of the business.
Answer F   Page 153

97. Neither the balance sheet method nor the adjusted balance sheet method of valuing a business consider the future earning power of the business.

Answer T   Page 153

98. In the excess earnings approach to business valuation, the earnings of comparable companies are needed to set the valuation of the company.
Answer F   Page 155

99. Goodwill is the difference between an established successful business, and one that has yet to prove itself.
Answer T   Page 155

100. Goodwill is a capital asset that the business buyer cannot depreciate or amortize for tax purposes.
Answer T   Page 157

101. Under the capitalized earnings approach to business valuation, firms with lower risk factors are more valuable than those with higher risk factors.
Answer T   Page 157

102. A purchaser should build his/her own pro forma income statement from an existing firm's accounting records and compare it to the same statement provided by the owner.
Answer T   Page 157

103. According to the discounted future earnings technique, a dollar earned in the future is worth more than a dollar earned today.
Answer F   Page 158

104. The reliability of the discounted future earnings approach to valuing a business depends on making realistic forecasts of future earnings and on choosing the proper present value rate.
Answer T   Page 158

105. The market approach to company valuation evaluates goodwill, risk-of-return, and estimated net earnings.
Answer F   Page 159

106. The market approach to valuing a company relies primarily on the price/earnings ratio of the company in comparison to the average P/E of similar companies.
Answer T   Page 159

107. A disadvantage of the market approach to valuing a business is finding similar companies for comparison.
Answer T   Page 160

108. Most business sales are relatively uncomplicated and take little time to arrange.
Answer F   Page 160

109. When Kurtz and Alexander sought to buy the company where Kurtz worked, they looked carefully at the cash flow to be sure it could service the debt they would take on.
Answer T   Page 161

110. A recent survey of small businesses shows that 94% of the business sales were asset sales rather than stock.
Answer T   Page 162

111. Only about 10% of business sales studied included covenants not to compete.
Answer F   Page 162

112. Owners who do not want to sell a business outright, but want to either stay around for a while or surrender control gradually can use a restructuring strategy.
Answer T   Page 163

113. Executives at companies purchased by foreign buyers say that their relationships with their foreign owners improve over time.
Answer F   Page 163

114. A two-step sale is when the new buyer assumes the role of president and the current owner stays on as CEO, then in one to two years the current owner retires and the new buyer assumes both roles.
Answer F   Page 164

115. To use an ESOP successfully, a company should have pre-tax profits of at least $100,000 and a payroll exceeding $500,000 a year.
Answer T   Page 164

116. When negotiating the deal, it is important to remember that the seller is looking for the best terms and to maintain some conduct with the company, at least for a while.
Answer F   Page 165

117. The buyer of the business wants to minimize the cash up front and avoid enabling the seller to open a competing business.
Answer T   Page 165

118. The biggest reason Neimann had to close the doors on ADS is that its product line was obsolete and they couldn't compete.
Answer F   Page 166

119. It is important that both the buyer and seller have their objectives thought out, written down, and prioritized when they go into the negotiation.
Answer T   Page 166

120. One way to get a mutually satisfying deal when negotiating is to recognize and try to meet the other parties need(s).
Answer T   Page 167

Essay Questions
121. Briefly describe the advantages and disadvantages of buying an existing business.
Pages 135–138

122. Outline the logical approach one should take in buying a business, naming each step and explaining it briefly.
Pages 139–144

123. What key questions need to be answered in the process of due diligence?
Page 141

124. Discuss the seven-step process for ensuring a smooth transition between owners in the purchase of a company.
Page 143

125. What are the five critical questions a business buyer must ask when evaluating an existing business?
Pages 144–151

126. Review the five key legal issues an entrepreneur needs to consider when evaluating an existing business.
Pages 147–149

127. What financial records should be examined when determining the financial soundness of a company and what should the entrepreneur look for in each?
Pages 149–150

128. What guidelines should be kept in mind when deciding how to value a company?
Pages 151–152

129. How does one value a company using the balance sheet method? Why would an entrepreneur choose this method of valuation?
Pages 153–155

130. Describe the earnings approach for valuing a company, outlining the calculation and the strengths and weaknesses of this technique.
Pages 155–159
131. Explain five exit strategies business owners can use for their businesses.
Pages 162–164

Mini-Cases

Case 5-1: Can You Trust Mom and Pop?
"To tell you the truth, son, Mom and I just want to retire and take it easy. We've operated this restaurant for a lot of years and have built up a good customer base. Mom's cooking has always brought them in and the service has always been quick and courteous."

Jim Phillips is well aware that a restaurant can be a profitable business venture, but he doesn't know much about Mom & Pop's Diner and how successful it really is. Fred and Ethel, the owners, appear to be straightforward, honest people. Jim recently saw the ad for the restaurant in the state trade association magazine and has driven 200 miles to check it out.

Mom & Pop's Diner is located in a working class neighborhood in a large Eastern city. It is housed in an older building and could use some renovation. When Jim mentions the condition of the equipment, Ethel laughs and says, "They don't make stuff like this anymore, Sonny." Jim also is concerned by the fact that several franchised restaurant chains have opened in the past few years within one mile of the diner. Jim is puzzled when he askes Fred if he can study the diner's financial statements for the past five years and Fred says, "What financial statements? What do you think we are, a corporation? I guess last year we cleared about $22,000."

Questions

1. If you were Jim Phillips, how would you further investigate Mom & Pop's Diner?

2. Identify any warning signs to Jim that all may not be as it seems.

3. What are some of the potential problems Jim faces if he buys the diner?

Case 5-2: What's It Worth?

Lauren Holcombe has wanted to open her own clothing store since she was in high school. Her career interest and dynamic personality enabled her to get a part-time job at a small women's clothing shop in her hometown after school. When Lauren enrolled in the state university to major in retail management, she got a part-time job in the ladies' clothing section of a prestigious department store in the city. Lauren's supervisor was impressed with her business acumen and her congenial personality: "Lauren is one of the best workers we've ever had in this department. She's very bright, quite attractive, and very outgoing. Lauren is eager to learn everything she can about the business; she's always asking questions!"

During Lauren's senior year in college, her Aunt Bessie died and left her an inheritance totaling nearly $300,000. "I'll miss dear old Aunt Bessie, but have I got plans for my inheritance! Now, I'll be able to run my own clothing store just like I've always dreamed." Lauren immediately began planning to launch her business venture, but progress was slow. During a trip to her hometown over the Christmas break, Lauren discovered that a well-established ladies' clothing shop was up for sale. The shop was well known and quite successful, but the owner, Kathleen Todd, was quitting to retire in Tahiti. Lauren contacted Ms. Todd to discuss the sale of the business.

Ms. Todd hired a company to conduct an independent appraisal of the business, which concluded that tangible assets were $230,000 and assumable liabilities were $18,000. The appraisal estimated net profit for the next fiscal year to be $73,800 before deducting any managerial salaries. Lauren expects to draw $20,000 in salary since she believes this is the salary she could expect when working for someone else. Lauren estimates that a reasonable rate of return on an investment of similar risk is 25%. Ms. Todd has set a value of $85,000 for intangibles such as goodwill, and is asking $297,000 for the business.

Questions

1. Using the capitalized earnings method, calculate the value of the business.

2. Based on the excess earnings approach, what do you estimate the business to be worth?

3. Given the following earnings estimates, compute the value of the business using the discounted future earnings technique:

Number of years into the future	Pessimistic	Most Likely	Optimistic
1	$62,000	$73,800	$75,000
2	65,000	75,000	77,000
3	68,000	77,000	79,000
4	71,000	79,000	80,000
5	73,000	80,000	82,000

4. Is Ms. Todd's asking price reasonable? How much should Lauren offer Ms. Todd at the beginning of the negotiation process?

Chapter 6 –
Creating the Marketing Plan

Multiple Choice

1. A business plan for the small business owner:
   a) is of relatively little importance due to the dynamic nature of the marketplace.
   b) is synonymous with the marketing plan.
   c) tends to stress how the entrepreneur will operate rather than detailing what he/she wants to accomplish.
   d) contains both a marketing plan and a financial plan.
   Answer d   Page 172

2. _____ is the process of creating and delivering desired goods and services to customers, and involves all of the activities associated with winning and retaining loyal customers.
   a) Marketing
   b) Personal selling
   c) Promotion
   d) Advertising and public relations
   Answer a   Page 172

3. Small businesses can compete with larger rivals with bigger budgets by employing unconventional, low-cost creative techniques known as:
   a) market research.
   b) astonishing customer service.
   c) guerrilla marketing techniques.
   d) psychographics.
   Answer c   Page 172

4. The focus of the small company's marketing plan is:
   a) its product or service.
   b) the customer.
   c) attracting capital.
   d) an evaluation of key competitors.
   Answer b   Page 172

5. The marketing plan builds a strategy for success:
   a) from the customer's point of view.
   b) as described by the marketing manager.
   c) based on eliminating all competition.
   d) by focusing on product development and market management.
   Answer a   Page 173

6. The marketing plan should include certain key objectives, such as:
   a) determining product costs through market research.
   b) pinpointing the specific target markets a small business will serve.
   c) determining what costing strategies to use.
   d) discovering what the company's ETDB index is.
   Answer b   Page 173

7. Shifting patterns in the age, income, education, race, and other characteristics of the population are the subject of _____ and exert a potent force on a company's marketing plan.
   a) psychographics
   b) geographics
   c) demographics
   d) geo-demographics

Answer c   Page 174

8. A demographic trend is like a train for the small business owner in that:
   a) he/she needs to catch it and ride it to wherever it is going.
   b) he/she needs to discover where it is going early and decide whether or not to get on board.
   c) the small business will be "run over" if it doesn't get out of the way and try to work with the "spin-offs" from the trend.
   d) it is a slow process that is easily caught at several points, and the small business owner has lots of time to consider his/her options.

Answer b   Page 174

9. Market research:
   a) provides the information that is foundational to the marketing plan.
   b) is the process used to set the goals and objectives of the marketing plan.
   c) is prohibitively expensive for the small business owner.
   d) is relatively unimportant to the small business owner if the owner is close to his/her customers.

Answer a   Page 174

10. Market research answers what important question for the small business owner?
    a) How shall I set up my distribution system?
    b) What should my goals and objectives be in my marketing plan?
    c) Who are my customers and what are they looking for?
    d) What form of business ownership would be most effective in this market?

Answer c   Page 174

11. Marketing consultant Faith Popcorn recommends small business owners track market trends by:
    a) hiring one of the top 10 market research firms to track trends for you.
    b) watching what the large corporations in your industry are doing.
    c) talking with 2–3 people at random each week to hear what they're buying and why.
    d) reading as many current publications as possible.

Answer d   Page 176

12. Once the entrepreneur has some sense of the trends in his/her market, the next step is:
    a) to invest more money in products that don't fit the trends in order to better promote them.
    b) to compare how his/her products match the trends and dump any that aren't fitting the trends.
    c) to hire a market research company to advise him/her as to the product mix that will best fit the trends.
    d) to focus on product development.

Answer b   Page 176

13. A number of key trends are driving the marketing strategies of companies in the '90s, including:
    a) people working longer and retiring later.
    b) a move to more uniformity in attire and homes.
    c) a resurgence of trust in established icons and symbols.
    d) increased environmental and health concerns.

Answer d   Page 177

14. The primary goal of marketing research is to:
    a) discover potential competitors.
    b) reduce the risks associated with business decisions.
    c) determine how to allocate distribution resources.
    d) help management choose the appropriate promotional tool.

Answer b   Page 177

15. The first, and most critical, step in conducting market research is to:
    a) define the research problem clearly.
    b) collect data from available sources.
    c) design questionnaires and surveys.
    d) choose how to collect the data.

Answer a   Page 177

16. John wants to answer the question, "What drives my customers' buying behavior?" The best information to address this question comes from:
    a) demo/geographic data.
    b) geographics data.
    c) demographics data.
    d) psychographics data.

Answer d   Page 178

17. When it comes to gathering market research on customers, most small companies tend to be:
    a) as good at it as large companies.
    b) at a severe disadvantage in comparison to large companies.
    c) data rich, lots of facts, but information poor, little in a useful form.
    d) less effective at defining the research problem than larger companies.

Answer c   Page 178

18. One-to-one marketing is a '90s marketing strategy that:
    a) gathers data on individual customers and then tailors an appeal to their needs and tastes.
    b) uses technology to make customers feel like they are being treated special.
    c) focuses on the use of personal selling and consultative advising of customers.
    d) relies heavily on geographic data but ignores demographic and psychographic data.

Answer a   Page 178

19. For the results of market research to provide a solution to a small business owner's problem:
    a) it has to be acted on.
    b) the owner much attach meaning to it.
    c) it must be converted into numeric information.

d) the data should be less than two weeks old.

Answer b   Page 179

20. Effective one-to-one marketing involves:
    a) identifying your best customers.
    b) seeing customer complaints as an opportunity to improve service.
    c) learning what the customers' buying cycle is.
    d) all of these.

Answer d   Page 179

21. The first step in building a useful database is to:
    a) gather the information.
    b) identify the target customer.
    c) determine what information to collect.
    d) decide how much time and money to spend on the project.

Answer c   Page 180

22. Most marketing experts contend that the greatest marketing mistake small businesses make is:
    a) failing to identify the target market.
    b) spending too little on advertising.
    c) underpricing their products and services.
    d) spending too little on quality improvement.

Answer a   Page 181

23. When it comes to the target market, most successful businesses:
    a) have broad target markets, permitting them to offer a wide variety of products.
    b) have little concern for the image of their company, focusing solely on how their products meet target market needs.
    c) have well-defined "portraits" of the customers they want to attract.
    d) don't have a clue as to their target market but put forth enough effort to succeed anyway.

Answer c   Page 182

24. The key to marketing success in the ⁻90s is:
    a) economy of scale in promotion by creating broad-based ad campaigns.
    b) understanding customers' unique needs, wants and preferences.
    c) the use of direct-marketing and E-commerce.
    d) catering to teenagers.

Answer b   Page 182

25. Larissa Janus' idea for a CyberCafe came from:
    a) extensive market research conducted in her undergraduate marketing class.
    b) her personal experience while studying abroad.
    c) reading general circulation magazines.
    d) a friends' failed effort to do the same thing.

Answer b   Page 183

26. A company's competitive edge is:

    a)   dependent on the availability of its products.
    b)   largely a function of its pricing strategies.
    c)   the superiority of its market research.
    d)   based on customers' perception of its products and services.
Answer d   Page 184

27. One "natural" advantage small businesses have over large business, which can be a significant competitive advantage, is:
    a)   relationship marketing.
    b)   their ability to conduct market research.
    c)   their lower costs.
    d)   their ability to serve many highly diverse target markets.
Answer a   Page 184

28. Peter has a small coffee/pastry shop. He and his employees know that there is a large market out there for their goods because they see all the young professionals walking by to and from work and at lunch time. He's not sure what type of coffee or pastry they like. Peter is most likely at which level of customer involvement?
    a)   Level 1—customer awareness
    b)   Level 2—customer sensitivity
    c)   Level 3—customer alignment
    d)   Level 4—customer partnership
Answer a   Page 184

29. When managers and employees understand the central role of the customer and spend considerable time talking to them and about them, a company is at which level of customer involvement?
    a)   Level 1—customer awareness
    b)   Level 2—customer sensitivity
    c)   Level 3—customer alignment
    d)   Level 4—customer partnership
Answer c   Page 185

30. When customer service is part of a firm's culture and customers are part of all major issues, the company has reached what level of customer involvement?
    a)   Level 1—customer awareness
    b)   Level 2—customer sensitivity
    c)   Level 3—customer alignment
    d)   Level 4—customer partnership
Answer d   Page 185

31. The majority of customers who stop patronizing a particular store do so because:
    a)   its prices are too high.
    b)   its quality is too low.
    c)   an indifferent employee treated them poorly.
    d)   it failed to advertise enough.
Answer c   Page 186

32. ____% of dissatisfied customers never complain about rude or discourteous service, but __%
    will not buy from that business again.
    a) 10; 55
    b) 26; 75
    c) 45; 67
    d) 96; 91

Answer d   Page 186

33. Attracting a new customer costs _____ as much as keeping an existing one.
    a) twice
    b) five times
    c) half
    d) three-fourths

Answer b   Page 187

34. Companies do a number of things to focus on their customers, including:
    a) fixing customer complaints quickly.
    b) conducting market research on what superior customer service is.
    c) offering quality products at low prices.
    d) implementing a TCM management system in their production facility.

Answer a   Page 187

35. To build an effective customer service program, it is important to:
    a) offer low prices.
    b) train key employees to watch for and intervene when there are problems.
    c) swiftly discipline employees who mistreat customers.
    d) let managers wait on customers occasionally.

Answer d   Page 188

36. The worst catastrophe to befall any business would be to:
    a) encourage customers to complain and have employees give management feedback on the
        complaints.
    b) have great advertising and poor quality products.
    c) have poor customer service and a highly effective promotional campaign.
    d) have a great product and an inaccessible location.

Answer b   Page 188

37. The Total Quality Management (TQM) concept:
    a) strives to achieve quality not just in the product or service itself, but in every aspect of the
        business and its relationship with the customer.
    b) relies on quality inspections through an army of quality control inspectors.
    c) focuses on reducing the time it takes to fulfill a customer's request for a product.
    d) is built on market research.

Answer a   Page 189

38. ____ recognizes any improvement in quality must have a reasonable positive bottom line
    impact.

a) Customer service
b) Return on quality
c) Total quality management
d) Total customer satisfaction

Answer b   Page 189

39. Companies with strong reputations for quality follow certain guidelines, such as:
a) establishing long-term relationships with suppliers.
b) fostering individual effort and pride of workmanship.
c) rewarding employees for compliance to rules and procedures.
d) building an extensive quality inspection system with many quality inspectors.

Answer a   Page 189

40. Studies show that customers want ____ from businesses almost more than anything else.
a) quality
b) low cost
c) cutting edge technology
d) convenience

Answer d   Page 190

41. 99.9% quality is exemplified by which of the following?
a) 1 hour of unsafe drinking water every month
b) blackout of power for 1 hour each week in the average size town
c) 100,000 documents lost by the IRS each year
d) 2 million phone calls misrouted each year

Answer a   Page 190

42. Which company would rate the highest on an "Easy to do Business With" index?
a) Thomas's bakery won't take credit cards.
b) Louies Lower Level sandwich shop is in the basement of a building with a alley entrance.
c) Jane's Tailor shop is open from 10 a.m to 10 p.m six days a week.
d) Country Tom Motors service department only allows the service manager to answer the phone.

Answer c   Page 191

43. A study of companies with revenues under $50 million showed that:
a) 40% of the CEOs thought that customer service was relatively unimportant.
b) α of the companies had developed partnerships with customers for developing new products.
c) nearly β of their CEOs thought new product development was a major competitive advantage.
d) 75% spent 15% of their annual budget on R & D and innovation-related efforts.

Answer c   Page 192

44. When it comes to innovation, the small business and entrepreneur:
a) often can't afford to pursue it.
b) tend to lead the way in business.
c) do it through imitation of large companies.

   d) make heavy use of market research instead.
Answer b   Page 192

45. Small businesses are able to maintain a leadership role in innovation by:
   a) using their size, flexibility, and speed to their advantage.
   b) spending much more money on R & D than large companies do.
   c) foreseeing trends better and far enough in advance that they can spread innovation costs over several years.
   d) making better use of technology than large companies.
Answer a   Page 192

46. A key to effective innovation by the entrepreneur is:
   a) dedicating at least 20% of pre-tax revenues to R & D.
   b) always looking for new product and service ideas.
   c) hiring managers with a track record for innovation.
   d) none of these.
Answer b   Page 193

47. Small companies with limited financial resources can often use _____ as a way to differentiate themselves from larger competitors.
   a) innovation
   b) lower prices with higher quality
   c) high price and high quality
   d) customer service
Answer d   Page 193

48. Numerous surveys have concluded that the most important element of service is:
   a) the personal touch.
   b) convenient business hours.
   c) speedy transactions.
   d) innovative product design.
Answer a   Page 194

49. Time compression management (TCM) involves:
   a) speeding new products to market.
   b) enhancing the quality of existing products.
   c) decreasing the time it takes a product to move from introduction to the maturity stage of the product life cycle.
   d) shortening the sales clerks' response time to customers entering the retail store and then being served.
Answer a   Page 196

50. Companies using time compression management (TCM) have found that manufacturing consumes about _____ of the total time between receiving an order and getting the product into the customer's hands.
   a) 50%
   b) 75%

    c) 10% to 15%
    d) 5% to 10%
Answer d   Page 196

51. The primary opportunity for time compression management (TCM) lies in its application to:
    a) the purchasing process.
    b) the production process.
    c) the administrative process.
    d) the marketing process.
Answer c   Page 197

52. Well-designed web pages:
    a) have extensive graphics and make heavy use of pictures and clip art.
    b) are interactive and offer question and answer capability.
    c) focus on product and price information.
    d) do not use links to avoid misdirecting the customer.
Answer b   Page 197

53. Currently, the average web user is:
    a) male, 18–23, in college, with an annual income of $27,000 to $33,000.
    b) female, over 40, some college, with an annual income of less than $43,500.
    c) of either gender, between 12–17, in high school, with an annual income of $6,000–$12,000.
    d) male, 35, has a college degree and an annual income over $69,000.
Answer d   Page 198

54. Killer web sites:
    a) offer customers links to other sites.
    b) include a 1-800 phone number option.
    c) have a complex and colorful design.
    d) have all of these elements.
Answer a   Page 199

55. The cost of marketing a product is highest in the:
    a) introductory stage.
    b) growth and acceptance stages.
    c) maturity stage.
    d) saturation stage.
Answer a   Page 200

56. Granite Rock Company has learned to compete by offering its customers:
    a) the lowest prices.
    b) offering value and quality.
    c) convenience.
    d) credit terms.
Answer b   Page 201

57. The time span between stages in the product life cycle:
    a) generally runs about six months to one year per stage.

b) is highly influenced by the amount of promotion that is done.

c) depends entirely on the type of products involved.

d) depends on the types of market strategy the small business owner is pursuing.

Answer c   Page 202

58. The product life cycle concept means that small businesses must:

a) constantly be involved in product innovation.

b) track demographic and psychographic trends carefully.

c) create both place and time utility if they are to survive.

d) use a market penetration strategy if they are to be successful.

Answer a   Page 202

59. The most common channel of distribution for consumer goods is:

a) manufacturer ----> consumer.

b) manufacturer ----> retailer ----> consumer.

c) manufacturer ----> wholesaler ----> retailer ---> consumer.

d) manufacturer ----> broker ----> consumer.

Answer c   Page 204

True or False Questions

60. Too often, business plans describe in great detail what the entrepreneur intends to accomplish but pay too little attention to how he plans to accomplish it.

Answer T   Page 171

61. The marketing function cuts across the entire company, affecting every aspect of its operation.

Answer T   Page 172

62. Market-driven companies have little concern about lowering costs and/or improved product or service performance because they don't have to be cost- or service-oriented with their marketing focus.

Answer F   Page 172

63. The product or service offered is the foundation of any marketing-oriented business.

Answer F   Page 173

64. The primary goal of any business, according to Theodore Levitt, is to create and keep a customer.

Answer T   Page 173

65. A marketing plan should have four objectives: profit, profit, profit, and profit.

Answer F   Page 173

66. Tracking demographic trends is interesting, but it is not essential to building or implementing a successful marketing plan.

Answer F   Page 174

67. The purpose of spotting major trends is to compare your company's products or services to the trends to see how well they match.
Answer T   Page 174

68. Market research frequently only confirms the intuition of the small business owner.
Answer F   Page 175

69. Small companies are at a definite disadvantage compared to larger ones when it comes to conducting market research since it is so expensive.
Answer F   Page 176

70. While market research is a sophisticated and complex process, the small business owner can conduct some of it for him/herself, but will need assistance interpreting it.
Answer F   Page 176

71. The primary general goal of market research is to identify and profile the target market and most profitable customer in it.
Answer F   Page 177

72. Bill wants to conduct market research to find out why sales are dropping. He should define his market research problem as, "To discover why sales are declining."
Answer F   Page 177

73. The goals of one-to-one marketing are to attract, retain and increase the purchases by the target customer.
Answer T   Page 178

74. Small business owners can use market research to uncover potential market opportunities.
Answer T   Page 178

75. When interpreting the market research data, the small business owner should be careful to follow the standard rules used for interpreting that data.
Answer F   Page 179

76. The market research process is completed with the analysis of the collected data and its translation into useful information.
Answer F   Page 179

77. Most marketing experts contend that the greatest marketing mistake small businesses make is defining their target market too specifically or clearly.
Answer F   Page 181

78. Most small business follow a "shotgun" approach in marketing their new products.
Answer T   Page 181

79. The most effective way to market to the diversity of the American market is to choose a single ethnic segment and market to it as if it were a homogeneous market.
Answer F   Page 182

80. The increasing diversity of our population is creating a marketing "threat" to small businesses because they can't profitably serve small niches.
Answer F   Page 182

81. When Larissa began considering the start-up of her CyberCafe, her first act was to think through a series of questions she felt she needed to answer in order to create a business plan.
Answer T   Page 183

82. Price is the safest criterion upon which to build a competitive edge.
Answer F   Page 184

83. Generally speaking, small businesses are more effective at relationship marketing than larger companies.
Answer T   Page 184

84. In Relationship Marketing, the highest level of customer involvement is Level 4, Customer Alignment.
Answer F   Page 185

85. While customer contact is important to a small business, excellent products and low prices can offset any problems a small business may have with customer service.
Answer F   Page 186

86. Most dissatisfied customers complain about rude or discourteous service to the owner or manager.
Answer F   Page 186

87. 70% of the average company's sales come from 20–30% of its present customers.
Answer T   Page 186

88. The difference between weak customer service and "world-class" customer service is attitude and attention to detail.
Answer T   Page 187

89. Giving customers a chance to complain about a problem usually is fruitless; once a business makes a customer angry, he typically will not buy from that company again under any circumstances.
Answer F   Page 188

90. Since front-line service workers are not able to predict the causes of customer complaints, managers must be the ones to identify potential customer service problems.
Answer F   Page 188

91. Perhaps the worst of all marketing catastrophes is to have great advertising and a poor quality product or service.
Answer T   Page 188

92. American customers rate reliability as the top component in quality.
Answer T   Page 189

93. The best way for a small business to ensure quality products is to use quality inspections.
Answer F   Page 189

94. If employees are committed to quality, management's commitment becomes unimportant.
Answer F   Page 190

95. When asked what they want from a business they deal with, most customers say convenience.
Answer T   Page 190

96. Because of their organizational and managerial flexibility, small businesses often can detect and act on new opportunities faster than large companies.
Answer T   Page 191

97. Hours of operation, quick answering of phone calls, and ease of use of credit cards are just three "measures" of a company's ETDBW index.
Answer T   Page 191

98. The ability to innovate is one of the greatest weaknesses of the entrepreneur.
Answer F   Page 192

99. Because the key to successful innovation is spending "megadollars" on research and development and hiring staff who are very creative.
Answer F   Page 192

100. The level of customer service in most small companies is excellent.
Answer F   Page 193

101. It is the position of your authors that companies that do not offer quality customer service will eventually fail, for that reason.
Answer T   Page 193

102. Truly customer-oriented companies seek to go beyond customer satisfaction, striving for customer astonishment.
Answer T   Page 194

103. Listening to customers and responding to what you hear from them is a highly effective way to achieve stellar customer service.
Answer T   Page 194

104. Satisfied customers exhibit at least one of three characteristics: loyalty, resistance to competition's attempts to lure them away with lower prices, and increased purchases.
Answer T   Page 194

105. Technology has little impact on the quality of customer service a small company offers.
Answer F   Page 195

106. TCM focuses solely on reducing administrative time in product development.
Answer F   Page 196

107. The key to successful time compression management is speeding up the manufacturing process, since manufacturing consumes 90% of the time it takes to get the order into the customer's hand.
Answer F   Page 196

108. While still new to small companies, there are nearly 1.4 million small companies on the world wide web with their own home pages.
Answer F   Page 197

109. It is the position of the authors of your text that while the web holds some significant potential for small businesses, it will be 5–10 years before there is an significant use of it for E-commerce.
Answer F   Page 198

110. Effective web sites include navigation buttons on the bottom of each page, avoid fancy type faces and small fonts, and do not make heavy use of music.
Answer T   Page 199

111. Profits generally are low and marketing cost high in the introductory stage of the product life cycle.
Answer T   Page 200

112. Sales and profits peak in the growth stage of the product life cycle.
Answer F   Page 202

113. Marketing experts recommend introducing a new product only when the existing one is in the maturity stage of the product life cycle.
Answer F   Page 202

114. One of the most commonly cited reasons for a new product failing is that it is not adequately differentiated from competitive products.
Answer T   Page 203

115. When a company makes a product available to the customer when he/she wants, it the company is providing place utility to the customer.
Answer F   Page 203

116. Service companies tend to use the manufacturer-to-customer distribution channel more than any other.
Answer T   Page 203

117. Relatively few consumer goods use the manufacturer-to-retailer-to-consumer distribution channel.
Answer F   Page 204

118. The price element of the marketing mix affects both sales volume and profits.
Answer T   Page 204

119. A small company's promotional goals may include creating a brand image, persuading customers to buy, and/or to develop brand loyalty.
Answer T   Page 205

Essay Questions

120. What is the role of marketing in the small business and what part does the marketing plan play?
Pages 172–173

121. What is the value of market research to the small business owner? How can he/she use it?
Pages 174–176

122. Faith Popcorn has identified 16 trends that will shape the future business environment. Name and briefly explain eight of them.
Page 177

123. Describe the four steps of the marketing research process.
Pages 177–179

124. Outline the three main steps in setting up a customer database and briefly explain the action necessary within each step.
Page 180

125. How is the target market important to the small business? What does this concept signify about changes in marketing?
Pages 181–182

126. What is relationship marketing? What characterizes each of the four levels of customer involvement that is part of relationship marketing?
Pages 184–185

127. Discuss strategies that a company can use to focus on their customers.
Pages 187–188

128. What characterizes companies that "get it right the first time," that have an emphasis on quality?
Pages 189–190

129. What can an entrepreneur do to be more effective at innovation?
Pages 192–193

130. Discuss how a company can achieve stellar customer service and satisfaction.
Page 194–196

131. What is time compression management and what does it involve?
Pages 196–197

132. What characterizes a "killer" web site?
Page 199

133. Describe the product life cycle, naming and explaining what characterizes each stage.
Pages 200–202

134. Identify the four common channels of distribution, briefly explaining their use by small
     businesses in moving their product to the customer.
Pages 203–204

Mini-Cases

Case 6-1: Customers; key to success

Lloyd Dixon has owned and operated a small dress shop for the past three years. Each fashion season,
Lloyd attends the apparel shows and he is always very impressed by the glamour—hundreds of
different manufacturers, all with the merchandise that they say will be this season's biggest sellers.
Lloyd caters to an older market and baby boomers. He hopes to tap into the upscale market.

After his first year of operation, Lloyd recognized that some of his merchandise was not selling. The
"inventory close-out sale" did rescue his investment in this merchandise, but did not make him a profit
or contribute much to his overhead. Lloyd knew that it was not reasonable to expect to sell everything
you bought, but he was not sure exactly how much of his inventory was comprised of slow movers.
Lloyd believed that when he went into the business he knew what women wanted in dresses. He had
always prided himself in having good taste. When he had the opportunity to open this store, he was
confident that he could choose merchandise that would be well received. In the first three years of
operations, sales have not met Lloyd's expectations.

Questions

1. Faith Popcorn offers several ways Lloyd Dixon could collect information about his customers and
   competitors. Explain at least five of those ways.

2. What trends in the 1990s should Lloyd pay attention to?

3. How could Lloyd realistically create a competitive advantage by giving customer service focus in
   his business?

Case 6.2: TQM and TV in Omaha

Nobody who knew Marvin Tollison ever met a man who liked television better. In the Navy he had
the opportunity to learn a great deal about his trade. When he finished his tour of duty, Marvin
opened a television repair shop back home in Omaha, Nebraska. Over the years the quality of his
workmanship, his fair prices, and his general overall good nature made his business flourish. Marvin
had a way of finding men and women like himself when expansion was needed.

Over 17 years, the business had grown from a one-man shop operating in his garage to a 38-employee
television repair staff that was dispatched to customers by two-way truck radio. Over the years, the
time between a customer's call and the television repairman getting to their home had increased to
about two days because the repairmen were taking longer with each call. Callbacks, having to rerepair

equipment, is up significantly. Marvin wasn't sure, but he thought some of his customers were going elsewhere for service.

Questions

1. Can Marvin use TQM to develop a competitive edge? If so, what would you recommend he do?

2. How can Marvin develop "stellar" customer service?

Chapter 7 –
Creating the Financial Plan

Multiple Choice Questions

1. About ___ of all entrepreneurs report they do not spend adequate time tracking their financials.
   a) 10%
   b) α
   c) β
   d) :

Answer b   Page 209

2. The _____ shows what assets the business owns and what claims creditors and owners have against those assets.
   a) balance sheet
   b) income statement
   c) sources and uses of funds statement
   d) pro forma

Answer a   Page 210

3. The _____ is built on the basic accounting equation: Assets = Liabilities + Capital.
   a) income statement
   b) sources and uses of funds statement
   c) balance sheet
   d) cash budget

Answer c   Page 210

4. John is reviewing the company's costs and expenses against revenue for the last year. John is reviewing the firm's:
   a) balance sheet.
   b) income statement.
   c) sources and uses of funds statement.
   d) pro forma.

Answer b   Page 210

5. The first section of a balance sheet lists:
   a) current and intangible assets.
   b) current liabilities.
   c) claims creditors have against the firm's assets payable within one year.
   d) the owner's equity in terms of initial capital invested and retained earnings.

Answer a   Page 210

6. _____ are those items of value the business owns; _____ are those things the business owes.
   a) Assets; liabilities
   b) Liabilities; assets
   c) Ratios; equities
   d) Equities; liabilities

Answer a   Page 210

7. Bill is studying those expenses that contribute directly to manufacturing and distribution of goods. He's reviewing:
   a) cost of goods.
   b) general expenses.
   c) operating expenses.
   d) current liabilities.

Answer c   Page 213

8. The statement of cash flow:
   a) compares costs and expenses against a firm's sales.
   b) is built on the basic accounting equation: Assets = Liabilities + Capital.
   c) shows what assets the business owns and what claims creditors and owners have against those assets.
   d) shows changes in working capital by listing sources and uses of funds.

Answer d   Page 213

9. The _____ shows the change in the firm's working capital since the beginning of the year.
   a) balance sheet
   b) income statement
   c) pro forma
   d) statement of cash flows

Answer d   Page 213

10. Depreciation is:
   a) the difference between the total sources available to the owner and the total uses of those assets.
   b) listed as a source of funds because it is a noncash expense, deducted as a cost of doing business.
   c) the owner's total investment at the company's inception plus retained earnings.
   d) creditors' total claims against the firm's assets.

Answer b   Page 213

11. Pro forma statements help the small business owner to:
   a) track and monitor current expenses.
   b) transform business goals into reality.
   c) calculate his/her return on the amount invested in the company.
   d) measure liquidity of the firm.

Answer b   Page 214

12. One of the most important tasks facing an entrepreneur is:
   a) establishing a large enough reserve of capital.
   b) earning enough the first year to provide an adequate return on investment.
   c) the deferment of taxes.
   d) determining the funds needed for a company start-up.

Answer d   Page 214

13. When creating the pro forma income statement, the owner needs to translate the target profit into a net sales figure. To do this, the owner needs:
    a) to operate the business for one to two years to build a record.
    b) published statistics for his/her specific type of business.
    c) to divide actual net sales by the net profit projected.
    d) a sales forecast, the amount of retained earnings, and current depreciation on assets.

Answer b   Page 214

14. The first step in creating the pro forma income statement is to:
    a) determine a reasonable salary and return on investment in the company.
    b) forecast potential sales and expenses.
    c) find published figures on the specific type of business in order to forecast sales.
    d) figure out operating costs and make a realistic sales estimate.

Answer a   Page 215

15. Michelle Becker's target income in her business for the upcoming year is $78,500. The company's gross profit margin averages 32.6% of sales, and its total operating expenses run 24.7% of sales. To achieve her target income, sales of Michelle's company should be:
    a) $148,773.
    b) $993,671.
    c) $317,814.
    d) $1,271,348.

Answer b   Page 215

16. If Michelle Becker expects her company's cost of goods sold for the upcoming year to be $669,734, and its average inventory turnover to be 5.3 times, she should expect an average inventory level of:
    a) $3,549,590.
    b) $669,734.
    c) $126,365.
    d) cannot be determined with information provided.

Answer c   Page 216

17. _____ are those things that a business owns which have value.
    a) Assets
    b) Liabilities
    c) Owners' equities
    d) Liquidities

Answer a   Page 219

18. _____ are those things that a business owes; they represent creditors' claims against the business.
    a) Assets
    b) Liabilities
    c) Owners' equities
    d) Liquidities

Answer b   Page 220

19. A technique that allows the small business owner to perform financial analysis by understanding the relationship between two accounting elements is called:
    a) creating the pro forma.
    b) budgeting.
    c) break-even analysis.
    d) ratio analysis.

Answer d   Page 220

20. _____ ratios tell whether or not the small company will be able to meet its maturing obligations as they come due.
    a) Leverage
    b) Profitability
    c) Liquidity
    d) Operating

Answer c   Page 223

21. The ____ ratio is a measure of the small company's ability to pay current debts from current assets.
    a) debt-to-net worth
    b) current
    c) quick
    d) debt-to-assets

Answer b   Page 223

22. The _____ ratio is the liquidity ratio most commonly used as a measure of short-term solvency.
    a) current
    b) quick
    c) debt-to-net worth
    d) turnover

Answer a   Page 224

23. As a general rule, financial analysts suggest that a small business maintain a/an _____ ratio of at least 2:1.
    a) debt-to-net worth
    b) current
    c) inventory turnover
    d) quick

Answer b   Page 224

24. The Shell Shop has a current ratio of 2.61:1. Its owner could liquidate its current assets at _____ of their book value and still manage to pay its current liabilities in full.
    a) 2.61%
    b) 38.3%
    c) 100%
    d) insufficient information given to determine

Answer b   Page 224

25. When a company is forced into liquidation, owners are most likely to incur a loss when selling:
    a) accounts receivable.
    b) inventory.
    c) marketable securities.
    d) real estate.
Answer b   Page 224

26. The _____ ratio is a conservative measure of a firm's liquidity and shows the extent to which a firm's most liquid assets cover its current liabilities.
    a) current
    b) quick
    c) turnover
    d) net profit
Answer b   Page 224

27. _____ ratios measure the financing supplied by business owners and that supplied by the firm's creditors.
    a) Leverage
    b) Profitability
    c) Liquidity
    d) Operating
Answer a   Page 224

28. Joe is examining the percentage of total funds in a business provided by its creditors. He is working with the _____ ratio.
    a) current
    b) quick
    c) debt
    d) turnover
Answer c   Page 225

29. A high debt ratio:
    a) means that creditors provide a large percentage of the company's total financing.
    b) gives a small business more borrowing capacity.
    c) decreases the chances that creditors will lose money if the business is liquidated.
    d) decreases the creditor's interest in the business.
Answer a   Page 225

30. _____ is one indication that a small business may be undercapitalized.
    a) A current ratio below 1:1
    b) A quick ratio above 2:1
    c) A debt-to-net worth ratio above 1:1
    d) A net-sales-to-working capital ratio equal to 3:1
Answer c   Page 225

31. If Mary wants to compare what her small business owes to what it owns in order to assess her ability to meet obligations in case of liquidation, she needs to look at the _____ ratio.
    a) quick
    b) total debt turnover
    c) asset turnover
    d) debt-to-net worth

Answer d   Page 225

32. The higher the ____ ratio, the lower the degree of protection afforded creditors and the closer creditors' interest approaches the owner's interest.
    a) debt-to-net worth
    b) quick
    c) asset turnover
    d) current

Answer a   Page 225

33. The _____ ratio is a measure of a company's ability to make the interest payments on its debt.
    a) debt-to-net worth
    b) times-interest-earned
    c) net sales-to-working capital
    d) net profit-to-equity

Answer b   Page 226

34. Which of the following would be a sign that a company is overextended in its debt?
    a) A low debt ratio compared to the industry average
    b) A debt-to-net worth ratio of 0.12 to 1
    c) A times-interest-earned ratio that is far below the industry average
    d) A high inventory turnover ratio

Answer c   Page 226

35. _____ ratios help a business owner evaluate the company's performance and indicate how effectively the business employs its resources.
    a) Liquidity
    b) Leverage
    c) Operating
    d) Profitability

Answer c   Page 226

36. An above average inventory turnover indicates that the business:
    a) has an illiquid inventory.
    b) is healthy, with a salable inventory.
    c) needs to review its pricing policies.
    d) has below average performance and is facing bankruptcy if not corrected quickly.

Answer b   Page 227

37. Sarah's Smart Shop has an inventory turnover ratio of 3 times per year and an average inventory of $156,000. If Sarah could manage her inventory better and increase the number of turnovers

to the industry average of 6 times per year, what average inventory would she need to generate the same level of sales?
a) $78,000
b) $52,000
c) $468,000
d) $312,000

Answer a   Page 227

38. A business that turns its receivables over 5.9 times a year would have an average collection period of about:
a) 30 days.
b) 2/10, net 30.
c) 71 days.
d) 62 days.

Answer d   Page 229

39. A business with a payables turnover ratio of 10.4 times a year would have an average payable period of about:
a) 3 days.
b) 30 days.
c) 35 days.
d) 62 days.

Answer c   Page 229

40. The _____ ratio measures the small company's ability to generate sales in relation to its assets.
a) net sales-to-working capital
b) net sales-to-total assets
c) average collection period
d) average inventory turnover

Answer b   Page 230

41. _____ ratios indicate how efficiently the small firm is being managed.
a) Liquidity
b) Profitability
c) Leverage
d) Operating

Answer b   Page 231

42. The _____ ratio measures the owner's rate of return on the investment in the business.
a) net profit-to-equity
b) net profit on sales
c) quick profit
d) net sales-to-working capital

Answer a   Page 231

Given the following data on Port Royal, Inc. answer questions 44 through 46.
Net sales = $927,641   Gross profit = $301,483 Net profit = $48,457

Total assets = $203,869   Total liabilities = $74,325

43. Port Royal's profit margin on sales is:
    a) 5.2%.
    b) 32.5%.
    c) 16.1%.
    d) 8.0%.
Answer a   Page 216

44. Port Royal's net profit-to-equity ratio is:
    a) 23.8%.
    b) 37.4%.
    c) 16.1%.
    d) 232.7%.
Answer b   Page 231

45. Port Royal's debt-to-net worth ratio is:
    a) 0.36:1.
    b) 0.08:1.
    c) 1.57:1.
    d) 0.57:1.
Answer d   Page 225

46. _____ publishes key business ratios for 22 retail, 32 wholesale, and 71 industrial business categories.
    a) Robert Morris Associates
    b) Boston Consulting Group
    c) Bank of America
    d) Dun and Bradstreet, Inc.
Answer d   Page 232

47. _____ publishes Annual Statement Studies, showing ratios and other financial data for over 350 different industrial, retail, and wholesale categories.
    a) Robert Morris Associates
    b) Boston Consulting Group
    c) Bank of America
    d) Dun and Bradstreet, Inc.
Answer a   Page 232

48. The break-even point occurs where:
    a) the firm's fixed expenses equal its variable expenses.
    b) the creditors' interest equals the owner's interest in the business.
    c) total revenue equals total expenses.
    d) assets and liabilities are equal on the balance sheet.
Answer c   Page 237

49. Which of the following expenses would likely be classified "semi-variable"?
    a) rent

    b)   electric utilities

    c)   wages

    d)   sales commissions

Answer b   Page 237

50. Which of the following expenses would be considered "fixed?"

    a)   wages

    b)   raw materials

    c)   utilities

    d)   rent

Answer d   Page 237

51. Topkin Corporation estimates its fixed cost for producing an industrial chemical to be $123,000 for the upcoming year. Variable costs are $8.60 per gallon, and the selling price per gallon is $10.00. Approximately how many gallons must Topkin sell to break even?

    a)   8,787

    b)   12,300

    c)   4,393

    d)   Cannot be determined from information given.

Answer a   Page 239

52. Refer to question 112. Topkin's break-even sales volume (in dollars) is:

    a) $123,000.

    b) $ 43,930.

    c) $ 87,860.

    d) $439,300.

Answer c   Page 239

Use the following information to answer questions 54 through 57.

Gunther's Gum Emporium expects net sales of $2,396,919 for the upcoming year, with variable expenses totaling $1,813,443 and fixed expenses of $412,190.

53. Using break-even analysis, what is Gunther's contribution margin?

    a)   4%

    b)   32%

    c)   24%

    d)   12%

Answer c   Page 240

54. What is Gunther's break-even point?

    a) $1,876,324

    b) $1,693,276

    c) $5,667,009

    d)   Insufficient information given to determine.

Answer b   Page 239

55. If the net profit target for the year is $190,000, what sales level must he achieve?

    a) $2,473,796

b) $1,876,324
c) $5,667,009
d) none of the above
Answer a   Page 240

Break-even Chart 7.1

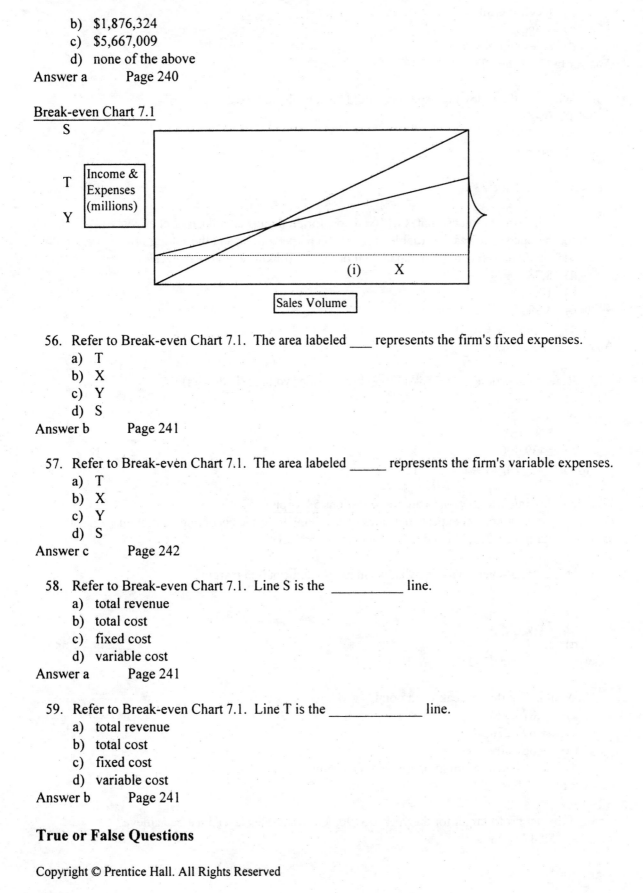

56. Refer to Break-even Chart 7.1. The area labeled ___ represents the firm's fixed expenses.
    a) T
    b) X
    c) Y
    d) S
Answer b   Page 241

57. Refer to Break-even Chart 7.1. The area labeled _____ represents the firm's variable expenses.
    a) T
    b) X
    c) Y
    d) S
Answer c   Page 242

58. Refer to Break-even Chart 7.1. Line S is the _____ line.
    a) total revenue
    b) total cost
    c) fixed cost
    d) variable cost
Answer a   Page 241

59. Refer to Break-even Chart 7.1. Line T is the _____ line.
    a) total revenue
    b) total cost
    c) fixed cost
    d) variable cost
Answer b   Page 241

True or False Questions

60. With a strong marketing plan, an entrepreneur does not need a detailed financial plan.
Answer F   Page 209

61. Only 11% of entrepreneurs analyze their financial statements as part of their managerial planning.
Answer T   Page 210

62. Proper financial management requires more than gathering financial data and organizing it into financial statements; the small business manager must analyze those statements and use that information to make better business decisions.
Answer T   Page 210

63. The balance sheet provides owners with an estimate of the firm's worth for a specific moment in time.
Answer T   Page 210

64. The balance sheet represents: Assets = Liabilities + Depreciation + Equity
Answer F   Page 210

65. The small firm's income statement presents a picture of the firm's profitability at a particular point in time.
Answer F   Page 210

66. To determine sales revenue, the owner records sales revenue for the year and subtracts liabilities.
Answer F   Page 212

67. The cost of goods sold represents the total cost, including distribution, of the goods sold during the year.
Answer T   Page 212

68. All costs directly related to the manufacture and distribution of goods are covered under general expenses.
Answer F   Page 213

69. The statement of cash flows shows the change in a firm's working capital.
Answer T   Page 213

70. The difference between the total sources of funds and the total uses of funds represents the increase or decrease in a firm's working capital.
Answer T   Page 213

71. The pro forma shows the company's current overall financial condition.
Answer F   Page 214

72. The most common method of creating a projected income statement is to develop a sales forecast and then "work down" to the bottom line.
Answer F   Page 214

73. An adequate profit in a small business must include a reasonable return on the owner's total investment in the business.
Answer T   Page 215

74. When determining the owner's target income, you must consider a reasonable salary for the time spent running the business, less the depreciation of assets.
Answer F   Page 215

75. The formula for calculating net profit margin is net profit/net sales (annual).
Answer T   Page 216

76. A new business owner must operate for at least six months in order to collect sufficient information to calculate net sales from a profit target.
Answer F   Page 216

77. Most small businesses start out strong financially because of the care generally given in determining the total asset requirements for running the business.
Answer F   Page 218

78. Concerning how much cash to have at start-up, a rule of thumb is to have enough to cover operating expenses (less depreciation) for two inventory turnover periods.
Answer F   Page 219

79. When setting proper financial controls, an important rule to remember is to use the same timetable for all numbers to be able to compare results properly.
Answer T   Page 219

80. Performing financial ratio analyses enables a business owner to identify problems early—before they become crises.
Answer T   Page 220

81. Turnaround specialist Raleigh Minor offers five rules for proper financial control. The first and primary rule is to generate numbers for the financial statements only 30–45 days after the end of the month to ensure all expenses and revenues are accounted for.
Answer F   Page 221

82. Financial ratios are a common tool used by over 50% of small business owners in the daily management of their businesses.
Answer F   Page 222

83. Ratio analysis may become meaningless if it is too detailed.
Answer T   Page 223

84. Liquidity ratios measure the financing supplied by the firm's owners against that provided by its creditors.
Answer F   Page 223

85. A quick ratio greater than 1:1 indicates that a small firm is overly dependent on inventory and on future sales to satisfy short-term debt.
Answer F   Page 224

86. The higher the current ratio, the stronger the small firm's financial position.
Answer T   Page 224

87. The quick ratio is the most commonly used measure for a small firm's short-term solvency.
Answer T   Page 224

88. Leverage ratios are a gauge of the depth of a company's debt.
Answer T   Page 224

89. Small businesses with high leverage ratios are less vulnerable to economic downturns, but they have a lower potential for large profits.
Answer F   Page 224

90. The higher the debt-to-net worth ratio, the lower the degree of protection afforded creditors should the business fail.
Answer T   Page 225

91. As a company's debt-to-net worth ratio approaches 1:1, its creditors' interest in that business approaches that of the owners'.
Answer T   Page 225

92. The times-interest-earned ratio expresses the relationship between the capital contributions of creditors and those of the owners.
Answer F   Page 226

93. Debt is also a danger and generally detracts from a company's performance.
Answer F   Page 226

94. The average inventory turnover ratio tells the owner how fast merchandise is moving through the business.
Answer T   Page 227

95. There is a direct 1:1 relationship between a company's expected average inventory turnover ratio and the amount of cash required to launch it.
Answer F   Page 227

96. A low inventory turnover ratio demonstrates that the firm's inventory is liquid and its pricing policies are accurate.
Answer F   Page 228

97. The company's average collection period ratio indicates the length of time the firm's cash is tied up in credit sales.
Answer T   Page 228–229

98. Generally, the higher the small firm's average collection period ratio, the lower the chance of bad debt losses.
Answer F   Page 229

99. The average payable period tells the owner the average number of days it takes to pay its accounts payable.
Answer T   Page 229

100. Ideally, the average payable period should match or exceed the time it takes to convert inventory into sales and sales into cash.
Answer T   Page 230

101. The small firm's net sales to total assets ratio measures how many dollars in sales the business makes for every dollar of working capital.
Answer F   Page 230

102. The net profit on sales ratio measures the owners' rate of return on the investment in the business.
Answer F   Page 231

103. Ratio analysis provides an owner with a "snapshot" of the company's financial picture at a single instant; therefore, he/she should track these ratios over time, looking for trends that otherwise might go undetected.
Answer T   Page 232

104. When a firm's ratios vary from the average ratios of similar firms in the industry, this indicates that the small business is in financial jeopardy.
Answer F   Page 232

105. Norman Myne has made training his employees on company finances his primary tool for controlling costs and as a result there has been a significant increase in profits.
Answer T   Page 233

106. The Vest Pocket Guide to Financial Ratios is published by the IRS and offers the operating ratios for a number of different types of companies.
Answer F   Page 234

107. If a small business has a current ratio of 1.7:1 and its industry ratio median is 1.5:1, this indicates that while the small business is about the median its liquidity is still good.
Answer T   Page 234

108. If a firm has a net sales-to-total assets ratio of 2.3:1 while the industry median is 3.1:1 this means that the firm is generating more sales than the industry median.
Answer F   Page 235

109. Tom's Tacos has a net profit on sales ratio of 1.6% while the industry median is 3.4%. This means Tom has a problem with his gross profit margin or his operating expenses or both.
Answer T   Page 235

110. Sam's Subs has a 19.6% net profit-to-equity ratio, while the industry median is 9.2%. This
    means that Sam's is in good shape because they are at twice the yield of the industry median.
Answer F   Page 236

111. Break-even analysis is a valuable tool for screening business opportunities since it considers the
    importance of cash flows.
Answer F   Page 237

112. The first step in preparing a break-even analysis is to break business expenses down into "fixed"
    and "variable" categories.
Answer T   Page 237

113. To calculate break-even sales, use the equation: break-even sales (in dollars) = total variable
    costs divided by contribution margin as a percentage of sales revenue.
Answer F   Page 237

114. While Ilene Polansky's restaurant was bringing in revenues in excess of $1.5 million a year and
    had a net profit margin of 10–15%, around the industry average, her lack of financial controls
    resulted in her having periodic financial problems.
Answer T   Page 238

115. The break-even analysis provides an opportunity for integrated analysis of sales volume,
    expenses, income, and other relevant factors.
Answer T   Page 239

116. Most small businesses prefer to express their break-even point in dollars rather than units
    produced or sold, unless they are retailing.
Answer F   Page 239

117. On a break-even chart, the break-even point occurs at the intersection of the fixed expense line
    and the total revenue line.
Answer F   Page 240

118. Break-even analysis is somewhat complex to use, but it is a final screening device.
Answer F   Page 242

119. A break-even analysis has several drawbacks including the fact that it ignores the importance of
    cash flows and that its accuracy is dependent on the accuracy of revenue and expense estimates.
Answer T   Page 242

Essay Questions
120. Explain the three basic financial reports that a business uses in building a financial statement:
    the balance sheet, the income statement, and the statement of cash flows. What information is
    contained in each, what is their value to the small business owner, and how are they used to
    build financial statements?
Pages 210–213

121. Describe a pro forma statement, identifying the types of pro formas a small business owner could use, and how the small business owner would create each.
Pages 214–220

122. What is the value of ratio analysis to the small business owner and what are the four categories of ratios he/she can use?
Pages 220–231

123. What are liquidity ratios and how are they used by the small business owner? Name and briefly explain the current and quick ratios.
Pages 223–224

124. What do leverage ratios measure? Name and explain three of them.
Pages 224–226

125. Describe what operating ratios are. Identify the five operating ratios covered in your text, explaining how each of the five helps the small business owner manage his/her business.
Pages 226–231

126. Identify and explain the two profitability ratios a small business owner can use to measure how effectively he/she is managing the business.
Pages 231–232

127. How can the entrepreneur interpret and use the various business ratios available to him/her?
Pages 232–334

128. What does a break-even analysis tell the small business owner? Describe the steps used in calculating it. What is the difference between a break-even point in dollars versus one in units?
Pages 237–242

Mini-Cases

Case 7-1: Sharps and Flats

Anthony Gray has been interested in music since he was old enough to sit at the piano. He literally grew up with music, and he used his talent to earn his way through college. Anthony has grown tired of his job at a large music house in Houston and is seriously considering moving back to his hometown in Massachusetts to open his own small music shop. In researching this venture, Anthony notices that he must include a projected income statement in his loan application.

Questions

1. Using Anthony's target income of $23,000 and the following statistic from Robert Morris Associates' **Annual Statement Studies**, construct a pro forma income statement for Anthony's proposed music shop.

Net sales	100.0%
Cost of sales	59.9%
Gross profit	40.1%

Operating expenses	31.2%
Net profit (before taxes)	8.9%

2. Suppose that a market survey indicates that Anthony's proposed business is likely to generate only $190,000 in sales. What net profit should Anthony expect to earn?

Case 7-2: Bowden Brake Service (Part A)

Jim Bowden, owner of Bowden Brake Service, is planning to expand his six-year-old brake service to include tune-ups and tire services. Based on budget estimates for the upcoming year, Jim expects net sales to be $825,000 with a cost of goods sold of $530,000 and total operating expenses of $210,000. From the budget, Jim computes fixed expenses to be $168,000, while variable expenses (including cost of goods sold) are $572,000. Jim is worried that the new cost structure may damage his ability to produce a profit, so he wants to perform a quick break-even analysis for the upcoming year.

Questions

1. Help Jim compute the break-even point for his brake service.

2. Prepare a break-even chart which graphically portrays this analysis.

3. Prepare an outline for Jim describing the components he should include in the business plan when requesting a loan.

Case 7-2: Bowden Brake Service (Part B)

One day while you are in Bowden Brake Service getting your brakes repaired, Jim storms into his office, slamming doors and shouting about the local financial institutions. After a few minutes of building your courage, you approach Jim and ask him what the problem is. He shouts, "It's the financial institutions in this town! Not one of them will lend me the money I need to expand my business. They all said I needed to take a closer look at my financial position before I consider expanding. One of them said something about ratio analysis. I know a lot about cars and brakes, but what is ratio analysis?"

You tell Jim you'll perform a ratio analysis for the business if he gives you a brake job. Jim provides you with the financial statements on the following pages.

Questions

1. Refer to the following income statement and balance sheet. Prepare a ratio analysis for Bowden Brake Service.

2. Using the following industry statistics for firms like Jim's, explain and interpret what these ratios mean.

Current ratio	1:4:1
Quick ratio	0:7:1
Debt ratio	1:8:1
Debt-to-N/W ratio	1:9:1
Average inventory turnover	NA
Average collection period	21.22 days

Net sales-to-total assets	2.8%
Net sales-to-working capital	17.2%
Net profit on sales	9.0%
Net profit to equity	22.2%

3. Were the bankers correct? Do you think Jim should expand the business?

Bowden Brake Service
Income Statement
Year Ended 31 December 199X

Net Sales		$780,000
Costs of Goods Sold:		
Beginning inventory	$104,000	
Purchases	526,480	
Goods available for sale	$630,480	
Ending inventory	134,400	
Cost of Goods Sold		496,080
Gross Margin		$283,920
Operating Expenses:		
Rent	24,000	
Insurance	5,250	
Advertising	6,000	
Travel	2,500	
Interest	72,750	
Taxes (property, etc.)	2,500	
Salaries & admn. expenses	97,000	
Utilities	12,500	
Supplies	1,360	
Total Operating Expenses		223,860
Net Profit		$ 60,060

Bowden Brake Service
Balance Sheet
31 December 199X

Assets

Current Assets:		
Cash		$20,000
Accounts receivable		10,000
Notes receivable		5,000
Inventory		134,400
Total Current Assets		$169,400
Fixed Assets:		
Land		147,000
Machinery	$ 73,000	
Equipment	160,800	
Less accumulated depreciation	30,200	203,600
Total Fixed Assets		350,600
Total Assets		$520,000
		=======

Liabilities & Owner's Equity

Current Liabilities:	
Accounts payable	40,500
Notes payable	20,200
Accrued salaries payable	4,300
Total Current Liabilities	$65,000
Long-Term Liabilities:	
Long-term loan	$325,000
Owner's Equity, Jim Bowden	130,000
Total Liabilities and Net Worth	$520,000
	=======

Chapter 8 –
Cash Flow Management

Multiple Choice Questions

1. Cash flow is most important to a small business:
    a) in the earliest stages of its life.
    b) during the maturity stage of its products.
    c) when the market reaches saturation.
    d) during the growth stage of the product life cycle.
    Answer a   Page 246

2. A survey of small business owners revealed that the greatest financial obstacle to their companies'
    success was:
    a) the inability to obtain bank loans.
    b) uneven cash flow.
    c) slow payment of receivables.
    d) the burden of state and federal taxes.
    Answer b   Page 246

3. When the entrepreneur is allocating the cash to pay bills, forecasting cash disbursements, etc.,
    he/she is fulfilling the cash management role of:
    a) cash finder.
    b) cash planner.
    c) cash distributor.
    d) cash conserver.
    Answer c   Page 247

4. The first step in managing cash more effectively is:
    a) having an adequate cash reserve for emergency expenditures.
    b) rapid payment of accounts payable.
    c) speeding up payment of accounts receivable.
    d) understanding the company's cash flow cycle.
    Answer d   Page 248

5. _____ is the money that moves through the business in a continuous cycle.
    a) Profit
    b) Net income
    c) Cash
    d) Cash flow
    Answer c   Page 248

6. _____ companies are most likely to suffer cash shortages.
    a) Slow-growth
    b) Service
    c) Manufacturing
    d) Fast-growth
    Answer d   Page 250

7. Bill and Henry are discussing the volume of cash that has been coming into and going out of their business during the accounting period. They are discussing:
   a) profit.
   b) net income.
   c) accounts receivable and payable.
   d) cash flow.

Answer d   Page 248

8. _____ typically lead(s) sales; _____ typically lag(s) sales.
   a) Production; receivables
   b) Collections; purchases
   c) Receipts; production
   d) Purchases; collections

Answer a   Page 248

9. _____ is simply a "cash plan" which shows the amount and the timing of cash receipts and cash disbursements over time.
   a) The income statement
   b) A balance sheet
   c) A cash budget
   d) The pro forma

Answer c   Page 249

10. Rochelle Zabarkes runs a successful specialty foods store in New York City. Her successful business is growing rapidly. What happened to her when she defaulted on her bank loan?
   a) The bank closed her down and sold her business at auction.
   b) She had to sacrifice personal belongs and stock in order to fund the businesses operation.
   c) She found an angel who picked up the note for a 51% stake in the company and now she is essentially an employee.
   d) The Small Business Administration took over and she is now chasing court order payment deadlines and is still short of cash.

Answer d   Page 250

11. When creating the cash budget, keep in mind that:
   a) it should be a monthly plan, projected out for 3 years.
   b) the more variable the sales pattern, the shorter the planning horizon should be.
   c) it should be quarterly estimates for a period of 1 year.
   d) it is a verbal or mental "document" in order to permit maximum flexibility.

Answer b   Page 251

12. The cash budget is based on the _____ method of accounting.
   a) cash
   b) financial
   c) accrual
   d) hybrid

Answer a   Page 251

13. Which of the following items appear on a cash budget?
    a) depreciation
    b) bad debt expenses
    c) noncash items not involving cash transfers
    d) cash receipts and disbursements
Answer d   Page 251

14. Once the owner determines an adeaquate minimum cash balance, what is the next step in creating a cash budget?
    a) Forecasting profits
    b) Forecasting sales
    c) Forecasting cash receipts
    d) Forecasting cash disbursements
Answer b   Page 251

15. Jane is arguing with Joan about how much cash on hand their small retail outlet needs as they prepare their cash budget. Jane feels that with the Christmas season coming up, their busiest time, they need more cash handy. Joan feels they don't because their sales volume will be up significantly. Jane and Joan are discussing which step of the cash budgeting process?
    a) Determining an adequate minimum cash balance
    b) Forecasting sales
    c) Forecasting cash receipts
    d) Forecasting cash disbursements
Answer a   Page 256

16. The heart of the cash budget is the _____ forecast.
    a) cash receipts
    b) cash disbursements
    c) sales
    d) receivables
Answer c   Page 256

17. A cash budget is only as accurate as the _____ forecast from which it is derived.
    a) profit
    b) receivables
    c) income
    d) sales
Answer d   Page 256

18. Which of the following would be a potential source of information for a sales forecast?
    a) past records
    b) trade associations and the Chamber of Commerce
    c) similar firms
    d) all of these
Answer d   Page 256

19. When a firm sells goods or services on credit, the owner needs to remember that for cash budgeting purposes:
    a) the sale may be immediately posted as if it has been collected.
    b) the sale should be recorded in the month it was made.
    c) he/she must account for a delay between the sale and collection of proceeds.
    d) such a transaction counts as a cash disbursement.

Answer c   Page 257

20. When forecasting cash disbursements in the cash budget:
    a) they count as a cash receipt until they are paid.
    b) they should be recorded in the month they will be paid.
    c) the disbursement should be recorded in the month the obligation was incurred.
    d) the money can be used for other purposes until it is due for disbursement.

Answer b   Page 259

21. Generally speaking, most small business owners tend to:
    a) overestimate cash disbursements.
    b) underestimate cash receipts.
    c) underestimate cash disbursements.
    d) try to count unpaid cash disbursements as cash that can be spent.

Answer c   Page 259

22. When estimating the firm's end-of-month cash balance the owner should first:
    a) determine the cash balance at the beginning of the month.
    b) add up total cash receipts and subtract cash on hand.
    c) review the accounts receivable.
    d) make a daily list of cash disbursements.

Answer a   Page 259

23. The fact that the cash budget illustrates the flow of cash in a business helps the owner to:
    a) accelerate accounts payable payments.
    b) get a seasonal line of credit rather than an annual line of credit.
    c) slow accounts receivable payments.
    d) track the effect of depreciation and bad debt.

Answer b   Page 260

24. One recent study showed that about ___ of small businesses used formal techniques to track their cash balances.
    a) 85%
    b) 16%
    c) 26%
    d) 35%

Answer c   Page 260

25. The "big three" of cash management include:
    a) accounts receivable, overhead, and inventory.
    b) accounts payable, accounts receivable, and taxes.
    c) accounts receivable, accounts payable, and inventory.
    d) accounts receivable, prices, and expenses.

Answer c   Page 260

26. _____ is simply the money owed the firm by customers because they've purchased goods or services on credit.
    a) Accounts receivable
    b) Accounts payable
    c) Barter
    d) Cash management

Answer a   Page 260

27. Joe Sergio of Sergio's Pools found the number one thing affecting his company's cash flow was:
    a) his credit policy.
    b) the inability to establish a line of credit with the bank.
    c) too small of a profit margin due to high operating costs.
    d) the seasons of the year lead to significant dips in business.

Answer d   Page 261

28. The most important item on the balance sheet is:
    a) cash.
    b) disbursements.
    c) expenses.
    d) receivables.

Answer a   Page 261

29. Small businesses selling on credit find that:
    a) it is relatively inexpensive and simple.
    b) it is expensive and requires a great deal of effort.
    c) it is essentially borrowing money from the customer.
    d) many can get by without selling on credit because their business customers don't expect to use credit.

Answer b   Page 262

30. _____ percent of small businesses sell on credit.
    a) Ten
    b) Forty
    c) Seventy-five
    d) Ninety-five

Answer d   Page 262

31. The first step to building a workable credit policy is:
    a) screening customers carefully before granting them credit.
    b) establishing a firm credit policy in writing.
    c) developing a policy for pursuing past-due accounts.
    d) creating a thorough credit application.

Answer a   Page 262

32. The first line of defense against bad debt losses is:
    a) screening customers carefully before granting them credit.
    b) establishing a firm credit policy in writing.

    c) developing a policy for pursuing past-due accounts.

    d) creating a thorough credit application.

Answer d   Page 262

33. Which of the following are credit reporting services a small business owner could use to check a customer's credit?
    a) National Association of Credit Management
    b) TRW
    c) Dun & Bradstreet
    d) All of these

Answer d   Page 263

34. An important source of credit information that collects information on small businesses that other reporting services ignore is:
    a) National Association of Credit Management.
    b) TRW.
    c) Dun & Bradstreet.
    d) National Association of Small Business Owners.

Answer a   Page 263

35. Only about ___ of small companies protect themselves by checking customers' credit.
    a) 3
    b) 40%
    c) α
    d) 10%

Answer c   Page 263

36. When a small business is writing off more than ___ % of its sales as bad debts, it needs to tighten its credit and collection policies.
    a) 10
    b) 5
    c) 25
    d) 3

Answer b   Page 263

37. Once a small business has established a firm written credit policy and communicated it, the next step in building an effective credit policy is to:
    a) send invoices promptly.
    b) determine what percentage of sales are being written off as bad debt.
    c) create a simple credit application.
    d) create a "tracking file" of events.

Answer a   Page 263

38. Once a credit account becomes past due, a small business owner should:
    a) wait patiently; the customer will most likely pay the bill sooner or later.
    b) turn the account over to a collection agency the day it becomes past due.
    c) contact the customer immediately, ask for full payment, and set a deadline.
    d) call the "deadbeat" in the middle of the night and make harassing and threatening remarks until he pays.

Answer c   Page 263

39. Dona McKenzie found that when it came to collecting from a big bank for services rendered:
    a) the bank paid more promptly than small businesses.
    b) the bank largely ignored its obligation to her until forced to pay.
    c) the bank tried to renegotiate the amount they owed her.
    d) the bank offered her free banking services, i.e., barter, in trade for her services.
Answer b   Page 264

40. The Fair Debt Collection Practices Act prohibits business owners from:
    a) harassing people who are past due.
    b) sending invoices the same day the product is shipped.
    c) hiring debt collection attorneys.
    d) referring past due bills to collection agencies.
Answer a   Page 265

41. The American Collector's Association has found that only about ___ of accounts over 90 days delinquent will be paid voluntarily.
    a) 5%
    b) 10%
    c) 2%
    d) 13%
Answer a   Page 265

42. A small business owner could accelerate accounts payable by:
    a) having customers mail printed orders to you.
    b) sending or faxing invoices the day of shipment.
    c) slowing their own accounts payable.
    d) depositing customer checks and credit card receipts weekly.
Answer b   Page 265

43. If a small business owner receives a "Notice of Filing" from a customer, he should:
    a) send a second notice.
    b) ask that customer for a portion of the purchase price up front.
    c) arrange for a lockbox for future payments from that customer.
    d) immediately file a proof-of-claim.
Answer d   Page 265

44. When designing a collection system the small business owner should keep in mind that ____ makes it much easier to collect accounts receivable on time.
    a) dealing fairly
    b) starting collection the first day past due
    c) using an outside collection agency
    d) making the first collection contact through an attorney
Answer a   Page 266

45. An arrangement in which customers mail their payments on account to a post office box which the company's bank monitors, from which it collects the payments, and then immediately deposits the payments into the firm's interest-bearing account is called a:

a)   zero balance account.

b)   lockbox.

c)   sweep account.

d)   credit reference.

Answer b   Page 267

46. A bank account that technically never has funds in it but is tied to another master account so that when checks are presented for payment the master account is debited, permitting the company to use its own money during the "float" period, is called a/an:

    a)   cash account.

    b)   accrual account.

    c)   sweep account.

    d)   zero balance account.

Answer d   Page 267

47. When managing your accounts payable, as a small business owner you should:

    a)   take advantage of any float you have before your check is cashed.

    b)   send second notices when payables are only 15 days past due.

    c)   pay payables as early as possible.

    d)   stretch out all payables as long as possible.

Answer d   Page 267

48. Efficient cash managers:

    a)   disregard trade discounts because of their hidden expenses.

    b)   avoid the use of credit cards to stretch their firm's cash balance.

    c)   set up a payment calendar in order to both pay on time and take advantage of cash discounts for early payment.

    d)   use expressions like "the check's in the mail" to mollify creditors when short on cash.

Answer c   Page 267

49. When it comes to trade credit, the small business owner:

    a)   should avoid it as it generally leads to overextension of his/her credit line.

    b)   should almost always take advantage of it.

    c)   should only consider it if they have a strong accounts receivables situation.

    d)   should know that its use makes little difference in the company cash flow and therefore should be avoided.

Answer b   Page 268

50. The country with the worst payment record is:

    a)   Iran.

    b)   Syria.

    c)   Chile.

    d)   Argentina.

Answer a   Page 269

51. Late payments have what effect on European companies?

    a)   An increase in cash flow within the companies not being paid

    b)   A significant decrease in international business

    c)   An increase in interest rate costs

d) A slowing of their own accounts payable

Answer c   Page 269

52. It is not atypical for a manufacturing company to pay _____ of the value of the inventory for the cost of borrowed money.
    a) 50^{B}60%
    b) 10^{B}15%
    c) 25^{B}30%
    d) 70^{B}90%

Answer c   Page 271

53. Exchanging goods and services for other goods and services, or _____, is an effective way for a small business to conserve cash.
    a) leasing
    b) bartering
    c) arbitraging
    d) credit sales

Answer b   Page 271

54. It is estimated that nearly _____ companies, most of them small, engage in barter every year.
    a) 400,000
    b) 8 million
    c) 250,000
    d) 80,000

Answer a   Page 271

55. Barter among companies in the United States is worth more than:
    a) $250 million a year.
    b) $800 million a year.
    c) $7.3 billion a year.
    d) $9.1 billion a year.

Answer d   Page 271

56. The real benefit of barter for the entrepreneur is that:
    a) it is essentially without cost to the business owner.
    b) it is considered a depreciable item for tax purposes rather than as income.
    c) it saves the small business owner between $50,000 and $150,000 a year on average.
    d) it is "paid" for at the wholesale cost of doing business, yet it is credited at the retail price.

Answer d   Page 272

57. Nearly ___ of U.S. companies use leasing as a cash management strategy.
    a) 80%
    b) 50%
    c) 100%
    d) 60%

Answer a   Page 273

58. Which of the following is an effective way to trim overhead?

a) Leasing inventory
b) Accelerating accounts receivable
c) Establishing lockboxes or zero balance accounts
d) Negotiating fixed loan payments to coincide with company cash flow

Answer d   Page 273

59. The budgeting strategy that evaluates the necessity of every item on the budget each year by starting with a zero in each budget category is called:
   a) accrual budgeting.
   b) cash budgeting.
   c) zero-based budgeting.
   d) cash flow budgeting.

Answer c   Page 274

60. When investing surplus cash, the small business owner's key objectives should be:
   a) high yields.
   b) current income.
   c) liquidity and safety.
   d) long-term yield.

Answer c   Page 274

True or False Questions

61. The lack of cash has driven a number of small businesses, even those with solid profits, into bankruptcy.

Answer T   Page 245

62. It is possible for a business to make a profit and go out of business due to cash flow problems.

Answer T   Page 248

63. The objectives of cash management are to adequately meet the cash demands of the business and to avoid retaining unnecessarily large cash balances.

Answer T   Page 246

64. The cash management role of "cash conserver," controlling the cash needed to pay bills, and prioritizing and timing those payments, is the entrepreneur's first and foremost responsibility.

Answer F   Page 247

65. The cash flow cycle is the time lag between paying suppliers and receiving payment from customers.

Answer T   Page 248

66. The longer a company's cash flow cycle, the more likely it is to encounter a cash crisis.

Answer T   Page 248

67. For a small business, cash planning is relatively simple since cash and profits are the same.

Answer F   Page 248

68. Profit is the difference between a company's total revenue and its total expenses.

Answer T   Page 248

69. Cash is money that flows through the business and is not tied up in any asset.
Answer T   Page 248

70. A firm whose sales volume is expanding rapidly need not be concerned about managing its cash flow.
Answer F   Page 248

71. A study of 230 fast-growing companies showed that 73% tracked cash flow either daily or weekly.
Answer T   Page 249

72. A cash budget is the document that shows a company the margin between its profit and its costs of goods and how to manage it.
Answer F   Page 249

73. While in her cash crisis, Rochelle Zabarkes has managed to save her company by working with creditors and the Small Business Administration to repay her loans.
Answer T   Page 250

74. Typically, a small firm should prepare a monthly cash budget for at least one year into the future.
Answer T   Page 251

75. The cash budget is based on the accrual method of accounting.
Answer F   Page 251

76. A cash budget is a forecast of the firm's cash inflows and outflows over a specific time period.
Answer T   Page 251

77. The first step in preparing a cash budget is to forecast cash receipts.
Answer F   Page 256

78. Ideally, a small firm's cash balance should be two times its average weekly sales.
Answer F   Page 256

79. Some experts suggest that a small business should maintain a supply of cash on hand equal to one-fourth its current debts.
Answer T   Page 256

80. One of the most reliable methods of determining an adequate minimum cash balance is using past experience.
Answer T   Page 256

81. Since even the best sales forecast can be wrong, the small business owner should prepare three forecasts—optimistic, pessimistic, and most likely.
Answer T   Page 256

82. In a cash budget, credit sales to customers are recorded as soon as the sale is made.
Answer F   Page 257

83. The key factor in forecasting cash disbursements for a cash budget is to record them in the month when they are incurred, not when they are paid.
Answer F   Page 259

84. For cash planning purposes, it is better to underestimate cash disbursements than to overestimate them.
Answer F   Page 259

85. To avoid cash crises, many owners add a "cushion" to each cash disbursement account since many expenses run higher than expected.
Answer T   Page 259

86. To estimate a firm's cash balance for each month, the owner must first wait until the end of the month.
Answer F   Page 259

87. Seasonal sales patterns cause cash balances to fluctuate dramatically, creating the need for cash forecasts.
Answer T   Page 260

88. If a small firm's profits are climbing, the owner can be sure its cash balance also is rising.
Answer F   Page 260

89. Not only must the small company be concerned about its monthly cash balance, but it must also monitor the trend of its cash balance over time.
Answer T   Page 260

90. 40% of small business sales are on credit.
Answer F   Page 260

91. It is possible for a small business to have customers that are simply "too big" to manage on the small firm's cash flow.
Answer T   Page 261

92. According to the National Association of Credit Management, receivables are only the second most important item on the balance sheet.
Answer T   Page 261

93. The first line of defense against bad debt losses is to have a financial institution extend loans to credit-seeking customers.
Answer F   Page 262

94. Most small businesses conduct a thorough credit investigation before selling to a new customer.
Answer F   Page 262

95. An important first step in protecting the small business from bad debt losses is a detailed credit application.
Answer T   Page 262

96. One effective technique for improving cash management is to establish a firm credit policy in writing and let customers know in advance what it is.
Answer T   Page 263

97. The layout and readability of an invoice affects the likelihood of it being paid in a timely manner.
Answer T   Page 264

98. Small business owners should not press customers for payment of their past due accounts for fear of losing them as customers altogether.
Answer F   Page 265

99. The longer a debt is outstanding, the lower its probability of collection.
Answer T   Page 265

100. When it comes to debt collection, it is appropriate to seek to motivate the customer to pay and not get into why the bill hasn't been paid during the "discussion stage" of the collection process.
Answer T   Page 266, Table 8.5

101. A lockbox arrangement is very inexpensive to operate and is economical even for small businesses with a low volume of payments on account.
Answer F   Page 267

102. Some companies manage their accounts receivable and cash by using sweep accounts. These are accounts where all funds above a certain minimum are automatically moved into an interest-bearing account.
Answer T   Page 267

103. The wise small business owner should strive to stretch out his/her payables as long as possible without damaging the company's credit rating.
Answer T   Page 267

104. An invoice marked 3/12 net 30 means that you can take a 3% discount if you pay the bill in 12 days but you must pay the entire balance in 30 days.
Answer T   Page 268

105. Usually, trade credit from vendors is expensive, and small business owners should avoid it.
Answer F   Page 268

106. A letter of credit, while not guaranteeing payment, at least shows the small business owner has done a background and credit check on any international customer.
Answer F   Page 269

107. Small businesses doing international business should always bill in the currency of the customer's country to avoid losses due to the exchange rate.
Answer F   Page 269

108. The danger inventory poses to a small business is the amount of cash it ties up.
Answer T   Page 271

109. Because inventory is illiquid, cash invested there is tied up and cannot be used for other purposes.
Answer T   Page 271

110. Surplus inventory yields about a 3% return rate and tends to be very liquid.
Answer F   Page 271

111. One highly effective cash management strategy is to schedule inventory deliveries as early as possible to speed your payment of accounts payable.
Answer F   Page 271

112. The dollar value of bartering has almost doubled from 1985 until 1996.
Answer F   Page 272

113. The nice thing about barter is that there is almost no cost involved in the process.
Answer F   Page 272

114. Nearly 80% of companies in the United States use leases to help cash management.
Answer T   Page 273

115. A lease is treated as an operating expense and is not carried as a liability on a company's balance sheet.
Answer T   Page 273

116. Rather than build the current year's budget on increases from the previous year's budget, zero-based budgeting starts from a budget of zero and evaluates the necessity of every item.
Answer T   Page 274

117. Small business managers need not be concerned about investing surplus cash since small amounts of cash sitting around for a few days or weeks are not worth investing.
Answer F   Page 274

118. When investing surplus cash, the small business owner should seek the highest returns possible on the money.
Answer F   Page 274

119. Asset-management accounts are available to small businesses that have at least $1.5 million in annual revenues.
Answer F   Page 275

120. Proper management of cash accounts can yield the owner additional leverage, the equivalent to actually keep the capital in the accounts.
Answer T   Page 275

Essay Questions

121. What are the five cash management roles an entrepreneur needs to fulfill in his/her small business?
Page 247, Table 8.1

122. Define or describe the terms: revenue, cash, profit, cash budget, cash flow, and cash flow cycle. Why is it important to understand the differences among them?
Pages 248^{B}249

123. Discuss the five basic steps to establishing a cash budget for a business.
Pages 256^{B}260

124. What are the big three of cash management? How does each impact the operation of the small business?
Pages 260^{B}271

125. Create a credit and collection policy for a privately owned small bookstore/café which has a number of customers who buy pastries on account and numerous customers with standing book orders that they pay on once a month.
Pages 260^{B}265

126. If you were having difficulty getting your customers to pay in a timely manner, what could you do to speed payment?
Pages 265^{B}266

127. How should a small business owner manage his/her accounts payable?
Pages 267^{B}268

128. How can an entrepreneur manage inventory in order to improve cash flow?
Page 271

129. What role does barter and investing surplus cash play in improving a small firm's cash flow?
Page 271–272 and 274

130. Offer several suggestions on how to trim overhead expenses in order to avoid a cash crunch. Explain how each technique can reduce the cash requirements for a small business.
Pages 272^{B}274

Mini-Cases

Case 8-1: Golden Company

From the information below, prepare a monthly cash budget for the next quarter (October^{B}December) for the Golden Company.

	October	November	December
Sales	$750,000	$800,000	$900,000
Manufacturing costs	450,000	480,000	540,000
Operating expenses	225,000	240,000	270,000
Capital expenditures	....	60,000	....

Golden Company expects 25% of its sales to be in cash, and of the accounts receivable, 70% will be collected within the next month. Depreciation, insurance, and property taxes comprise $25,000 of monthly manufacturing costs and $10,000 of the operating expenses. Insurance and property taxes are paid in February, June, and September. The rest of the manufacturing costs and operating expenses will be paid off, one-half in the month in which incurred and the rest in the following month. The current assets on October 1 are made up of:

- Cash, $70,000
- Marketable securities, $50,000
- Accounts receivable, $600,000 ($450,000 from September, $150,000 from August) and current liabilities include $60,000, 6%, 90-day note payable due October 18
- Accounts payable of $200,000 for September manufacturing expenses
- Accrued liabilities of $100,000 for September operating expenses.

Dividends of $1,000 should be received in November. An income tax payment of $50,000 will be made in November. The firm's minimum cash balance is $20,000.

Case 8-2: The Laurens Corporation

In past years, Sue Salgado, owner of the Laurens Corporation, has been plagued by unexpected cash flow problems. Her banker, worried about her lack of cash flow management, has suggested that Sue create a cash budget for the upcoming quarter. Sue does this, using the following information:

	October	November	December
Sales	$800,000	$900,000	$950,000
Manufacturing costs	475,000	520,000	575,000
Operational expenses	250,000	270,000	290,000
Capital expenditures	20,000	70,000	-------

Laurens Corporation expects 35% of its sales to be in cash, and of the accounts receivable, 70% will be collected within the next month and 25% in the second month after sale. Depreciation, insurance, and property taxes comprise $25,000 of monthly manufacturing costs and $12,000 of operating expenses. Insurance and property taxes are paid in February, June, and September. One-half of the remaining manufacturing costs and operating expenses will be paid in the month in which incurred, and the rest in the following month. As of October 1, the following facts are relevant:

- Current assets consist of $50,000 in cash, $50,000 in marketable securities.
- Credit sales for August and September were $500,000 and $450,000, respectively.
- Current liabilities include a 90-day note for $60,000 at 9%, due October 18.
- The firm has a line of credit with a local bank at 18% APR, and the loan is due the following month.
- Accounts payable of $200,000 for September manufacturing expenses
- Accrued liabilities of $100,000 for September operating expenses

Dividends of $1,000 should be received in November. An income tax payment of $20,000 will be made in November. The firm's minimum cash balance is $10,000.

From the information just given, prepare a monthly cash budget for the next quarter (October^{B}December) for the Laurens Corporation.

Chapter 9 –
Crafting a Winning Business Plan

Multiple Choice Questions

1. A business plan performs a number of functions including:
   a) identifying how many employees will be needed in the business start-up phase.
   b) attracting capital for the start-up.
   c) providing the entrepreneur with a plan for managing inventory.
   d) providing the basis for purchasing property and casualty insurance for the new company.

   Answer b   Page 279

2. The _____ becomes the document that summarizes the analysis that has been done to justify a new business.
   a) business plan
   b) cash budget
   c) pro forma
   d) financial statement

   Answer a   Page 280

3. A business plan:
   a) is developed through an intuitive process by which the entrepreneur records his/her plans for the business in the future.
   b) focuses on the internal elements of the business.
   c) forces an entrepreneur to think a business idea through, considering both its positive and its negative aspects.
   d) is a strategic plan for a business that must be supplemented by operational plans once financing is secured.

   Answer c   Page 280

4. A well-developed business plan provides the entrepreneur with a number of benefits, such as:
   a) a way to identify probable financial backers.
   b) a valuable tool for recruiting management to help in running the business.
   c) assisting the entrepreneur in going public with his/her new venture on the stock market.
   d) determining the principle risks confronting the business.

   Answer d   Page 280

5. The primary purpose of building a business plan is to:
   a) raise capital.
   b) attract potential employees.
   c) provide direction, to create a "target" to shoot for.
   d) meet SEC requirements designed to protect lenders and investors.

   Answer c   Page 280

6. The second essential purpose for creating a business plan is:
   a) to guide the operation of the company by charting its future course and devising a strategy for following it.
   b) to attract lenders and investors.
   c) to file with the SEC before making a public stock offering.

d)   to attract potential managers and employees to run the new venture.

Answer a   Page 281

7.   Potential investors tend to believe that if an entrepreneur can't develop a good plan:
   a)   he/she is probably the action-oriented sort of person they need running a business.
   b)   he/she needs to hire a consultant to write the plan for him/her.
   c)   he/she probably lacks the discipline to run a business.
   d)   then the entrepreneur is just like the majority of entrepreneurs and will probably do quite well.

Answer c   Page 281

8.   The "β" rule means that:
   a)   entrepreneurs will only find about β of the financing they need to start their business; they will have to come up with the rest.
   b)   2 out of 3 new start-ups fail within the first year.
   c)   2 out of 3 new businesses with excellent business plans succeed.
   d)   only β of entrepreneurs with a viable new venture will find funding.

Answer d   Page 282

9.   The real value in preparing a business plan is:
   a)   in attracting experienced management talent to help grow the business.
   b)   in the creative process the entrepreneur has to go through.
   c)   in identifying viable funding sources while "fleshing out" the business concept.
   d)   in none of these.

Answer b   Page 282

10.   A business plan:
   a)   reduces the risk and uncertainty involved in starting a new company.
   b)   is a guarantee of success for the small company.
   c)   should be done by professional writers in consultation with the owner.
   d)   should be kept in outline form to avoid overstructuring the company.

Answer a   Page 282

11.   The _____ is the first part of the business plan. It summarizes all the relevant points of the deal, but it should be the last part written.
   a)   executive summary
   b)   mission statement
   c)   industry analysis
   d)   marketing strategy

Answer a   Page 283

12.   The _____ expresses the entrepreneur's vision for the company and what he/she hopes it will become.
   a)   executive summary
   b)   mission statement
   c)   industry analysis
   d)   marketing strategy

Answer b   Page 283

13. The _____ highlights significant financial and operational events in the company's life and should concentrate on the company's accomplishments.
    a) executive summary
    b) company history
    c) business and industry profile
    d) marketing strategy
Answer b   Page 284

14. The _____ acquaints lenders and investors with the nature of the business and the general goals and objectives of the company.
    a) executive summary
    b) company history
    c) business and industry profile
    d) marketing strategy
Answer c   Page 284

15. _____ are long-range, broad statements of what the company plans to accomplish in the distant future, and they guide the overall direction of the company.
    a) Policies
    b) Goals
    c) Procedures
    d) Objectives
Answer b   Page 284

16. The company's overall direction and answer to the question, "Why am I in business?" is answered in this section of the business plan.
    a) executive summary
    b) company history
    c) business and industry profile
    d) marketing strategy
Answer c   Page 284

17. _____ are short-term, specific targets which are attainable, measurable, and controllable.
    a) Objectives
    b) Policies
    c) Goals
    d) Standard operating procedures
Answer a   Page 284

18. The business and industry profile section of the business plan includes:
    a) significant financial and operational events in the life of the company.
    b) how the entrepreneur intends to accomplish the company's goals and objectives.
    c) the nature and characteristics of the target market.
    d) the historical evolution of the market, market size, ease of entry, etc.
Answer d   Page 284

19. A solid business plan is marked by a number of characteristics including:

a) broad, general market research on the overall industry and business environment.
b) a description of the management team.
c) a minimum of financial detail.
d) an optimistic financial projection and understandable risk statement.
Answer b   Page 285

20. Discussion of profitability and anticipated profitability of firms in the market segment, along with the entry, exit, and merger of those firms, is all part of the _____ section of the business plan.
   a) business strategy
   b) company history
   c) business and industry profile
   d) marketing strategy
Answer a   Page 286

21. In the business strategy of the business plan, the owner needs to explain to investors:
   a) significant financial and operational events in the life of the company.
   b) how the entrepreneur intends to accomplish the company's goals and objectives.
   c) the nature and characteristics of the target market.
   d) the historical evolution of the market, market size, ease of entry, etc.
Answer b   Page 286

22. Kyoto is writing a description of her new venture's product line and how it compares to her competitors' product lines. She is writing the ____ portion of her business plan.
   a) description of her firm's product
   b) marketing strategy
   c) competitive analysis
   d) business strategy
Answer a   Page 286

23. Defining the target market's potential and describing its characteristics is part of the:
   a) description of the product line.
   b) marketing strategy portion of the business plan.
   c) competitive analysis.
   d) business strategy section of the business plan.
Answer b   Page 287

24. Proving that a profitable market exists involves:
   a) proving that customers in the marketplace have a need for the good or service and are willing to pay for it.
   b) honestly comparing your firm's products with a competitor's products, showing your advantages.
   c) explaining how you will achieve your business objectives and market share goals.
   d) showing the linkage between your plan of operation and your financial profitability.
Answer a   Page 288

25. An effective market analysis identifies:
   a) your product's competitive advantage.

b)   how you will achieve your market goals, what methods will be used.

c)   the officers'/owners' resumes.

d)   how the product will be advertised.

Answer d   Page 289

26. An explanation of how the product will be distributed is contained within the:

a)   description of the product line.

b)   marketing strategy portion of the business plan.

c)   competitive analysis.

d)   business strategy section of the business plan.

Answer b   Page 290

27. The focus of the competitor analysis section of the business plan is to:

a)   demonstrate the existence of the market for your product.

b)   show that your experienced management team is better than your competitors'.

c)   demonstrate your company's advantage over competitors.

d)   describe your overall product line.

Answer c   Page 290

28. Investors look for which of the following when reviewing the experience of the management team of a new venture?

a)   Assets that can be used as collateral for the loan/investment

b)   Experience, talent, and integrity

c)   Plans for keeping the management team in place

d)   A hiring strategy that has the customer clearly in focus

Answer b   Page 291

29. The organization chart is described in which section of the business plan?

a)   The plan of operation

b)   The resumes of the officers/owners

c)   The business strategy

d)   The executive summary

Answer a   Page 291

30. The plan of operation of the company within the business plan should detail:

a)   the experience of the management team.

b)   the production process for the product being sold.

c)   the financial assets of each of the officers.

d)   plans for keeping the important officers in place with the company.

Answer d   Page 291

31. When creating financial forecasts in a business plan for a proposed venture, an entrepreneur should:

a)   be sure that all forecasts are realistic.

b)   embellish all forecasts to make the numbers look really impressive.

c)   include any assets of the officers/owners that can be used as collateral.

d)   list all previous loans which are in default.

Answer a   Page 291

32. Which of the following is true about the financial data included in the business plan?
    a) Some venture bankers discount owners' projections by 50%.
    b) Only the realistic forecast must be included, although the pessimistic and optimistic forecasts should be available if requested.
    c) The data must be accurate because it is often accepted without further verification.
    d) It should include only the pro forma and the firm's financial statement from the previous year.

Answer a   Page 292

33. Which of the following statements is true?
    a) The useful life of the financed asset must be less than the maturity of the loan.
    b) An entrepreneur should try to camouflage any weaknesses in the small business.
    c) Projected financial statements should prove the company's ability to repay the loan.
    d) Officers' personal assets that can be used as collateral must be included in the financial statement.

Answer c   Page 292

34. An equity investor's objective with the early stage financing of a business is to earn a _____ annual return over the life of the investment.
    a) 30% to 50%
    b) rate that is 10% more than going bank rates.
    c) 60% to 75%
    d) 15% to 25%

Answer a   Page 292

35. The loan proposal portion of the business plan should include:
    a) three sets of forecasts: optimistic, realistic, and pessimistic.
    b) a realistic time table for repayment or for investors to exit.
    c) pro forma for two to three years.
    d) a listing of anyone who owns more than 20% of the business.

Answer b   Page 292

36. David Cupp's business plan for starting Photos Online:
    a) lacked detailed market research.
    b) neglected to include a competitive analysis.
    c) only generated 40% of the capital he needed to start his business.
    d) was developed with the help of the SBA, SCORE, and a retired executive.

Answer d   Page 293

37. When dealing with the risks involved in the business start-up, the business plan should:
    a) leave them out entirely.
    b) only mention them in concept and then only in positive terms.
    c) deal with the most significant risks and describe how they will be addressed.
    d) show the entrepreneur's resolve to grow the company and follow the plan regardless of potential obstacles.

Answer b   Page 294

38. Business plans need to pass three tests:
    a) the financial test, the market test, and the management test.
    b) the appearance test, the substance test, and the concept test.
    c) the reality test, the competitive test, and the value test.
    d) the presentation test, the content test, and the application test.
    Answer c   Page 294

39. An external test of a business plan that revolves around proving that a market exists is the:
    a) competitive test.
    b) consumer test.
    c) value test.
    d) reality test.
    Answer d   Page 295

40. When the entrepreneur presents his/her business plan, he/she usually:
    a) takes 2 of a day.
    b) only gets 15 to 30 minutes.
    c) takes one hour.
    d) takes several days, and does it in sections.
    Answer b   Page 295

41. Entrepreneur America is a ____ begun by Rob Ryan to help entrepreneurs start their companies.
    a) venture capital firm
    b) management consulting firm
    c) bootcamp of plan building
    d) promotional agency
    Answer c   Page 296

42. At Entrepreneur America, Rob Ryan focuses on what part of the business plan?
    a) the presentation
    b) the financial section
    c) the strategy section
    d) the product concept
    Answer a   Page 296

43. According to Dean Suposs, the best business presentations:
    a) are kept low key, clear, complete with lengthy and detailed explanation.
    b) focus on the written document and verbal explanation.
    c) emphasize technical jargon to show the entrepreneur's expertise.
    d) cover the highlights while answering the question, "What's in it for the investor?"
    Answer d   Page 297

44. When presenting the business plan it is important to:
    a) show enthusiasm for the venture.
    b) use visual aids.
    c) avoid technical jargon.
    d) do all of these.

Answer d   Page 297

45. Which of the following is true about banks as a source of capital for new ventures?
    a) Banks are rarely the sole source of capital for a new venture.
    b) Banks are looking for an annual return of $30B50\%$ on loans to new ventures.
    c) A bank's risk is limited to 50% of the loan since the balance of the loan is always covered by owner collateral.
    d) Banks are usually the first source of capital for entrepreneurs and new ventures.
Answer a   Page 298

46. The C of the five Cs that is a synonym for "cash flow" is:
    a) capital.
    b) character.
    c) collateral.
    d) capacity.
Answer d   Page 298

47. The most common reason cited by banks for rejecting small business loans is:
    a) poor credit history.
    b) undercapitalization or too much debt.
    c) lack of collateral.
    d) insufficient cash flow or poor profitability.
Answer b   Page 298

48. Any assets pledged to the bank as security for repayment of the loan are the ____ of the five Cs.
    a) collateral
    b) capacity
    c) capital
    d) conditions
Answer a   Page 298

49. The intangible C that lenders examine in evaluating the business plan is that of:
    a) capital.
    b) character.
    c) collateral.
    d) capacity.
Answer b   Page 298

50. The problem that Kosha Bartel faced when receiving start-up capital from her uncle was:
    a) a loss of control of the company to the uncle.
    b) insufficient capital to sustain the business through the start-up phase.
    c) not having a business plan to guide her company's growth through any crisis.
    d) unrealistic financial projections, especially in terms of expected revenue growth.
Answer c   Page 299

51. The C of the five Cs that relates to the circumstances relating to the business, such as potential growth in the market, form of ownership, location, etc., is called:
    a) capital.

    b) capacity.

    c) conditions.

    d) character

Answer c   Page 300

52. The executive summary should contain which of the following information?
    a) A brief statement of the financial needs of the business and what the money would be used for
    b) A short description of potential buyers
    c) A brief history of the business
    d) A complete description of your business

Answer a   Page 300

53. A description of the key factors that will dictate the success of your business ^{X}quality, price competitiveness, etc. ^{X}should be contained in the _____ section of the business plan.
    a) market analysis
    b) executive summary
    c) description of the business
    d) competitor analysis

Answer c   Page 300

54. Which of the following elements should be identified in the business plan's market analysis?
    a) A brief description of the strategic actions you will take to make your firm a success
    b) Who your existing competitors are
    c) How your products stand up against existing products in the market
    d) External market influences, such as economic factors, social factors, and the like

Answer d   Page 301

55. If your product is a consumer product, in the market analysis section you should address:
    a) what competitors might try to enter your market.
    b) what is the nature of the buying cycle.
    c) the question about what makes your company unique.
    d) a projection of the cost of operation.

Answer b   Page 301

56. How you will market your products to your target market is the subject of this portion of the business plan.
    a) The business strategy
    b) The competitor analysis
    c) The strategic plan
    d) The market analysis

Answer c   Page 302

57. The form of ownership in your company should be explained in the _____ portion of the business plan.
    a) business strategy
    b) specifics of your organization and management structure
    c) executive summary

d)   market analysis
Answer b   Page 302

58. You should identify your key people, explain their backgrounds and what they bring to the
     business, in:
     a)   the executive summary.
     b)   the specifics of your organization and management structure.
     c)   the strategic plan.
     d)   the business strategy.
Answer b   Page 302

59. Your cash budget and an explanation of how much money you need to make your company and
     product a long-term success are the subject matter of the:
     a)   financial plan.
     b)   strategic plan.
     c)   business strategic plan.
     d)   strategic action plan.
Answer a   Page 302

60. A clear mission statement, a restatement of your production and marketing strategies, and a
     discussion of how you will translate those strategies into operation plans, should be detailed in
     the:
     a)   financial plan.
     b)   strategic plan.
     c)   business strategic plan.
     d)   the strategic action plan.
Answer d   Page 302

True or False Questions

61. A well-prepared business plan helps determine the risks facing the venture.
Answer T   Page 279

62. The business plan has two essential functions; it helps the entrepreneur determine if the
     business will succeed and it helps recruit management talent to run the new company.
Answer F   Page 280

63. The primary purpose of building a business plan is to raise capital.
Answer F   Page 280

64. Entrepreneurs who apply for loans without having prepared business plans are less likely to get
     the money they need.
Answer T   Page 281

65. The quality of the entrepreneur's business plan has little impact on the first impression potential
     lenders and investors have of the company.
Answer F   Page 281

66. Often, the presence or absence of a quality business plan is a determining factor in a lender's or investor's decision to put money into a business venture.
Answer T   Page 281

67. When preparing the business plan, the entrepreneur may assume that the investor understands the business the entrepreneur is starting.
Answer F   Page 281

68. Although an entrepreneur may decide to enlist the aid of professionals to help polish a business plan, the entrepreneur should create the essence of the plan.
Answer T   Page 281

69. The best service that a business plan can provide is to show that the business idea is not viable.
Answer T   Page 282

70. The entrepreneur should use a standard format and presentation for the sake of the venture capitalist's analysis and ease of use.
Answer F   Page 282

71. Investors read business plans in such detail that the executive summary is nice to have but it is optional.
Answer F   Page 283

72. The ideal business plan should be at least 100 pages long and somewhat hard to read in order to demonstrate your thoroughness and to capture the venture capitalist's attention.
Answer F   Page 283

73. The executive summary should summarize all of the relevant points of the proposed venture and should be concise^{X}no more than two pages.
Answer T   Page 283

74. The executive summary should highlight significant financial and operational events.
Answer F   Page 283

75. The business plan should cover key people, the opportunity, provide a business context, and explain the risks and rewards involved.
Answer T   Page 283

76. The company history should explain why the company was formed, its past successes, and its image in the marketplace.
Answer T   Page 284

77. Objectives are long-range, broad statements of what the company plans to accomplish in the distant future.
Answer F   Page 284

78. Company goals address the question, "Why am I in this business?"
Answer T   Page 284

79. The industry analysis should cover existing profitability and anticipated profitability of firms in the targeted market segment, and any significant entry or exit of firms.
Answer T   Page 284

80. Business strategy outlines how the owner plans to achieve business objectives in the face of a competitive environment.
Answer T   Page 284

81. The business plan should use a standard format covering standard material, regardless of the specific business and industry.
Answer F   Page 285

82. The executive summary should be written first and should be a broad general discussion of the business plan.
Answer T   Page 285

83. The "competitor analysis" section of the business plan is optional since few lenders and investors are concerned about a small company's rivals in the marketplace.
Answer F   Page 285

84. The business strategy section addresses how the firm will meet the key success factors necessary for success.
Answer T   Page 286

85. When the entrepreneur describes the product in terms of what the customer gains through its purchase and use, he/she is describing it in terms of its features.
Answer F   Page 286

86. Defining the target market is one of the hardest and most important things the entrepreneur can do in the business plan.
Answer T   Page 287

87. Some feel the worst mistake an entrepreneur can make is to fail to define the target market.
Answer T   Page 287

88. It is important to create enthusiasm for the venture by describing the market in broad optimistic terms such as, "The size of this market virtually guarantees success of this venture!"
Answer F   Page 288

89. One way to document customer interest in the market strategy section of the business plan is to include testimonials and evaluations from customers and potential customers.
Answer T   Page 288

90. In the market strategy portion of the business plan, the entrepreneur should explain the promotional strategy, pricing strategy and distribution strategy.
Answer T   Page 288^{B}289

91. How the product will be distributed should be explained in the plan of operation.
Answer F   Page 290

92. The focus of the "competition analysis" section of the business plan should be demonstrating how the company has an advantage over its competitors.
Answer T   Page 290

93. The business plan should include the resumes of anyone with more than a 20% interest in the company.
Answer T   Page 291

94. The business plan needs to address, in the management section, how important officers will be encouraged to remain with the company.
Answer F   Page 291

95. The business plan should include an existing firm's past three years of financial statements as well as its projected statements.
Answer T   Page 291

96. Essential pieces of information for potential investors and lenders are the assumptions the entrepreneur used to derive forecasts, projections, etc.
Answer T   Page 291

97. General requests for funds^{X}e.g., for "working capital"^{X}are sufficient for most loan offices.
Answer F   Page 292

98. Entrepreneurs should artificially inflate the amount of a loan request and expect the loan officer to "talk them down."
Answer F   Page 292

99. A business plan's financial forecasts should reflect the company's ability to repay loans.
Answer T   Page 292

100. An entrepreneur should not include an exit strategy^{X}a way to "cash out"^{X}for investors in the initial plan.
Answer F   Page 292

101. David Cupp receiving funding for his company Photos Online from his local banker, including a line of credit without a loan guarantee from the SBA, because of the quality of his business plan.
Answer T   Page 293

102. When presenting the risks involved, the entrepreneur should stress the risks in the business plan and then "lessen" them in the oral presentation of the plan.
Answer F   Page 293

103. Appearance has little, if any, impact on the acceptance of the business plan by lenders.
Answer F   Page 294

104. A business plan should always have a cash flow projection.
Answer T   Page 294

105. Always tell the truth, even if it's bad news, in the business plan.
Answer T   Page 294

106. The internal competitive test focuses on management's ability to create a company that will gain a competitive edge.
Answer T   Page 295

107. The reality test of a business plan is the explanation of how much of a return is expected, and when investors can expect it.
Answer F   Page 295

108. A business plan should cover five basic areas, including the company's background and its products or services.
Answer T   Page 295

109. Rob Ryan formed Entrepreneur America as a result of his own failures in securing financing for his start-up companies in order to help new entrepreneurs avoid his problems.
Answer F   Page 296

110. The business plan presentation should be slow, methodical, and detailed to show the depth of understanding and preparation the entrepreneur has gone to.
Answer F   Page 297

111. Regardless of how good the plan or its presentation, the entrepreneur should always be prepared for questions when he/she presents the venture.
Answer T   Page 297

112. The entrepreneur should begin the presentation with an explanation of the opportunity, the benefit to the investors, and what the new venture is.
Answer T   Page 297

113. In today's financial climate, more banks are becoming the primary and often only source of capital for new ventures.
Answer F   Page 298

114. A common reason cited by banks which reject small business loan applications is "undercapitalization or too much debt."
Answer T   Page 298

115. Most loans banks make to start-up businesses are unsecured by collateral but by the character of the entrepreneur.
Answer F   Page 298

116. Even though it is an intangible factor, the entrepreneur's "character"—and the quality of the presentation—are important factors in evaluating a loan proposal.
Answer T   Page 298

117. Even though Kosha Bartel easily convinced her uncle that he should fund her start-up, it wasn't until she talked with her friend Liz that she realized the importance of having a written business plan.
Answer T   Page 299

118. In presenting the idea of her company to her uncle, Kosha Bartel felt she would easily convince him because she wanted so little money, but her uncle pressed her for assurances on the probable return and for a clear explanation of the exit strategy.
Answer F   Page 299

119. The conditions in the business environment have little influence on lenders' decision to invest in a business start-up.
Answer F   Page 300

120. While every business plan will be unique, there are several areas of information that should be common to all good business plans.
Answer T   Page 300

Essay Questions

121. Why does the entrepreneur need to develop a business plan? What functions does it fulfill?
Pages 280^{B}282

122. Outline the elements of the business plan with a one to two sentence explanation of each element.
Pages 300^{B}302

123. What 10 characteristics mark a successful business plan?
Page 285

124. What should be included in the section on the firm's product/service? How should the product or service be described?
Pages 286^{B}287

125. What are the two primary steps to proving that a market exists in the market strategy section? What should an effective market analysis include?
Pages 288^{B}290

126. What financial data will lenders want to see in your financial section?
Pages 291^{B}294

127. What are the three tests any business plan should be put to? Name and explain the purpose of each.
Pages 294^{B}295

128. Review the business plan process, outlining the important elements of the presentation.
Pages 295^{B}298

129. What are the five Cs that creditors look for in the business plan? Name and explain each.
Pages 298^{B}300

130. What information should be included in the executive summary? Outline the main points.
Page 300

131. What ten questions should be addressed in the market analysis portion of the business plan?
Page 301

Mini-case

Case 9-1: No case for this chapter in the text.

Chapter 10 –
Pricing for Profit

Multiple Choice Questions

1. Most small business owners appear to use _____ to set their prices.
   a) hunches or guesses
   b) regression analysis
   c) competitive comparisons
   d) an ideal pricing strategy

Answer a   Page 305

2. Tom is working on a pricing strategy for his company's new product line. In order to determine the price ceiling for these products, Tom needs to know:
   a) what price range will work best.
   b) what his company's cost structures are.
   c) what his customers a willing to pay.
   d) what his competitors are charging.

Answer c   Page 305

3. When pricing products, it is important to remember that:
   a) there is an ideal price that customers will pay for a given product or service.
   b) once the acceptable price range is found, prices should not be changed again.
   c) pricing is more an intuitive than a quantitative process.
   d) a customer orientation in price setting is most important.

Answer d   Page 306

4. Small business owners get into trouble when determining their price floor when they:
   a) focus on what the customer will pay.
   b) assume their costs are the same as their competitors'.
   c) begin to track financial ratios to determine what they are doing.
   d) use the price floor as the minimum price in their acceptable price range.

Answer b   Page 307

5. The final price set by the entrepreneur for the products depends on:
   a) the desired image for the products.
   b) the cost structure.
   c) what customer will pay.
   d) what competitors are charging.

Answer a   Page 307

6. When small manufacturing companies face rapidly increasing raw material costs, they can adopt a number of strategies including:
   a) pass the increasing costs along to their customers without comment.
   b) absorb costs for the short term and plan for double price increases in the next pricing cycle.
   c) reconsider their competitive strategy and seek a niche they can service.
   d) emphasize the value their company provides customers.

Answer d   Page 308

7. When pricing a new product, a small business owner should strive to always satisfy three objectives:
    a) long-term acceptance, extensive distribution, and quickly recovering costs.
    b) recovering initial development costs, recovering initial promotional costs, and discouraging competition.
    c) product acceptance, maintaining market share, and earning a profit.
    d) discouraging competition, recovering development costs, and developing a prestigous image.

Answer b   Page 309

8. _____ pricing strategy introduces a new product at a low price to gain quick acceptance and extensive distribution in a mass market.
    a) Penetration
    b) Skimming
    c) Discount
    d) Sliding-down-the-demand-curve

Answer a   Page 309

9. _____ pricing policy is used to introduce a relatively low-priced good into a market where no "elite segment" exists.
    a) Penetration
    b) Skimming
    c) Discount
    d) Sliding-down-the-demand-curve

Answer b   Page 310

10. The basic objective of a penetration pricing policy is to:
    a) recover start-up costs as quickly as possible.
    b) transform the small firm into a discount outlet.
    c) gain quick access into a market to realize high sales volume quickly.
    d) discourage competition and gradually become a high volume producer.

Answer c   Page 310

11. A new product _____ pricing strategy is often used in markets with little competition and when the company seeks to recover start-up costs quickly.
    a) penetration
    b) skimming
    c) discount
    d) sliding-down-the-demand-curve

Answer b   Page 310

12. When using a skimming price strategy, small business owners should remember that:
    a) it is difficult to correct pricing mistakes with this strategy.
    b) is a long-term policy and it will take time to see appropriate results.
    c) if a price is set too low initially, it can be very hard to raise it later.
    d) it is an excellent strategy for discouraging competitors from entering the market.

Answer c   Page 310

13. A company that introduces a new product at a high price and then lowers the price ahead of its competitors is using a _____ pricing strategy.
    a) penetration
    b) skimming
    c) discount
    d) sliding-down-the-demand-curve
Answer d   Page 310

14. Sliding-down-the-demand-curve is a variation of the ___ pricing strategy.
    a) penetration
    b) skimming
    c) discount
    d) price lining
Answer b   Page 310

15. Gateway 2000 is a computer manufacturer that strives to constantly lower its costs so that it can cut the prices on its popular line of personal computers ahead of its competitors. Gateway 2000 is pursuing a _____ pricing strategy.
    a) skimming
    b) sliding-down-the-demand curve
    c) penetration
    d) loss leader
Answer b   Page 310

16. When a retailer routinely prices goods at $9.97 and $7.36 rather than $10.00 and $7.50, the retailer is using:
    a) variable pricing.
    b) penetration pricing.
    c) odd pricing.
    d) price skimming.
Answer c   Page 311

17. _____ is a technique which greatly simplifies the pricing function by setting the same price for items with similar characteristics.
    a) Odd pricing
    b) Leader pricing
    c) Price lining
    d) Geographical pricing
Answer c   Page 311

18. When a small business practices price lining, it most commonly carries lined merchandise in sets of __ different ranges.
    a) 2
    b) 3
    c) 4
    d) 5
Answer b   Page 311

19. Jerry is developing a pricing strategy for a an established line of home care products. His premium products are priced over $50, his best products are in the $25^{B}40 range, and his good products are $10^{B}15 range. Jerry is using a _____ strategy.
    a) penetration pricing
    b) leader pricing
    c) price lining
    d) geographic pricing

Answer c   Page 311

20. _____ is a technique in which a small firm marks down the price of a popular item below its normal price in an effort to increase customer traffic and to boost sales of other items.
    a) Odd pricing
    b) Leader pricing
    c) Price lining
    d) Suggested retail pricing

Answer b   Page 311

21. In _____ pricing, a type of geographical pricing, a small firm charges customers located in different territories different prices for the same products.
    a) FOB factory
    b) uniform delivered
    c) zone
    d) price lining

Answer c   Page 312

22. Geographical pricing includes numerous techniques, such as:
    a) uniform delivered pricing.
    b) loss-leader pricing.
    c) markdowns.
    d) multiple pricing.

Answer a   Page 312

23. _____ is a pricing strategy under which local customers "subsidize" the shipping charges the firm incurs when transporting merchandise to distant customers.
    a) FOB factory pricing
    b) Uniform delivered pricing
    c) Zone pricing
    d) Opportunistic pricing

Answer b   Page 312

24. Many small business owners use a _____ strategy to move stale, damaged, or slow moving goods or to encourage shoppers to purchase merchandise before an upcoming season.
    a) multiple pricing
    b) opportunistic pricing
    c) discount pricing
    d) price lining

Answer c   Page 312

25. Claudia Post's fundamental problem with her courier business was that:
    a) she couldn't win enough business to reach a profitable economy of scale.
    b) she followed a penetration pricing strategy and lost too much money to recover.
    c) she missed using opportunistic pricing when the other courier services were halted due to a strike.
    d) she had not done a profit analysis and didn't know which businesses were making money and which were losing money.
Answer d   Page 313^{B}314

26. The Pastry Shop normally sells cheese Danishes for 60 cents each. On Mondays and Tuesdays, its slowest days, The Pastry Shop offers cheese Danishes at "4 for $2.00." This is:
    a) price lining.
    b) leader pricing.
    c) multiple pricing.
    d) odd pricing.
Answer c   Page 314

27. Baseball cards usually sell for 10 cents each. The Card Shop advertises them at "12 for $1.00." This is:
    a) price lining.
    b) leader pricing.
    c) odd pricing.
    d) multiple pricing.
Answer d   Page 314

28. When a computer manufacturer offers its computer with software pre-installed, a printer, and Internet service, as all part of one price, the manufacturer is using a:
    a) bundling strategy.
    b) multiple pricing strategy.
    c) suggested retail price strategy.
    d) skimming pricing strategy.
Answer a   Page 314

29. When a small business owner doesn't want to make a pricing decision, he/she can use a _____ pricing strategy.
    a) price lining
    b) suggested retail
    c) opportunistic
    d) multiple unit
Answer b   Page 315

30. Probably the most important consideration a manufacturer has when setting the final price of its new exclusive perfume is:
    a) the perfume's production cost.
    b) competitor's prices.
    c) the image the company wants to create for the scent in the customer's mind.
    d) choosing between odd pricing and price lining.
Answer c   Page 315

31. Dotty has her competitors' price information. Her most effective use of that information would be to:
    a) seek to match her competitors.
    b) undercut competitors' prices.
    c) create a premium image by setting her prices higher than competitors.
    d) use it as one variable in her pricing mix.
Answer d   Page 316

32. When considering the competition in price setting, the small business owner should:
    a) consider the competitors' location.
    b) consider the competitors' motives for their prices.
    c) consider the nature of the goods being sold.
    d) consider all of these.
Answer d   Page 316

33. Which of the following factors is vital to determining the effects of competition on the small firm's pricing policies?
    a) The competitor's location
    b) The availability of capital for production
    c) The form of ownership of the small business
    d) The type of outlet the business is
Answer a   Page 316

34. When a small business is faced with price competition from a much larger competitor, it should consider:
    a) going head-to-head on prices by lowering its cost structure.
    b) using nonprice competition by offering value added service.
    c) make rapid, continual price changes to keep the competition off balance.
    d) move to a premium price strategy by offering higher scale goods and services.
Answer b   Page 316

35. Sasha and Seth Dowager wanted to use their pricing strategy for selling their brownies to:
    a) capture the maximum market share as fast as possible.
    b) regain their start-up costs as quickly as possible.
    c) establish a high-quality homemade image.
    d) establish an inexpensive medium-quality image.
Answer c   Page 317

36. When it comes to pricing, it is not uncommon for entrepreneurs to:
    a) use careful research to price their products.
    b) cut prices to the point of unprofitability just to compete.
    c) overprice their products and lose sales.
    d) underestimage the power of price cuts.
Answer b   Page 318

37. Alicia sells a home exercise product with a gross profit margin of 25%. If she cuts her price 10%, how much would sales have to increase for her to just break even?
    a) increase 50%

b) double
c) triple
d) increase 75%

Answer c   Page 318

38. If a haberdasher purchases a tie for $12 and plans to sell it for $18, the percentage of <u>retail price</u> markup would be:
a) 33%.
b) 50%.
c) 175%.
d) 100%.

Answer a   Page 319

39. If a haberdasher purchases a tie for $12 and plans to sell it for $18, the <u>percentage of cost</u> markup would be:
a) 33%.
b) 50%.
c) 175%.
d) 100%.

Answer b   Page 319

40. _____ is the average markup required on all merchandise to cover the cost of items, incidental expenses, and a profit.
a) Initial markup
b) Cost plus markup
c) Direct markup
d) Contributing margin

Answer a   Page 319

41. If an item costs a small business owner $15, and the desired markup on it is 60%, its retail price would be:
a) $24.00.
b) $25.00.
c) $37.50.
d) $43.25.

Answer c   Page 320

42. A common "me-too" pricing policy by which the small business owner establishes his/her prices by monitoring competitor's prices and then matching them is called:
a) follow-the-leader pricing.
b) below-market pricing.
c) price lining.
d) variable pricing.

Answer a   Page 320

43. John is considering using a below-market pricing strategy to compete. To do this, John needs to:
a) offer prices at least 15% below the average market price.

b) find a service customers really want to attract them to his store.
c) determine his price floor.
d) eliminate extra services and increase volume enough to offset the lower profit margins.
Answer d   Page 321

44. The most commonly used pricing technique for manufacturers is:
a) direct pricing.
b) margin pricing.
c) cost-plus pricing.
d) absorption pricing.
Answer c   Page 321

45. Cost-plus pricing:
a) is complete pricing in that it takes into consideration all manufacturing and overhead costs.
b) guarantees the manufacturer a desired profit margin.
c) does not encourage a manufacturer to operate efficiently.
d) clouds the true relationship of price, volume, and costs.
Answer d   Page 321

46. Cost-plus pricing has several disadvantages, including:
a) it clouds the relationships among price, volume, and costs.
b) it fails to consider the competition sufficiently.
c) a mentality of "I-can-do-it-cheaper," leading to price competition with larger companies.
d) it tends to be reactive rather than proactive in relation to competition and market forces.
Answer b   Page 321

47. A reliable cost accounting system is necessary for accurate pricing. The traditional method of product costing, where the costs of direct materials, direct labor, and   factory overhead are included, is called _____ costing.
a) absorption
b) break-even
c) direct
d) variable
Answer a   Page 321

48. _____ include(s) the unit cost of a manufacturer's product under an absorption costing system.
a) Opportunity costs
b) Depreciation
c) Insurance
d) Variable costs
Answer d   Page 322

49. _____ costing includes only those costs that vary directly with the volume of an item produced.
a) Absorption
b) Break-even
c) Indirect
d) Direct

Answer d   Page 322

50. _____ tells what portion of the total revenues remains after covering variable costs to contribute toward meeting fixed expenses and earning a profit.
    a) The full-absorption statement
    b) The break-even selling price
    c) The contribution percentage
    d) Cost-plus pricing

Answer c   Page 322

51. Even in the short run, a small business must set the price of a product at least equal to the _____ costs (per unit), or it must shut down.
    a) fixed
    b) variable
    c) total
    d) invariable

Answer b   Page 322

52. The Japanese approach to pricing:
    a) begins with the design of a product, then the calculation of the cost, computing its price, and then determining if the product will sell at that price.
    b) makes no allowance for what the product should cost.
    c) uses a cost management system and tends to maintain the status quo.
    d) Allows a target cost for a product, then designs and manufactures the product to meet that cost target.

Answer d   Page 324

53. The Japanese pricing process relies heavily on:
    a) teams of workers.
    b) the use of statistical method.
    c) cost accounting.
    d) the use of cost-plus pricing.

Answer a   Page 325

54. Most service firms base their prices on:
    a) fairly stable pricing policies.
    b) the cost of the service plus an estimate of the value they add in delivering the service.
    c) market surveys on their respective industries.
    d) an hourly basis for services rendered.

Answer d   Page 326

55. To establish a reasonable, profitable price for service, the small business owner needs to know:
    a) fixed and variable costs, the break-even point, and his/her contribution percentage.
    b) competitors' prices, and costs of direct and indirect labor.
    c) the cost of materials, direct labor, and overhead for each unit of service.
    d) full-absorption costs, direct and indirect labor, and the break-even point.

Answer c   Page 326

56. The total number of credit cards in the United States now tops:
  a) one million.
  b) one hundred million.
  c) one hundred and fifty million.
  d) one billion.
Answer d   Page 328

57. When small business owners let customers use credit cards, the small business:
  a) image will be enhanced.
  b) will find customers spending more than noncredit card users.
  c) will probably be rated higher on key performance measures than those who do not.
  d) loses its small business feel.
Answer c   Page 328

58. The normal fee that a credit service charges for using the system is ___ of total credit card charges.
  a) $1^B6\%$
  b) $7^B10\%$
  c) $8^B9\%$
  d) $2^B1\%$
Answer a   Page 329

59. A customer who purchases a television from Ace Appliance Store and pays for it in 36 monthly payments is using:
  a) trade credit.
  b) charge account credit.
  c) installment credit.
  d) debit card credit.
Answer c   Page 329

60. A firm sells small-ticket items to their regular customers on customer charge accounts and then bills the customers each month. This type of credit arrangement is called:
  a) trade credit.
  b) charge account credit.
  c) installment credit.
  d) debit card credit.
Answer a   Page 329

True or False Questions
61. It is common for start-ups to price their products and services too high.
Answer F   Page 305

62. Price is the monetary value of a good or service in the marketplace.
Answer T   Page 306 ·

63. Price is a measure of what the customer must exchange to obtain goods and services and is an indicator of value to the customer.
Answer T   Page 306

64. For most products, there is an ideal price.
Answer F   Page 306

65. The price floor of a product or service is set by the company's cost structure.
Answer T   Page 306

66. All firms within an industry have the same price floor.
Answer F   Page 307

67. Proper pricing is a balancing act, walking between a high enough price to cover profit margins and convey the right image and low enough to attract customers.
Answer T   Page 307

68. Managers sometimes introduce a new product at a less than cost price to gain acceptance, knowing they can easily raise the price later.
Answer F   Page 307

69. If a company wants quick acceptance and extensive distribution, when introducing a new product into a highly competitive market with a large number of similar products, penetration pricing is the best strategy.
Answer T   Page 309

70. Penetration pricing is a short-term pricing strategy and achieves tremendous profit.
Answer F   Page 310

71. A penetration pricing strategy is designed to recover a company's developmental and promotional cost of a new product very quickly.
Answer F   Page 310

72. A skimming pricing strategy sets a relatively high price for a product to appeal to the segment of the market which is not sensitive to price.
Answer T   Page 310

73. The skimming pricing strategy is used when there is a lot of competition in the market.
Answer F   Page 310

74. A skimming pricing strategy permits a small business owner to correct pricing mistakes more quickly and easily than a penetration pricing strategy.
Answer T   Page 310

75. A sliding-down-the-demand-curve pricing strategy is a short-term strategy which assumes that competition will emerge.
Answer T   Page 310

76. A sliding-down-the-demand-curve pricing strategy is often used in conjunction with a penetration pricing strategy.
Answer F   Page 310

77. Odd pricing is a form of psychological pricing.
Answer T   Page 311

78. Price lining occurs when a small company raises the price of all of its goods by the same percentage to cover operating expenses.
Answer F   Page 311

79. Price lining, leader pricing, and odd pricing are three geographic pricing strategies that can be used for established products.
Answer F   Page 312

80. Under uniform delivered pricing, a company charges all of its customers the same price, even though the cost of selling or transporting the merchandise varies.
Answer T   Page 312

81. Under FOB Factory terms, the customer pays all shipping costs.
Answer T   Page 312

82. Claudia Post was excellent at sales but had a very poor understanding of the "business side" and this resulted in her problems with cash flow in the running of her courier service.
Answer T   Pages 313-314

83. Multiple pricing is a technique used to simplify the pricing decision by setting the same price for items in the same line.
Answer F   Page 314

84. Most small business managers follow the manufacturer's suggested retail price when it is available.
Answer T   Page 315

85. The manufacturer's suggested price takes into account the small firm's cost structure and its competitive situation.
Answer F   Page 315

86. It is more common for a small business to underprice its products and services than overpricing them.
Answer T   Page 315

87. Even if a small business <u>cannot</u> differentiate its product by creating a distinctive image in the consumer's mind, it can afford its own line of prices.
Answer F   Page 315

88. The prices a small business charges influence its image in the marketplace.
Answer T   Page 315

89. Two factors that determine the effects of competitors' prices on a small business owner's pricing decisions are the location of the competitors and the nature of the competing goods.
Answer T   Page 316

90. Although competitor's prices can have a dramatic effect on a small business's own prices, monitoring competitor prices is illegal in many states.
Answer F   Page 316

91. If a firm lacks a unique business image, it must match its competitor's prices or risk losing customers.
Answer T   Page 316

92. The reason Sasha and Seth Dowager built a web page rather than use a more traditional method of direct marketing is because they wanted a better way to reach customers and a better response rate than traditional direct marketing would normally get.
Answer T   Page 317

93. Nonprice competition is using personal service, free delivery, and other extras to attract and keep customers without changing prices.
Answer T   Page 318

94. The underlying forces that dictate price are generally the same across industries, so that all business in that industry have the same underlying cost factors.
Answer F   Page 318

95. A firm's initial markup is the average markup required on all merchandise to cover the cost of items, incidental expenses, and a profit.
Answer T   Page 319

96. The costs of merchandise used in computing markup includes wholesale price, incidental costs, and profit minus any discounts.
Answer T   Page 319

97. A retailer who buys a product for $19.75 and has a desired markup of retail price of 55% should establish a retail price of $43.89.
Answer T   Page 319

98. The initial markup on a product is the total markup on all merchandise to cover the cost of the items and a reasonable profit.
Answer F   Page 319

99. Most stores use a standard markup across all products due to the heavy labor costs involved in individual pricing.
Answer F   Page 320

100. The most effective pricing strategy for small businesses is follow-the-leader pricing due to its simplicity and its ability to keep price parity for the small business.
Answer F   Page 320

101. The primary advantage of cost-plus pricing is its simplicity.
Answer T   Page 321

102. Even though cost-plus pricing is simple, it does not encourage a small business to use its resources efficiently.
Answer T   Page 321

103. The traditional method of product costing, absorption costing, is extremely useful in helping the manufacturer determine prices or the effect of price changes.
Answer F   Page 321

104. The problem with using full absorption cost information when setting prices is that it clouds the true relationships among price, volume, and costs by including fixed expenses in unit cost.
Answer T   Page 322

105. Contribution margin is the portion of sales revenue left after covering fixed expenses and a profit.
Answer F   Page 322

106. The break-even selling price is calculated by dividing the profit desired plus the variable cost per unit times the quantity produced plus the total fixed cost by the quantity produced.
Answer T   Page 323

107. The formula for calculating the break-even is:

$$\text{Break-even selling price} = \frac{\text{Profit} + (\text{Variable cost} \times \text{Quantity produced}) + \text{Total fixed cost}}{\text{Quantity produced}}$$

Answer T   Page 323

108. The Japanese approach to pricing is to start with a target cost based on the price customers are likely to accept; then, manufacturers design and develop the product to meet that target cost.
Answer T   Page 324

109. The Japanese approach to pricing a product focuses on pinning down the major cost components of a product in the planning and design phase since that's where virtually all of its subsequent costs are built in.
Answer T   Page 325

110. The Japanese approach to pricing relies on the expertise of upper management and their ability to stay in touch with the market.

Answer F   Page 325

111. The American approach to pricing stresses constant improvement, pushing costs down and prices up to increase profit margins.
Answer F   Page 325

112. Because service firms have no quantitative pricing techniques available to them, they must charge the "going rate" for their services.
Answer F   Page 326

113. For a service firm, labor and materials comprise the largest portion of the cost of the service provided.
Answer T   Page 326

114. The use of credit cards increases the probability, speed, and magnitude of customer spending.
Answer T   Page 328

115. The use of a credit card by small business customers costs the small business from 10 to 15 percent of the price of the product.
Answer F   Page 329

116. One advantage of installment loans for a small business is that the business owner retains a security interest in the item sold as collateral on the loan.
Answer T   Page 329

117. Because installment credit is so profitable for the small business, most small businesses finance themselves.
Answer F   Page 329

118. Trade accounts are the equivalent of a credit card that is issued by the business.
Answer F   Page 329

119. Qualifying for merchant status is relatively easy for most small businesses.
Answer F   Page 330

120. Merchant status permits a small business to accept credit card payments and enhances the reputation of the small business.
Answer T   Page 330

Essay Questions

121. Define and explain the terms: price, price range, price ceiling, and price floor. Why is it important to keep these terms distinct in the entrepreneur's thinking?
Pages 306–307

122. Name and explain the three basic pricing strategies a small business owner has in establishing a new product's price.
Pages 309–310

123. There are at least eight different pricing strategies for established goods and services. Explain four of those strategies and why you'd use them.

Pages 311–315

124. How does price convey an image for the product or service?
Page 315

125. Explain the impact of competition on pricing strategy and what an entrepreneur should do about competitors' prices.
Pages 316–317

126. Retailers have three pricing techniques available to them. Describe each technique, explain why a retailer would use it, and offer advantages or disadvantages that exist for each technique.
Pages 319–321

127. What pricing strategies are available to manufacturers? Explain each, why it is used, and what it does for the manufacturer.
Pages 321–326

128. Compare and contrast the typical American pricing strategy for developing a new product with the typical Japanese practice.
Pages 324–325

129. Discuss pricing strategies for service firms.
Pages 326–327

130. Explain the different kinds of credit a small business can offer its customers and the impact each has on pricing.
Pages 328–329

131. How does a small business achieve merchant status? Why would it want to?
Page 330

Mini-Cases

Case 10-1: The Price is Right?

"It is obvious what women want; I can't imagine why someone never thought of it before. What good is it to be rich if you have to stay around the house all day waiting for service representatives or doing paperwork?" Penny Matthews decided she would take those responsibilities off the backs of the well-to-do women of Tucson, Arizona. "My business will arrange for all the services you need around the home (lawns mowed, plumbing, carpets cleaned, televisions repaired, pools cleaned, everything). My clients will be free to enjoy their lives without worrying about their houses. We will also arrange for parties to be completely catered. In addition, if you wish, we will pay all your bills and reconcile your bank statements. A life without the irritations of domestic hassles; that's our service."

Penny was explaining the idea to her close friend and banker, Wallace Trevillian. "You have definitely thought about this for some time and puts months of work into its planning," said Wallace. "What do you plan to charge for these services?"

"That's a good question, Wallace. I haven't thought about it."

Question

1. How would Penny Matthews go about determining how to price the services her business plans to offer?

Case 10-2: Pricing for Profit

Miller Manufacturing, Inc. produces electronic components for television circuitry. Variable costs comprise 67% of the product's selling price. The variable costs of producing a component include:

> Direct material $1.83/unit
> Direct labor $6.72/unit
> Variable factory overhead $ 0.86/unit

Vicki Miller, President, expects to produce 80,000 electronic components and to incur $280,000 of fixed costs.

Questions

1. What is the minimum price that Miller Manufacturing would sell its electrical components for?

2. What is Miller Manufacturing's break-even price?

3. If Miller desires a profit of $120,000, what price should she set?

Chapter 11 –
Creative Use of Advertising and Promotion

Multiple Choice Questions

1. In reality, advertising:
    a) is a "luxury expense" to be undertaken only when the budget permits.
    b) requires a large budget to be successful.
    c) is an investment in the future; without steady advertising the customer base will dry up.
    d) is relatively ineffective in increasing sales but it does increase customer awareness.

    Answer c   Page 334

2. Tami is developing an advertising strategy for her small business. The first step in this process is to:
    a) choose an advertising agency to assist her.
    b) determine how much she can spend.
    c) identify her target audience.
    d) set her advertising goals and objectives.

    Answer d   Page 335

3. It is more difficult to measure the results of ____ ads; they should produce an increase in sales within six to nine months.
    a) name recognition
    b) purchasing results
    c) stimulation of purchase
    d) attraction of new customers

    Answer a   Page 335

4. Effective ads are built on:
    a) a clear picture of the competition's products.
    b) a multimedia approach.
    c) a unique selling proposition.
    d) clearly defined features of the product.

    Answer c   Page 336

5. The most meaningful unique selling proposition:
    a) identifies as many product features as possible.
    b) stresses price.
    c) counters the strengths of the competition.
    d) describes the primary benefit of the product.

    Answer d   Page 336

6. The choice of advertising medium is primarily determined by:
    a) what media the competition uses.
    b) what media the industry focuses on.
    c) the target audience and the message.
    d) the unique selling proposition and budget.

    Answer c   Page 337

7. There are a number of tips a small business owner can follow to build effective advertising, including:
   a) run one advertisement at a time.
   b) limit the content of each ad.
   c) focus on short-term advertising goals.
   d) all of these.
Answer b   Page 338

8. _____ is any form of persuasive communication designed to inform consumers about a product or service and to influence them to purchase those goods or services.
   a) Promotion
   b) Publicity
   c) Personal selling
   d) Advertising
Answer a   Page 339

9. _____ is any commercial news covered by the media that boosts sales but for which the small business does not pay.
   a) Promotion
   b) Publicity
   c) Personal selling
   d) Advertising
Answer b   Page 339

10. The Last Hole, a small golf shop, sponsors a hole-in-one contest in a golf tournament to raise money for charity. Anyone scoring a hole-in-one on #16 wins a complete set of clubs; the golfer closest to the pin on #16 wins a golf wardrobe. The Last Hole is the subject of several reports and stories in the local media. This is an example of:
   a) sales promotion.
   b) advertising.
   c) personal selling.
   d) publicity.
Answer d   Page 339

11. When Chapters, a small book store, brings in a famous author for a special autograph session promoting her latest book and gets her on the local radio station, Chapters is using:
   a) sales promotion.
   b) advertising.
   c) publicity.
   d) personal selling.
Answer c   Page 339

12. A recent study of top salespeople found that they:
   a) do most of the talking during the sales call.
   b) work from the customer's perspective and use past "success stories."
   c) tend to be indirect, taking their time to get to the point with the customer.

    d) see themselves as vendors and tend to not leave sales materials with the customer.

Answer b   Page 340

13. Top salespeople:
    a) spend 60% of their time presenting the benefits of the product.
    b) offer the product or service in the first 30 minutes of the sales call.
    c) spend 60–70% of their time listening.
    d) do all of these.

Answer c   Page 340

14. The cost of making a sales call is approximately:
    a) $84.
    b) $128.
    c) $25.
    d) $225.

Answer d   Page 341

15. A study by the Dartnell Corporation showed that:
    a) 80% of salespeople are highly effective.
    b) 20% of salespeople can sell and are selling the right product.
    c) the average salesperson worked approximately 60 hours per week.
    d) 55% of salespeople have sales ability but are selling the wrong product.

Answer b   Page 341

16. The small business owner should track a number of measures of sales activity including:
    a) actual advertising and promotion costs.
    b) the effectiveness of advertising supporting the sales call.
    c) the cost of sales promotion materials used by the salesperson.
    d) profit contribution by product, salesperson, territory, and/or customer.

Answer d   Page 342

17. _____ is any sales presentation that is nonpersonal in nature and is paid for by an identified sponsor.
    a) Publicity
    b) Advertising
    c) Specialty advertising
    d) Personal selling

Answer b   Page 342

18. The Hilderbrand's initial effort at personal selling used what type of sales force to sell their educational products for children?
    a) They relied solely on their own sales force of 5.
    b) They only used 35 independent sales representatives.
    c) They didn't have a sales force; they sell strictly via the web.
    d) They used an in-house sales force of 5, supplemented by 350 independent representatives.

Answer d   Page 343

19. The _____ cost of an advertising medium compares the actual dollar cost of an ad with the number of potential customers it reaches.
    a) relative
    b) continuous
    c) absolute
    d) comparative

Answer a   Page 344

20. When selecting the advertising vehicle the small business owner should ask him/herself:
    a) what are the characteristics of my product?
    b) who are my target customers?
    c) what medium will best support my sales force?
    d) what can I legally say in my advertisements?

Answer b   Page 344

21. Which of the following media account for the greatest portion of advertising expenditures?
    a) Internet
    b) radio
    c) newspapers
    d) magazines

Answer c   Page 345

22. Newspaper advertising is characterized by:
    a) broad territory coverage.
    b) high costs.
    c) long ad life
    d) prompt responses to the ads.

Answer d   Page 336

23. Newspapers have a number of disadvantages for the small business, such as:
    a) poor timeliness; its already old news.
    b) high expense.
    c) lack of prominence of the ads.
    d) readership of primarily older women.

Answer c   Page 336

24. Radio has a number of advantages for the small business owner, such as:
    a) friendliness, in that radio ads are more active than print media ads.
    b) easily measurable results and testable strategies.
    c) long life span.
    d) the ability to personalize the ads to the specific customers.

Answer a   Page 347

25. Radio:
    a) is the one medium that customers spend the most time paying attention to.
    b) can reach nearly any target market.
    c) is very susceptible to "zapping."
    d) is the most expensive advertising medium in terms of <u>relative</u> costs.

26. Radio's power as an advertising medium comes from:
    a) the high production qualities available to the advertiser.
    b) the long life of its ads.
    c) its nearly universal presence in society.
    d) the powerful graphic abilities of the medium.

Answer c   Page 347

27. _____ radio ads are most common.
    a) 10-second
    b) 15-second
    c) 30-second
    d) 60-second

Answer d   Page 348

28. Which of the following times would be considered radio "prime time?"
    a) 7 p.m. to midnight
    b) 6 a.m. to 4 p.m.
    c) 10 a.m. to 4 p.m.
    d) midnight to 6 a.m.

Answer b   Page 349

29. If a small business owner wants to use television advertising, he/she should:
    a) go for national advertising to get the maximum absolute cost advantage.
    b) try to use cable which costs $200 or less for a 30 second spot.
    c) consider radio instead because they have identical advantages.
    d) remember that television is one of the least flexible media.

Answer b   Page 349

30. Television ads are most commonly sold in what time increments?
    a) 20 seconds
    b) 30 seconds
    c) 60 seconds
    d) 15 seconds

Answer b   Page 349

31. Flashing from one television channel to another, especially during commercials, is called:
    a) zapping.
    b) skipping.
    c) cluttering.
    d) zipping.

Answer a   Page 350

32. Today, nearly ____ web sites belong to small businesses.
    a) 1 million
    b) 3.4 million
    c) 59,000
    d) 141,000

Answer d   Page 350

33. John wants to gather information on the potential customers that "hit" his small company's home page. The technology that would let him do this is:
    a) hypertext tech link.
    b) a cookie.
    c) a banner ad.
    d) push technology.
Answer b   Page 351

34. Magazines are a powerful advertising medium in that:
    a) nearly 6 out of 10 adults read a magazine every day.
    b) there are nearly 500 trade magazines in circulation.
    c) the average magazine attracts 4 hours and 32 minutes of adult reading time.
    d) the average reader of a magazine is exposed to 89% of the ads in the copy.
Answer d   Page 351

35. Magazines have a number of advantages for the small business owner, including:
    a) low cost.
    b) short closing time.
    c) high quality ad reproduction.
    d) prominence of the ads in the medium.
Answer c   Page 352

36. Which of the following is a <u>disadvantage</u> of magazine ads?
    a) the long closing times
    b) poor ad quality
    c) an inability to target a market
    d) lack of flexibility
Answer a   Page 352

37. Which advertising medium offers the greatest ability to selectively target a specific audience?
    a) newspaper
    b) television
    c) direct mail
    d) radio
Answer c   Page 353

38. Direct mail ads have a number of advantages to them, such as:
    a) low relative costs.
    b) long life spans.
    c) flexibility.
    d) multiple exposure.
Answer c   Page 353

39. The key to the success of direct mail advertising is:
    a) designing the right envelope.
    b) the accuracy of the customer mailing list.

    c) creative use of color and photographs in the mailing.
    d) using key words such as "free," "hurry," and "savings."
Answer b   Page 353–354

40. Which of the following media has the highest cost per thousand?
    a) radio
    b) newspaper
    c) direct mail
    d) outdoor ads
Answer c   Page 354

41. A successful direct mail ad is characterized by:
    a) text written as if it were being spoken.
    b) thorough text descriptions of the benefit.
    c) making statements rather than asking questions.
    d) minimal use of pictures and color, to reduce costs.
Answer a   Page 355

42. The typical direct mail campaign is right only about ___ % of the time.
    a) 2
    b) 5
    c) 15
    d) 8
Answer a   Page 356

43. The advantage of "hi-tech" direct mail is:
    a) it is much lower in cost than traditional direct mail.
    b) customers spend more time interacting with it and remember it better.
    c) it is much easier to produce and mail than traditional direct mail.
    d) it works even with poor or outdated mailing lists.
Answer b   Page 356

44. The reason Anne Kelly's direct mail marketing for her Junonia, Ltd is successful is:
    a) because of her use of hi-tech interactive direct mail.
    b) the accuracy of her mailing list.
    c) because shopping is so painful for her customers; they prefer direct mail shopping.
    d) the way the letter is written and the because of the use of color in the catalog.
Answer a   Page 357

45. Which of the following is an <u>advantage</u> of outdoor ads?
    a) prominence of the ads
    b) narrow reach
    c) long exposure
    d) flexibility
Answer d   Page 358

46. Which of the following is a <u>disadvantage</u> of outdoor ads?
    a) high absolute and relative costs
    b) legal restrictions

    c) narrow reach
    d) lack of flexibility
Answer b   Page 359

47. The best <u>color</u> combination for an outdoor ad is:
    a) blue on green.
    b) red on black.
    c) yellow on orange.
    d) black on white.
Answer d   Page 359

48. Transit advertising's <u>advantages</u> include:
    a) its flexibility.
    b) the high quality color reproduction.
    c) its wide coverage.
    d) the prominence of display.
Answer c   Page 360

49. Transit advertising has several disadvantages, such as:
    a) legal restrictions.
    b) high cost.
    c) low frequency and short exposure.
    d) the inability to target specific audiences.
Answer d   Page 361

50. _____ are an important advertising medium for reaching customers who have already made the purchase decision and are looking for the product or service.
    a) Direct mail ads
    b) Directory listings
    c) Television ads
    d) Transit ads
Answer b   Page 361

51. The form of advertising that gives the small business owner a preselected audience and an economical way to make sales calls would be:
    a) outdoor advertising.
    b) trade shows.
    c) directories.
    d) direct mail.
Answer b   Page 362–363

52. A hardware store giving customers nail aprons and yardsticks emblazoned with its name, address, phone number, logo, and slogan is using which advertising medium?
    a) point-of-purchase ads
    b) cooperative advertising
    c) specialty advertising
    d) shared ads
Answer c   Page 364

53. An important advantage of specialty advertising is its:
    a) ability to significantly lower the cost of sales calls.
    b) low specific costs.
    c) versatility.
    d) potentially broad reach.

Answer c   Page 364

54. The Aerobic Shop sponsors a "Fun Run" to raise money for the local Muscular Dystrophy chapter. As a result, The Aerobic Shop's sales increase by 12%. The Aerobic Shop is using:
    a) special events and promotions advertising.
    b) specialty advertising.
    c) personal selling.
    d) point-of-purchase advertising.

Answer a   Page 366

55. Under the _____ method of establishing an advertising budget, the owner sees advertising as a luxury.
    a) what-is-affordable
    b) matching competitors
    c) percentage of sales
    d) objective-and-task

Answer a   Page 366

56. The most commonly used method of establishing an advertising budget for a small business is:
    a) a percentage of sales.
    b) spending what competitors spend.
    c) objective-and-task method.
    d) what is affordable.

Answer a   Page 366

57. The _____ method is the most difficult and least used technique of establishing an advertising budget.
    a) percentage of sales
    b) spending what competitors spend
    c) objective-and-task
    d) what is affordable

Answer c   Page 367

58. Under _____, a manufacturer splits the cost of advertising with a small retailer if the retailer features its product.
    a) cooperative advertising
    b) shared advertising
    c) direct advertising
    d) integrated marketing

Answer a   Page 368

59. Timex designs a set of newspaper ads promoting its watches, making them available at no cost to jewelers selling its watches so they can add their names, addresses, and phone numbers. It is using _____ advertising.
    a) institutional
    b) generic
    c) cooperative
    d) shared

Answer c   Page 368

60. In a _____ advertising program, a group of similar businesses forms a "syndicate" to produce "generic" ads that allow the individual businesses to dub in local information.
    a) cooperative advertising
    b) shared advertising
    c) direct advertising
    d) integrated marketing

Answer b   Page 370

61. A successful public relations technique used by local businesses to sponsor and promote fundraising activities of nonprofit groups is called:
    a) cooperative advertising.
    b) shared advertising.
    c) cause marketing.
    d) integrated marketing.

Answer c   Page 370

True or False Questions

62. When using advertising, the small business owner should ask him/herself certain questions such as; "What business are we in?", "What image do we want to project?", etc.

Answer T   Page 335

63. The most powerful unique selling proposition is tied to the tangible practical features of the product.

Answer F   Page 336

64. One way ad effectiveness can be measured is to simply measure the increased volume of traffic into the store as a result of the ad.

Answer T   Page 337

65. Effective advertising involves running multiple ads at one time.

Answer T   Page 338

66. Advertising is a synonym for promotion.

Answer F   Page 339

67. Contacting local business and civic groups, sponsoring a seminar, offering to be interviewed on a radio show are types of publicity a small business owner could use.

Answer T   Page 339

68. A recent study of top salespeople found that most sales representatives see themselves as vendors and sellers of products.
Answer F   Page 340

69. Experts estimate that salespeople fail to ask for the order 60% of the time.
Answer T   Page 341

70. The most effective sales calls begin with an explanation or a demonstration of the product.
Answer F   Page 341

71. One of the most important advertising decisions the small business manager must make is selecting the specific media to employ in disseminating the manager's personal message.
Answer T   Page 342

72. The Hilderbrands had the most success when they hired two sales managers, installed a computer system for tracking results, handled international sales themselves, and hired 100 independent sales representatives.
Answer T   Page 343

73. The small business manager should employ the same advertising media as competitors to increase the likelihood of advertising success.
Answer F   Page 344

74. When choosing a medium for an advertising message, a small business owner needs to consider the <u>absolute</u> costs of the ad, the ad's cost per potential customer reached.
Answer F   Page 344

75. Newspaper circulation as a percentage of total households reached has climbed over the past two decades, making it an excellent value for the advertising dollar.
Answer F   Page 345

76. Newspapers are flexible and provide selected coverage in the firm's trading area.
Answer T   Page 346

77. One disadvantage of newspaper ads is their long closing time.
Answer F   Page 346

78. Newspaper ad space is typically sold by lines and columns or inches and columns.
Answer T   Page 347

79. Because of radio's nearly universal presence, advertising messages receive a tremendous amount of exposure in the target market.
Answer T   Page 347

80. By choosing a radio station with the appropriate listener profile, a small business owner can reach almost any target market desired.
Answer T   Page 347

81. Radio ads require repeated broadcasting in order to be effective; one time exposures don't work.
Answer T   Page 348

82. In radio advertising, 30-second ads are the most common.
Answer F   Page 348

83. The primary benefit of television ads is their ability to demonstrate a good or service in a graphic, vivid manner.
Answer T   Page 349

84. A significant disadvantage of television advertising is the difficulty in changing an ad to match the rapidly changing marketplace.
Answer F   Page 349

85. The typical television viewer sees 1,500 advertisements a day and in a recent survey only 10 percent of respondents could correctly identify a particular television ad.
Answer T   Page 350

86. The world wide web is an effective small business advertising tool for reaching the international market as nearly 27% of "browsers" are from outside the United States.
Answer T   Page 350

87. Push technology on the web allows small business owners to track and gather information on the customers that "hit" their home page.
Answer F   Page 351

88. Magazines have a wide audience reach in that nearly 9 out of 10 adults read an average of seven different magazines a month.
Answer T   Page 351

89. The average readership of a magazine is 33 adult readers.
Answer F   Page 351

90. Most magazines printed today are broad, general interest publications, printed as national editions.
Answer F   Page 352

91. Magazines have a shorter closing time than newspapers, making them timely and highly flexible.
Answer F   Page 352

92. Direct mail has been a popular method of small business advertising for a long time. Catalogs were printed as early as the 15th century.
Answer T   Page 353

93. The greatest strength of direct mail is its ability to allow the owner to select the specific audience to receive the message.
Answer T   Page 353

94. Direct mail ads typically produce quick results; in most cases, the ad will generate sales within three or four days after it is received.
Answer T   Page 353

95. The cost of designing direct mail is less than in other media and is considered quite low.
Answer F   Page 354

96. Successful direct mailers include an order form separate from the offer letter.
Answer T   Page 355

97. Direct mail advertisers have found that recipients of direct mail computer disks throw them away at a higher rate than they do magazines or newspapers.
Answer F   Page 356

98. The key to the success of a direct mailing campaign is the accuracy of the customer list.
Answer T   Page 356

99. Due to the low cost, most small businesses rely almost solely on outdoor/billboard advertising.
Answer F   Page 357

100. When located near a store, billboards can be effective "last-minute" reminders.
Answer T   Page 358

101. Outdoor ads tend to reach people who are older, poorer, and not as well educated as the average person.
Answer F   Page 358

102. Outdoor advertising has the highest cost per thousand (CPM) of all advertising media.
Answer F   Page 359

103. Some cities have put restrictions or outright bans on the use of outdoor ads.
Answer T   Page 359

104. When designing an outdoor ad, the small business owner must remember that "more" is better and put as much information as possible in the ad.
Answer F   Page 359

105. To be most effective, an outdoor ad should be located on the right-hand side of the highway.
Answer T   Page 359

106. Transit advertising traces its history back to the pre-Civil War era.
Answer T   Page 359

107. Transit ads offer the advantages of wide coverage and low costs for advertising messages.
Answer T   Page 360

108. Directories have a very long life but can become obsolete.
Answer T   Page 361

109. Trade show advertisements reach a particular type of customers—those who have already made a purchase decision.
Answer F   Page 361

110. A major advantage of trade shows is their ability to provide a pre-selected audience of potential customers.
Answer T   Page 362

111. One significant disadvantage of trade shows is inability to bring in new customers or international customers.
Answer F   Page 363

112. Specialty advertising is an example of narrow casting in advertising.
Answer T   Page 364

113. Specialty advertising gives small businesses an opportunity to fine tune or personalize their advertising to a specific customer.
Answer T   Page 364

114. A popular form of in-store advertising which reaches the customer at a crucial point is specialty advertising.
Answer F   Page 366

115. Under the "what is affordable method" of establishing an advertising budget, advertising is viewed as an investment which produces sales and profits in the future.
Answer F   Page 366

116. The objective-and-task method is the easiest and most used technique for establishing an advertising budget.
Answer F   Page 367

117. The normal cooperative advertising plan involves a united advertising effort by a group of small businessmen in related businesses.
Answer F   Page 368

118. Ben and Jerry's Ice Cream has found the use of promotions to be effective. It offers several tips for effective promotions including special off-season promotion to keep customers interested.
Answer T   Page 369

119. Small businesses need not worry about public relations since their impact on the local community is small.
Answer F   Page 370

120. Small businesses can save on advertising expenditures by repeating successful ads and running ads when customers are most likely to buy.
Answer T   Page 370

Essay Questions

121. What questions does the small business owner need to answer in the developing of an advertising strategy?
Pages 335–336

122. What is the "six-sentence advertising strategy?"
Page 337

123. How can a small business owner use publicity to the benefit of his/her business?
Page 339–340

124. Outline the six-step process for increasing sales.
Pages 341–342

125. List and explain the questions a small business owner needs to answer when choosing a media vehicle for the advertising message.
Page 344

126. Your small firm is considering using print media, specifically, newspapers and magazines for an advertising campaign. Explain the advantages and disadvantages of each of these media.
Pages 346–347 & 351–353

127. Discuss the advantages and disadvantages of using radio and television advertising. How and why would you choose one over the other?
Pages 347–350

128. How could an entrepreneur use the world wide web to advertise his/her business?
Pages 350–351

129. Why would a small business owner use direct mail in his/her advertising strategy? Why wouldn't he/she?
Pages 353–356

130. What is the value of outdoor and transit advertising to the small business?
Pages 357–361

131. Why would the small business owner use trade shows in his/her advertising strategy?
Pages 361–364

132. Name and discuss the four methods of establishing an advertising budget.
Pages 366–368

133. How can the entrepreneur use cooperative and shared advertising, and publicity to effectively advertise his/her business and products while holding down promotional costs?
Pages 366–370

Mini-Cases

Case 11-1: The Pen Is Mightier Than the Sword, But the Word Processor Beats Both

Upon her retirement, after working at the university for 35 years, Betty Woodall opened an editorial service for both faculty and townspeople. Known for years as the best editorial assistant at the university, Betty purchased the latest state-of-the-art computer and word processing software package for her business. Her home was within walking distance of both the university and the town. Her office was in her basement. "With my low overhead and my high-speed word processor, I can move this work along at top-notch speed." Betty was all set to start. Now she needed to make the community aware of her new service.

Questions

1. How can Betty use the world wide web to promote her new business?

2. How would you promote the opening of the business?

3. Who will be the target market for her editorial services and how can this group best be reached?

Case 11-2: The Banner vs. The Bulletin

Lawnmowers Unlimited was a new business in town. After working for 10 years in a factory job, Harry Owens decided it was time to be his own boss. Harry had taken courses at the local community college for the past two years and was ready for the grand opening. When it came to advertising, Harry thought it would be valuable to put a major ad in one of the two local newspapers, the **Banner** or the **Bulletin**. He could not afford a full page ad in both, and Harry did not want to have only a half-page ad, so it was obvious that the choice was one paper or the other. Harry called both newspapers and the next day a sales representative from each visited Harry to sell the merits of their newspapers.

The **Banner** had evidence that its circulation was 29,000, and its full-page ad cost $1,600. The **Bulletin's** circulation was only 20,000 but the cost for a comparable ad was only $1,000. Harry was undecided after talking with both sales representatives, so be began to conduct an informational survey to determine which of his potential customers read either or both papers. Early in the morning on two consecutive days, Harry went around the neighborhood from which he hoped to draw customers. Each day he would stop the newspaper delivery people and ask how many papers they delivered each day and what territory they served. From this research, Harry concluded that 36% of his potential customers read the **Banner** while 25% read the **Bulletin**.

Questions

1. Based on the data supplied by the two newspaper sales representatives and the survey Harry conducted, which newspaper should Harry use for his ad?

2. Could Harry effectively use the World Wide Web? Why or why not?

Case 11-3: "Dr. Boogy Calling"

"I don't know if my customers listen to Dr. Boogy in the morning on their way to work." Bob Wentworth was concerned over where to spend his advertising budget and was talking with one of his younger and brighter employees.

"Everybody listens to Dr. Boogy. He is the final word on what's happening," replied Frank.

"Frank, I appreciate your opinion, but I am not sure that you are an example of our customers."

"Be serious, Mr. Wentworth. In today's world, I am about as typical as you can get. Trust me on this. The audience for Dr. Boogy's morning show covers the city from border to border."

Bob Wentworth knew that he was naive about advertising and was even more out-of-step with this younger generation, but he was very concerned about the image of his business. Prior to now, all advertising was limited to newspapers. Bob knew that radio could reach large numbers and there was no question that the Dr. Boogy radio program had the largest audience in the city. Bob was still concerned. Would advertising on the Dr. Boogy radio show reach the right markets for Wentworth Mortuary?

Questions

1. From what you know about radio advertising, how would you respond to Bob Wentworth?

2. If Bob Wentworth owned a shoe store, would your advice be different? Why?

Chapter 12 –
International Opportunities for Small Business

Multiple Choice Questions

1. Since World War II, the amount of trade as a percentage of global income:
   a) doubled.
   b) tripled.
   c) quadrupled.
   d) increased five-fold.

Answer b   Page 375

2. Expanding a small business into international markets:
   a) guarantees its success in the marketplace.
   b) makes it a member of GATT automatically.
   c) often helps it to grow faster and better survive competition.
   d) leads to business failure for companies under $100 million in annual revenue.

Answer c   Page 375

3. In the 1950s, ____ of the goods manufactured in America faced foreign competition; in the year 2000, ____ will go up against foreign goods.
   a) 5%; 80%
   b) 10%; 50%
   c) 75%; 35%
   d) 35%; 70%

Answer a   Page 376

4. Entrepreneurs who go global may find a number of benefits such as:
   a) less pressure in meeting day-to-day operating goals.
   b) less competition.
   c) consumers hungry for American products and willing to buy regardless of cost.
   d) a way to offset declines in sales in their domestic market.

Answer d   Page 376

5. Which of the following is true about global competition?
   a) There is less of a focus on quality and more of a focus on price internationally.
   b) It makes companies more customer focused.
   c) It is largely the domain of small businesses due their flexibility.
   d) It tends to shorten the life cycle of a product or service.

Answer b   Page 377

6. The Competitiveness Policy Council reports that:
   a) fewer small businesses are entering international markets.
   b) there is an absence of global thinking in our society.
   c) the ability to think globally is increasing significantly in the United States
   d) the formation of the EC has put the United States at a significant competitive disadvantage.

Answer b   Page 377

7. The first step to becoming a truly global company is to:
   a) establish an export program.
   b) find a joint venture partner.
   c) begin to think globally, taking on a global attitude toward a business.
   d) hire motivated, multilingual managers.

Answer c   Page 378

8. A small business owner needs to consider several questions before launching an international venture, such as:
   a) "Do we have the correct multinational management in place?"
   b) "Can we find an appropriate international partner for this venture?"
   c) "What nontariff barriers do we have to be prepared to overcome?"
   d) "Are we sensitive to the cultural differences of conducting international business?"

Answer d   Page 378

9. A.T. Kearney, Inc. developed a matrix to assess the level of global competitiveness. In the basic stage (Stage I) of this matrix a company:
   a) focuses on the domestic market with products designed for the domestic market.
   b) has tailored products for overseas markets, locally provided services, and locally hired management.
   c) recognizes the need to adapt products to international markets but is slow to do so; senior management understands international management but is not expert.
   d) has so much foreign presence in senior management that the company could be dubbed country-neutral with financial goals tied to strategic plans with 5- to 10-year planning cycles.

Answer a   Page 379

10. Companies at Stage _____ in A.T. Kearney's matrix operate with worldwide strategies and are at home in every market. Senior managers have foreign experience and are "country-neutral."
   a) I
   b) II
   c) III
   d) IV

Answer d   Page 379

11. In the A.T. Kearney, Inc. matrix, a Stage III multinational firm:
   a) focuses on the domestic market with products designed for the domestic market.
   b) has tailored products for overseas markets, locally provided services, and locally hired management.
   c) recognizes the need to adapt products to international markets but is slow to do so; senior management understands international management but is not expert.
   d) has so much foreign presence in senior management that the company could be dubbed country-neutral with financial goals tied to strategic plans with 5- to 10-year planning cycles.

Answer b   Page 379

12. The growth in the globalization of business:
    a) actually favors small businesses because of their size.
    b) favors large corporations because of their economies of scale.
    c) is due to federal government programs assisting domestic businesses in going global.
    d) has led to the collapse of many domestic small businesses.
Answer a   Page 380

13. Small businesses go global:
    a) for very different reasons than large businesses do.
    b) through joint ventures with large companies.
    c) when they realize their success and survival depends on them going global.
    d) often between their fifth and seventh year of existence as a domestic company.
Answer c   Page 380

14. The simplest and least expensive way to conduct international business is through:
    a) foreign licensees.
    b) the world wide web.
    c) joint ventures.
    d) trade intermediaries.
Answer b   Page 381

15. John is taking his company global on the world wide web. He is currently conducting market research on the international market. In the evolution of small businesses going international via the web, John's company is at which step in the evolutionary process?
    a) Step 1
    b) Step 2
    c) Step 3
    d) Step 4
Answer c   Page 382

16. A relatively easy way of getting into international marketing, which currently handles about 10% of all U.S. exports, is through _____ who act as distributors in foreign countries for domestic companies of all sizes.
    a) foreign licensees
    b) international franchises
    c) joint ventures
    d) trade intermediaries
Answer d   Page 383

17. A/an _____ is a business that buys and sells products in a number of countries, offering a range of services—importing, exporting, shipping, distributing, and others—to their clients.
    a) foreign joint venture
    b) export trading company
    c) foreign licensee
    d) resident buying office
Answer b   Page 383

18. An export trading company is:
    a) a government-owned or business-owned facility set up in a foreign country to buy products that are made there.
    b) a firm in an overseas distribution network selling noncompetitive products made by other firms.
    c) formed by an agreement by which a licenser gives a foreign licensee the right to use a patent, trademark, copyright, technology, and products in return for a percentage of the licensee's sales or profits.
    d) a business that buys and sells products in many countries, either in its own name, or as an agent for its buyer-seller clients.
    Answer d   Page 383

19. Anna Chong and Eric Kelly sell their demolition service in the international market through:
    a) resident buying offices.
    b) direct export.
    c) joint venture with another firm.
    d) an export trade company.
    Answer b   Page 384

20. _____ is/are one of the trading intermediaries a small company can use to enter the global marketplace.
    a) Export merchants
    b) Joint ventures
    c) International franchising
    d) Establishing international locations
    Answer a   Page 385

21. A/an _____ is a government- or privately-owned company established in a foreign country for the purpose of buying goods made there.
    a) export trading company
    b) resident buying office
    c) foreign distributor
    d) export merchants
    Answer b   Page 385

22. A resident buying office is:
    a) a business that buys and sells products in many countries, either in its own name, or as an agent for its buyer-seller clients.
    b) a firm in an overseas distribution network selling noncompetitive products made by other firms.
    c) a government-owned or business-owned facility set up in a foreign country to buy products that are made there.
    d) formed by an agreement where a licenser gives a foreign licensee the right to use a patent, trademark, copyright, technology, and products in return for a percentage of the licensee's sales or profits.
    Answer c   Page 385

23. Evie works for a domestic wholesaler who does business in foreign markets, buying goods from domestic companies and selling them in foreign markets. Evie's firm is an:
    a) resident buying office.
    b) export trading company.
    c) foreign distributor.
    d) export merchant.

Answer d   Page 385

24. In a _____, two or more UNITED STATES small businesses form an alliance for the purpose of exporting their goods abroad. The companies get antitrust immunity and share responsibility for the business equally.
    a) foreign joint venture
    b) trade intermediary
    c) domestic joint venture
    d) export management company

Answer c   Page 386

25. In a/an _____, a domestic small business forms an alliance with a company in the target nation for the purpose of exporting to that market.
    a) foreign joint venture
    b) trade intermediary
    c) domestic joint venture
    d) export management company

Answer a   Page 386

26. The average success rate of joint ventures is ____%.
    a) 26
    b) 35
    c) 43
    d) 12

Answer c   Page 386

27. The U.S. Commerce Department, the SBA, and the Trade Administration provide a number of services. TOP—the trade opportunity program—is one and through it entrepreneurs can:
    a) receive up-to-the minute pre-screened sales leads, including joint venture possibilities.
    b) establish business relationships in major markets by helping them make networking contacts.
    c) gain access to contact and product information for more than 82,000 foreign distributors.
    d) place advertisements that will reach thousands of foreign customers.

Answer a   Page 387

28. If you can't afford to invest in foreign facilities, don't have time to even learn the foreign market, but you are willing to give someone else the right to make and market your product for a fee and royalties, your best bet for entering the foreign market is:
    a) a foreign management company.
    b) joint venturing.
    c) foreign licensing.
    d) international franchising.

Answer c   Page 388

29. Foreign licensing has its greatest potential in the licensing of:
   a) products.
   b) intangibles.
   c) goods.
   d) franchises.

Answer b   Page 388

30. Domino's Pizza, McDonald's, etc., in Japan and Europe are examples of:
   a) foreign management companies.
   b) joint venturing.
   c) foreign licensing.
   d) international franchising.

Answer d   Page 389

31. In international franchising, ____ is the primary market for U.S. franchisers.
   a) Japan
   b) Russia
   c) Canada
   d) Europe

Answer c   Page 389

32. Countertrade is necessary in nearly ___ of all countries because they lack a convertible currency.
   a) 15%
   b) 60%
   c) 70%
   d) 90%

Answer c   Page 390

33. Countertrades have significant drawbacks, including:
   a) getting goods that are of no direct use to the seller.
   b) receiving currency that cannot be exchanged outside the foreign nation.
   c) needing a trading intermediary to arrange the countertrade, thereby raising costs.
   d) being limited in size to $100,000 per deal.

Answer a   Page 390

34. Nearly ___ of UNITED STATES companies with annual revenues under _____ export goods.
   a) 30%; $50 million
   b) 50%; $100 million
   c) 15%; $1 million
   d) 75%; $10 million

Answer b   Page 391

35. The first step an entrepreneur should take when starting an export business is to:
   a) recognize that the tiniest companies and least experienced entrepreneurs have the potential.
   b) research and pick target markets.

      c) develop a distribution strategy.

      d) find his/her customer.

Answer a   Page 391

36. To break into international markets the entrepreneur needs to take several steps including:

    a) analyzing his/her commitment to the effort.

    b) researching the markets and picking a target market.

    c) developing a distribution strategy.

    d) all of these.

Answer d   Page 392

37. Candi is thinking through a number of management issues in making her exporting decision. She is thinking about her company's _____ capacity when she is thinking about how exporting will affect meeting domestic orders, her pricing structure, collection process, and what it will cost her for the company to make enough product for foreign export.

    a) financial

    b) management

    c) production

    d) marketing

Answer c   Page 393

38. The biggest barrier to small business exports is:

    a) the lack of experience.

    b) the lack of financing.

    c) not understanding other cultures.

    d) not having appropriate products for export.

Answer b   Page 394

39. Specialty Building Supplies is considering exporting. Where are they on A.T. Kearney's export matrix?

    a) Stage I–domestic

    b) Stage II–international

    c) Stage III–multinational

    d) Stage IV–global

Answer a   Page 395

40. When collecting for the sale of foreign goods, a small business will use a _____, an agreement between their bank and the foreign buyer's bank that guarantees payment.

    a) bank draft

    b) foreign sales agreement

    c) tariff voucher

    d) letter of credit

Answer d   Page 396

41. Sometimes, once established in international markets, businesses _____, despite the frustrations of securing services, the significant capital investment involved, etc.

    a) offer foreign licenses

    b) sell international franchises

    c) establish an international location
    d) use trade intermediaries
Answer c   Page 397

42. Key to successfully establishing an international location is:
    a) securing the necessary licenses to operate in the foreign country.
    b) finding the right person to manage the international office.
    c) making a substantial investment in personnel.
    d) being able to speak the language of the foreign country.
Answer b   Page 397

43. International trade has:
    a) been cut by 50% by international trade barriers.
    b) declined three-fold over the last decade.
    c) grown 26-fold to over $6.6 trillion over the last 30 years.
    d) centered around the Pacific Rim for the last five years.
Answer c   Page 398

44. Of the three domestic barriers exporters face, _____ is the biggest.
    a) information
    b) attitude
    c) financing
    d) language
Answer b   Page 398

45. John wants to expand into the foreign markets, but he can't convince his partners. They feel international markets are the domain of large corporations. John is facing which barrier to international trade?
    a) financing
    b) political
    c) cultural
    d) attitude
Answer d   Page 398

46. An entrepreneur wants to move into international markets but can't quite figure out how to do it. He's not clear on his target market or how to approach it but he knows he needs to "go global." This entrepreneur is experiencing which barrier to international trade?
    a) financing
    b) information
    c) cultural
    d) attitude
Answer b   Page 398

47. A recent survey of exporters found that ____ said they had lost export business because they couldn't get financing.
    a) 53%
    b) 46%
    c) 23%

d)   78%
Answer a   Page 399

48. Malcolm won a contract to provide nuts, bolts, and washers to a small African country's military. Unfortunately, neither his bankers nor venture capitalists would provide the loans needed to buy the material to produce the order. The bank didn't do international loans. Which barrier to international trade is Malcolm experiencing?
    a)   information
    b)   cultural
    c)   financing
    d)   attitude
Answer c   Page 399

49. The tax that a government puts on products that are imported into a country is called a/an:
    a)   embargo.
    b)   tariff.
    c)   quota.
    d)   nontariff barrier.
Answer b   Page 399

50. A quota is:
    a)   a duty, or tax, that a government puts on products that are imported into the country.
    b)   the maximum amount of a product that can be imported or exported.
    c)   a prohibition or suspension of foreign trade of specific imports or exports.
    d)   a law that a government uses to regulate products that are imported into the country.
Answer b   Page 399

51. An embargo is:
    a)   a duty, or tax, that a government puts on products that are imported into the country.
    b)   the maximum amount of a product that can be imported or exported.
    c)   a law that a government uses to regulate products that are imported into the country.
    d)   a prohibition or suspension of foreign trade of specific imports or exports.
Answer d   Page 399

52. The members of the European Community have limited the number of cars Japanese automakers can export into the European market. This is an example of which type of trade barrier?
    a)   tariff
    b)   quota
    c)   embargo
    d)   dumping
Answer b   Page 399

53. In preparing to sell overseas, Specialty Building Supplies has largely neglected to:
    a)   secure financing for their venture into Japan.
    b)   think through the impact of GATT on their business venture.
    c)   learn and understand the Japanese culture.
    d)   address the political barriers that will come up doing business in Japan.

Answer c   Page 400 & 402

54. An American executive went to a foreign country to sign a business contract. While there, he found that there were numerous government regulations his company needed to meet before closing the deal. This executive was experiencing which barrier to international trade?
    a) nontariff
    b) political
    c) cultural
    d) domestic

Answer b   Page 401

55. Wanda is an American manager with a U.S. firm in Japan. Wanda is having difficulty "conducting business." When invited to play golf she attempts to talk business, but her Japanese hosts gently refuse. When she meets a new corporate customer, she tries to get "right down to business" to show respect for their time, but they insist on talking about nonbusiness matters for several meetings. Wanda is experiencing what international barrier to doing business?
    a) cultural
    b) political
    c) domestic
    d) nontariff

Answer a   Page 402

56. The General Agreement on Tariffs and Trade has had what effect on tariffs around the world?
    a) It has had little effect, only lowering them an average of 4.7%.
    b) It has eliminated tariffs among member nations and raised them to nonmembers.
    c) It has had no effect.
    d) It has reduced them by 90% since 1947.

Answer d   Page 403

57. The Uruguay Round of General Agreement on Tariffs and Trade accomplished which of the following?
    a) Negotiators agreed to the formation of a World Trade Organization with the power to settle disputes.
    b) It weakened protections for patents and copyrights throughout the world.
    c) There were no new changes to tariff and trade policy as a consequence of the Uruguay Round.
    d) It eliminated all tariffs over the next fifteen years.

Answer a   Page 403

58. The North American Free Trade Agreement:
    a) brought Chile, Mexico, the United States, and Canada together as one market.
    b) eliminated all tariffs among member nations, effective immediately, and raised them to nonmembers.
    c) benefits the trading relationship between Canada and the United States most.
    d) created a unified market of 370 million people and $6.5 trillion in goods and services.

Answer d   Page 405

59. The North American Free Trade Agreement has which of the following provisions?

a) The immediate elimination of all tariff and quota barriers on all goods
b) The elimination of nontariff barriers by 2008
c) A lowering of safety and air quality standards
d) The formation of a North American Trade Organization

Answer b   Page 406

True or False Questions

60. Even though large companies must view themselves as "global companies" if they are to succeed, small companies cannot because they have a significant competitive disadvantage in the global environment.

Answer F   Page 375

61. A recent study concluded that American manufacturers with global operations grew faster and earned more than purely domestic companies.

Answer T   Page 375

62. Multinational companies are only 25% more likely to survive the decade than domestic companies.

Answer F   Page 375

63. For many businesses across the world, "going global" is now a matter of survival, not preference.

Answer T   Page 376

64. Currently, only about 40% of goods made in America face foreign competition but that percentage will rise dramatically over the next decade.

Answer F   Page 376

65. Small businesses go into global markets for a number of reasons such as to offset declining domestic sales.

Answer T   Page 376

66. Going global tends to make companies more quality and customer conscious.

Answer T   Page 377

67. Going global often shortens the products' life cycles and raises manufacturing costs, but it does enhance a company's reputation.

Answer F   Page 377

68. An important question for the small business owner to ask before entering global markets is, "If we go global, can we get back out?"

Answer T   Page 378

69. A.T. Kearney's four stages of global development matrix reflect a company's ability to compete internationally, based on its financial resources and product.

Answer F   Page 379

70. In terms of the stages of global development, global companies operating with worldwide, "country-neutral" strategies have the greatest chance for prospering in international markets.

Answer T   Page 379

71. John Nesbitt, author of <u>The Global Paradox</u>, believes increasing globalization in business favors small businesses.
Answer T   Page 378–380

72. Some small companies go international because domestic sales are booming and they decide to invest excess cash in international expansion.
Answer F   Page 380

73. The least expensive way to enter international markets is by using a trade intermediary.
Answer F   Page 381

74. When using the world wide web to enter international markets, companies go through a four-step evolutionary process that begins with doing market research on their target company,
Answer F   Page 382

75. The use of trade intermediaries currently accounts for nearly 50% of all UNITED STATES exports.
Answer F   Page 383

76. One form of trade intermediary, the export management company, is a merchant intermediary that works on a buy-and-sell arrangement with domestic small companies.
Answer T   Page 383

77. Unlike an EMC or an ETC, manufacturer's export agents are international sales representatives who work on commission in a short-term relationship with the small domestic company.
Answer T   Page 383

78. In order to grow their international business, Chong and Kelly's Engineered Demolitions, they have had to become more culturally sensitive.
Answer T   Page 384

79. Export merchants represent a limited number of noncompeting domestic companies.
Answer F   Page 385

80. Selling to a resident buying office is just like selling to domestic customers since the buying office handles all of the details of exporting the products.
Answer T   Page 385

81. Foreign distributors work in a close partnering relationship with a small business, providing a wide range of services to a limited number of domestic companies.
Answer F   Page 385

82. The key to establishing a successful relationship with a trade intermediary is to thoroughly screen in order to determine what type of intermediary the small company needs.
Answer T   Page 385

83. In a domestic joint venture, a domestic company forms an alliance with a company in the target nation.
Answer F   Page 386

84. When two small businesses in the target nation form an alliance, they have formed a foreign joint venture.
Answer F   Page 386

85. Choosing the "right" joint venture partner is crucial to the its ultimate success.
Answer T   Page 386

86. The Commerical Service International Contacts List (CSIC) and the Country Directories of International Contacts (CDIC) provide the same information but organized in different ways.
Answer T   Page 387

87. One way to avoid the failure of a joint venture is to not use any kind of an agreement that details what to do if the business fails, as this just predestines the joint ventures failure.
Answer F   Page 388

88. Foreign licensing is when a business buys and sells products in many countries, either in its own name, or as an agent for its buyer-seller clients.
Answer F   Page 388

89. The licensing potential for intangibles, such as technology, trademarks, etc., is often greater than the licensing opportunities for products.
Answer T   Page 388

90. While franchise outlets are throughout the world, Europe is the primary market for U.S. franchisers.
Answer F   Page 389

91. A small business exporting to Hungary would likely have to engage in barter or countertrade since Hungarian currency is not convertible into any other currency.
Answer T   Page 390

92. Successful bartering is easier than countertrade but requires finding a business with complementary needs.
Answer T   Page 390

93. Small companies tend to dominate exporting.
Answer F   Page 391

94. The first and most difficult step to exporting for the small business is breaking the psychological barrier.
Answer T   Page 391

95. Most products sold in the United States require major modifications before they can be sold in foreign markets.

Answer F   Page 392

96. An important management issue to consider before going international is to decide who will be responsible for the export entity's organization and staff.
Answer T   Page 393

97. Lack of export financing remains a significant barrier to small businesses selling in foreign markets.
Answer T   Page 394

98. The best way for Specialty Building Supplies to move into international markets, given their expertise and their Autovent product, would be direct exporting.
Answer F   Page 395

99. Small businesses just starting out in global markets often rely heavily on international freight forwarders and custom-house agents for the shipping of their goods.
Answer T   Page 396

100. Small businesses are using foreign sales corporations in entering global markets in order to utilize the tax advantages offered.
Answer T   Page 397

101. The key to successfully establishing an international location is properly screening for the right partner company with compatible goals and products/services.
Answer F   Page 397

102. Usually, the first step a small business takes when getting its products into international markets is setting up permanent offices in foreign countries.
Answer F   Page 397

103. An advantage to establishing an international location is lower start-up costs in the foreign country.
Answer T   Page 397

104. Small companies often find that competing in foreign markets and selling to foreign customers makes them tougher competitors at home.
Answer T   Page 398

105. Very few nations interfere with free international trade by erecting trade barriers with tariffs, quotas, and embargoes.
Answer F   Page 398

106. The three biggest domestic barriers to exporting facing small businesses are the appropriateness of the product, political and cultural information, and finding a suitable foreign agent to assist them.
Answer F   Page 398

107. A recent survey of exporters found that over half of them said they had lost export business because they couldn't get financing.
Answer T   Page 399

108. When a government imposes a quota on a particular imported good, the effect is to raise the price customers must pay for that good.
Answer T   Page 399

109. Specialty Building Supplies' primary barrier in entering Japan was political.
Answer F   Page 400

110. American small business owners are often astounded at how much less government regulation there is in foreign countries.
Answer F   Page 401

111. In most other countries, American business owners and managers find human resource laws to be very similar, if not more stringent, than they are in the United States.
Answer F   Page 401

112. Cultural differences among countries have little impact on international trade.
Answer F   Page 402

113. Fortunately for U.S. business owners, American customs and habits have become the standard for proper business behavior around the world.
Answer F   Page 402

114. The World Trade Organization was formed as a consequence of the growth of the European Community.
Answer F   Page 403

115. GATT will probably bring 2 million jobs and as much as $1 trillion to the U.S. economy over the next decade.
Answer T   Page 403

116. In Spain, patience is a must for conducting business; Spaniards like to get to know business associates before working with them.
Answer T   Page 404

117. An American business owner greeting a Japanese executive should use both a handshake and a bow.
Answer T   Page 404

118. NAFTA is an agreement between the United States, Canada, Mexico, Argentina, and Chile, forming a free trade arena among these countries.
Answer F   Page 405

119. NAFTA includes provisions reducing tariff and nontariff barriers and toughening health and safety standards.

Answer T   Page 406

Essay Questions

120. Why it is important for small businesses to "go global?"
Pages 376–377

121. Describe the four stages of global competitiveness developed by A.T. Kearney, Inc.
Page 379

122. How can a small business use the world wide web to go global?
Pages 381–382

123. One of the seven ways a small business owner can "go global" is through trade intermediaries. Identify the six types of trade intermediaries and explain why a small business person might use each one.
Pages 383–386

124. Discuss joint ventures, identifying the two primary types, and why a small business might consider using a joint venture to go global.
Pages 386–388

125. How do foreign licensing and international franchising differ? Why would a small business owner choose one over the other in going global?
Pages 388–390

126. Explain the concepts of countertrade and barter and what role they play in international business.
Pages 390–397

127. Describe how culture can be a barrier to "going global" and offer examples from three different countries.
Pages 402-403

128. For the small business owner there are two major trade agreements, GATT and NAFTA. Explain each one and its impact on the small business "going global."
Pages 403-406

Mini-Cases

Case 12-1: The Grass Is Really Greener

It's not usual for city people to be concerned about plants or grass—they see so little of them. But Martha Goldman has been interested in these things since her first biology course back in Brooklyn, New York. Martha won all the awards in the science fairs and eventually was the recipient of a scholarship to college. She chose to major in botany and became fascinated with the creation of hybrid plants and grasses. Martha was also concerned about the problems of hunger around the world. She knew what improved plants and grains had done to increase the productivity of American agriculture and hoped that someday she would find a way to play a small part in reducing world hunger.

After college, with the help of her dad, she opened a small wholesale greenhouse. The business was a modest success while allowing Martha to experiment with new growing methods. Two years ago Martha's research paid off. She had been working on developing a fast-growing grass that needed less water. One of the experiments produced a grass that seemed to have real potential. She tested it with a local cattleman. All tests so far have shown that the new hybrid grass is better for feeding cattle than many presently being grown. Martha may have realized her dream—a grass which will grow better in parts of the world that could not previously support cattle. High protein beef cattle may now be able to thrive in parts of the world where previously it was not possible.

Question
1. How should Martha proceed to determine the best way to export her new grass seed?

Chapter 13 –
Sources of Equity Financing

Multiple Choice Questions

1. When raising money to launch new businesses, the entrepreneurial segment of the nation's economy:
   a) needs $60 billion per year in seed capital to fuel its growth.
   b) finds it easier every year to find risk capital.
   c) is spending less time and finding more money than in the past decade.
   d) knows where to find it, as traditional sources are full of venture capital.

Answer a   Page 411

2. Unlike entrepreneurs of the past, today's entrepreneurs:
   a) are finding more government interest and funding for business start-ups than ever before.
   b) find fewer closed doors as small business start-ups have become less risky.
   c) have to piece their capital together from several sources.
   d) are spending nearly 75% of their time raising capital.

Answer c   Page 412

3. When raising start-up money, most entrepreneurs are looking for:
   a) $10 million or more.
   b) $7.5-5 million.
   c) $5 to 3.5 million.
   d) less than $1 million.

Answer d   Page 413

4. The reward for investing in a successful start-up usually comes in the form of:
   a) regular dividends paid annually.
   b) the appreciation of the company's value.
   c) significant interest payments, made quarterly.
   d) the satisfaction of having succeeded in helping a small business grow.

Answer b   Page 413

5. _____ is any form of wealth used to produce more wealth.
   a) Debt
   b) Equity
   c) Capital
   d) Capacity

Answer c   Page 414

6. Tien is looking for capital to purchase new buildings and equipment for her small manufacturing company. Tien is looking for _____ capital.
   a) working
   b) fixed
   c) growth
   d) asset-based

Answer b   Page 414

7. _____ capital is the pool of temporary funds of the business used to support the normal operation of the business on a short-term basis.
   a) Growth
   b) Fixed
   c) Equity
   d) Working

Answer d   Page 414

8. The money Bert uses to build inventory for the upcoming Christmas season would be classified as _____ capital.
   a) growth
   b) working
   c) fixed
   d) efficiency

Answer b   Page 414

9. _____ financing includes the personal investment of the owner(s) and is often called "risk capital."
   a) Equity
   b) Asset-based
   c) Debt
   d) Growth

Answer a   Page 415

10. The most common source of equity funds used to start a small business is:
    a) private investors or "angels."
    b) loans from commercial banks.
    c) the entrepreneur's pool of personal savings.
    d) public stock issues.

Answer c   Page 416

11. Studies show that ___% of all business owners get at least some of their capital from their own pockets.
    a) 25
    b) 33
    c) 67
    d) 75

Answer d   Page 416

12. As a general rule, an entrepreneur needing $72,000 to launch a business venture should expect to provide how much?
    a) $72,000
    b) $18,000
    c) $48,000
    d) $36,000

Answer d   Page 418

13. An advantage of using friends and relatives as investors is that:
    a) they tend to be more patient.
    b) they take a lower return.
    c) they don't want controlling interest in the company.
    d) they don't tend to have unrealistic expectations.
Answer b   Page 418

14. When receiving investment money from friends and relatives entrepreneurs should:
    a) use a clear verbal contract to ensure no misunderstandings.
    b) only borrow from close friends and relatives who won't cause them trouble.
    c) discuss all the details of the investment up front.
    d) not borrow more than 30% of the necessary capital from them.
Answer c   Page 418

15. Entrepreneurs can make a number of mistakes when seeking start-up capital such as:
    a) paying too much attention to the sales and marketing strategies.
    b) offering too much documentation to support financial projections.
    c) being too specific in the amount of money needed and how it will be used.
    d) failing to differentiate themselves and their businesses from the competition.
Answer d   Page 419

16. A study by Coopers and Lybrand shows that ___ of founders use their own or relatives' money to start their companies.
    a) 25%
    b) 50%
    c) 70%
    d) 80%
Answer c   Page 420

17. The largest single source of external equity capital for small businesses is:
    a) angels.
    b) venture capitalists.
    c) Small Business Administration loans.
    d) commerical bankers.
Answer a   Page 420

18. Most "angel" investments:
    a) are for growth or fixed capital.
    b) are for between $250,000 and $1,000,000.
    c) come from international or foreign investors.
    d) are seeking a high and quick return on their investment.
Answer d   Page 420

19. "Angels":
    a) are hard investors to please. Nearly 70% are dissatisfied with their investment.
    b) tend to be easy to get money from as they accept nearly 60% of the opportunties presented.
    c) have an average of $131,000 invested in 3.5 firms at any given time.
    d) only finance deals requiring over $1 million in capital.
Answer c   Page 421

20. When looking for an angel, the key is:
    a) networking.
    b) using the SBA as a contact point.
    c) searching the web.
    d) using business incubators' computer matching services.
Answer a   Page 421

21. When structuring a deal with an "angel," an entrepreneur should remember that:
    a) "angels" tend to prefer a controlling interest in the business.
    b) the deal needs an annual return of 60–75%.
    c) "angel" money is patient, often waiting seven or more years to cash out.
    d) they prefer to earn their returns through dividends and interest.
Answer c   Page 421

22. Private "angel" investors tend to:
    a) take 80% ownership by the time the company goes public.
    b) provide seed money and less than $500,000.
    c) look for returns of 60–75%.
    d) only finance projects outside of their local area or region.
Answer d   Page 422

23. When structuring a deal with an angel, the entrepreneur should:
    a) take the money and run, run the business and ignore their advice.
    b) nail down the angel's exit path from the business.
    c) offer them no more than 25% of the company.
    d) not place the angel on the board or he/she might take over the company.
Answer b   Page 422

24. An entrepreneur can find an angel if he/she keeps several things in mind.
    a) The angel wants to invest and be left alone.
    b) Most angels tend to invest out of state so look in other regions for them.
    c) Join philanthropic organizations, advisory boards, etc., and network through them.
    d) Most angels have web sites with applications on them.
Answer c   Page 423

25. The key for Lammert and Weber of Wisconsin Technology in finding their angel was:
    a) networking through family.
    b) in joining the local Chamber of Commerce and Kiwanis club.
    c) taking the advice of their banker.
    d) the Small Business Administration.
Answer a   Page 423

26. Venture capital firms look for a return of _____ the amount invested.
    a) twice
    b) three to five times
    c) six to eight times
    d) ten times
Answer c   Page 425

27. A/An ____ is a private, for-profit organization that purchases equity positions in young businesses that will potentially produce returns of 300 to 500 percent over five to seven years.
    a) commerical bank
    b) venture capital company
    c) "angel"
    d) SB-1 filing
Answer b   Page 425

28. The minimum investment venture firms seek to make is in the range of:
    a) $10,000 to $3,000,000.
    b) $50,000 to $500,000.
    c) under $250,000.
    d) $1,000,000 to $10,000,000.
Answer a   Page 426

29. The average venture capital firm receives over _____ proposals a year and ultimately invests in _____ of them.
    a) 10,000; 100
    b) 1,000; 1 or 2
    c) 500; 10
    d) 5,000; 5 or 6
Answer b   Page 426

30. Although there is no limit on the amount of stock it can buy, a typical venture capital firm will purchase _____ of the ownership in a small firm.
    a) 10–20%
    b) 50–60%
    c) 80–90%
    d) 30–40%
Answer d   Page 426

31. Most venture capitalists purchase ownership in a small business through:
    a) a common stock or convertible preferred stock.
    b) an ESOP.
    c) loans with an option to buy stock.
    d) a general partnership.
Answer a   Page 426

32. One recent survey showed that ___ of venture capitalists eventually become involved in managing or selecting outside managers.
    a) 50%
    b) 65%
    c) 80%
    d) 90%
Answer d   Page 426

33. As Garfinkle, Ben-Yaacov and Jaffe prepare their company—PictureVision—for an IPO, they made their company more attractive by:
    a) investing heavily in refurbishing their facilities.

b) trimming costs by laying off workers and reducing inventory.
c) building a more professional management team and an active board.
d) doing all of these.
Answer c   Page 428

34. Venture capitalists look for _____ as the <u>most important</u> ingredient in the success of any business.
a) innovation
b) a growth industry
c) a competitive edge
d) competent management
Answer d   Page 429

35. Less than ___% of all U.S. companies are publicly-held corporations.
a) 1
b) 5
c) 10
d) 12
Answer a   Page 430

36. When taking a company public, investment bankers look for:
a) a leading position in a stable market.
b) 3 to 5 years of audited financial statements.
c) a strong record of revenues.
d) a moderate growth rate.
Answer b   Page 430

37. One of the biggest advantages of going public is:
a) the ability to attract low cost equity funding.
b) the ability to retain control while gaining maximum funding.
c) better employee morale and productivity.
d) enhanced credibility and improved corporate image.
Answer d   Page 431

38. Probably the biggest disadvantage of "going public" to the entrepreneur is the:
a) dilution of ownership interest.
b) diminished corporate image.
c) future threat of being acquired through the use of stock.
d) loss of key employees.
Answer a   Page 432

39. For the typical small company, the cost of a public stock offering is approximately ___% of the capital raised.
a) 4
b) 12
c) 50
d) 35
Answer b   Page 433

40. The largest cost in a public stock offering is:
    a) printing expenses.
    b) filing fees with the SEC.
    c) the underwriter's commission.
    d) legal fees.

Answer c   Page 433

41. The single most important ingredient in making a successful public offering is:
    a) choosing a capable underwriter.
    b) negotiating a favorable letter of intent.
    c) preparing a suitable registration statement.
    d) filing Regulation D with the SEC.

Answer a   Page 435

42. In a public offering, the underwriter:
    a) advises the owner as to the best structure of the business going into the sale.
    b) serves as an adviser and consultant to the small business in preparing the registration statement for the SEC.
    c) is bound to the offering until it is executed.
    d) is listed as one of the officers of the company.

Answer b   Page 435

43. The document outlining the details of the agreement between the entrepreneur and the stock underwriter is called:
    a) Regulation D.
    b) a filing.
    c) the letter of intent.
    d) the registration statement.

Answer c   Page 435

44. Under a _____ agreement, the underwriter agrees to purchase all of the shares in a company's public offering and then resells them to investors.
    a) best effort
    b) lock-up
    c) final price
    d) firm commitment

Answer d   Page 435

45. To ensure an "aftermarket" for a company's stock, most underwriters prefer to offer a minimum of _____ shares.
    a) 10,000 to 20,000
    b) 100,000 to 150,000
    c) 400,000 to 500,000
    d) 1,000,000 to 1,500,000

Answer c   Page 437

46. Most underwriters recommend selling _____% of a small company in an initial public offering (IPO).
    a) 8 to 10

b)   25 to 40
c)   55 to 60
d)   80 to 85
Answer b   Page 437

47. A lock-up agreement:
   a)   prevents the sale of "insider" shares for a specific period of time—often 12 to 36 months—after an initial public offering (IPO).
   b)   prevents a small company from signing on with other underwriters to make an IPO.
   c)   prevents a company about to make an IPO from signing a union contract.
   d)   establishes the final price of the IPO so that it cannot fluctuate before the stock offering is actually made.
Answer a   Page 437

48. When filing with the SEC, the initial registration statement:
   a)   prohibits a "road show."
   b)   is filed without share price, proceeds, or commissions listed.
   c)   signals the time to sign the formal underwriting agreement.
   d)   is generally accepted without corrections by the SEC.
Answer b   Page 437

49. The "wait to go effective" is the time period when:
   a)   the SEC registration statement is being prepared.
   b)   the underwriter decides what regulation to file under.
   c)   the firm prices the stock for the offering.
   d)   the company is waiting for SEC approval after filing the registration statement.
Answer d   Page 438

50. The formal underwriting agreement is signed:
   a)   on the last day before the registration statement becomes effective.
   b)   when the statement of registration is filed.
   c)   during the road show.
   d)   at the time of the letter of intent.
Answer a   Page 438

51. It typically takes _____ to take a company public.
   a)   30 days
   b)   one year
   c)   60 to 180 days
   d)   two weeks
Answer c   Page 438

52. _____ governs private placements and is designed to reduce the registration requirements for small companies going public.
   a)   Regulation D
   b)   Form SB
   c)   Form S-1
   d)   Regulation A
Answer a   Page 441

53. The Small Company Offering Registration (SCOR):
    a) is a simplified registration process designed to make it easier for small companies to make public stock offerings but it is more expensive than an S-1 filing.
    b) has a capital ceiling of $10 million, and the price of each share must be at least $25.
    c) filing uses a standardized disclosure statement, consisting of fifty fill-in-the-blank questions.
    d) can be accomplished without a professional broker or securities firm.
Answer c   Page 441

54. The maximum number of shares a company can sell under a SCOR is:
    a) 200,000.
    b) 10,000.
    c) 100,000.
    d) 1,000,000.
Answer a   Page 441

55. A SCOR filing has a number of advantages to it, such as the fact that:
    a) it can be used by partnerships.
    b) it is recognized in every state.
    c) a company may raise between $3 and $5 million per year.
    d) there is no requirement for an audited financial statement if the offering is under $500,000.
Answer d   Page 442

56. In a Regulation D—private placement (Rule 505 and 506)—a company:
    a) sells its shares directly to private investors.
    b) "goes public" with under 10,000 shares.
    c) registers its shares with the SEC.
    d) must be licensed to do business in all 50 states.
Answer a   Page 443

57. To qualify for a Rule 147 (Intrastate) public stock offering, a company must:
    a) be a limited partnership.
    b) file an SB-1 with the SEC 60 days before the offering.
    c) derive 60% of its revenues in the state in which it makes this offering.
    d) use 80% of the offering proceeds for business in the state in which it makes this offering.
Answer d   Page 443

58. An increasingly popular method of selling stock directly to investors that is used by 31% of all companies seeking to raise capital is:
    a) an IPO.
    b) a direct public offering.
    c) an ESOP.
    d) a Form S-1 filing.
Answer b   Page 445

59. Direct public offerings are characterized by:
    a) offerings too small to be listed on most stock exchanges.
    b) being very time consuming for the entrepreneur.
    c) the company keeping investors informed.

d) all of these.

Answer d   Page 446

60. A foreign stock market that caters to small companies is:
a) OFEX.
b) the London Stock market.
c) the NASDAQ.
d) DPOX.

Answer a   Page 447

True or False Questions

61. Choosing the right source of capital is as important as choosing the right form of ownership for the small business owner.

Answer T   Page 411

62. The problem with the lack of funding for start-ups is that the seed capital and funding sources just aren't there.

Answer F   Page 412

63. Layered financing is the process of piecing start-up capital together from a variety of sources rather than relying on a single source of funds.

Answer T   Page 412

64. Seed capital for the entrepreneur is risk capital for investors.

Answer T   Page 413

65. Most entrepreneurs seeking money to launch their businesses need more than $1,000,000.

Answer F   Page 413

66. The owner of a small retail shoe store and the owner of a small furniture manufacturer would likely have very different capital requirements.

Answer T   Page 414

67. Lenders of fixed capital expect the assets purchased to increase the borrowing firm's efficiency, profitability, and cash flows.

Answer T   Page 414

68. A small company needs fixed capital to expand and grow the business.

Answer F   Page 414

69. The need for growth capital is created by the uneven flow of cash into and out of the business due to normal seasonal fluctuations.

Answer F   Page 414

70. The primary advantage of equity capital is that it does not have to be repaid with interest.

Answer T   Page 415

71. The most common source of equity funds used to start a small business is an SBA loan.

Answer F   Page 416

72. Most entrepreneurs, more than 60%, are forced to look to external sources to meet their start-up capital requirements.
Answer F   Page 417, Figure 13.3

73. If an entrepreneur is not willing to risk funds in a business venture, other potential investors and lenders are not likely to provide capital either.
Answer T   Page 418

74. An entrepreneur should <u>not</u> take advantage of offers from family and friends to lend or invest money for the business venture.
Answer F   Page 418

75. Investors like to see entrepreneurs devote at least 30% of a business plan to marketing and selling.
Answer T   Page 419

76. Investors are usually more interested in the assumptions behind an entrepreneur's.
Answer T   Page 419

77. When a potential investor asks, "How much money do you need?" the best answer an entrepreneur can give is "How much can I get?"
Answer F   Page 419

78. "Angels" typically invest in businesses in the start-up phase, providing the seed capital needed to get the business going.
Answer T   Page 420

79. "Angels" control a larger pool of venture capital than venture capitalists.
Answer T   Page 420

80. "Angels" usually prefer to invest in businesses they know something about.
Answer T   Page 421

81. Private investors, or "angels," seek 60–75% annual return-on-investment and tend to take a 51%+ share of the business.
Answer F   Page 422

82. A typical venture capital firm seeks annual returns of 35–50% over three to five years.
Answer F   Page 422

83. Most venture capitalists make investments in promising business ventures in return for a share of the ownership.
Answer T   Page 422

84. Locating "angels" to finance a business is essentially a matter of networking—finding the right contacts.
Answer T   Page 423

85. A relatively recent source of financing for small businesses is large corporations.

Answer T   Page 424

86. Foreign corporations invest in U.S. small businesses through strategic partnerships in order to gain access to new technology, new products, and U.S. markets.

Answer T   Page 425

87. To justify the cost of investigating the offers they receive, venture capitalists typically seek investments in the $200,000 to $500,000 range.

Answer F   Page 426

88. Venture capital companies reject 90% of the proposals they receive because they don't meet the firms' standards.

Answer T   Page 426

89. The majority of venture capital firms which provide capital to small businesses strive to not be involved in running the business.

Answer F   Page 426

90. Most venture capitalist companies prefer to finance start-up companies to maximize their return.

Answer F   Page 428

91. The most important ingredient that venture capitalists look for in judging the potential success of a small business is a competent management team.

Answer T   Page 429

92. Most venture bankers want to invest in a business that can become a $50 million company in 5 to 7 years.

Answer T   Page 429

93. A small business with a 25–35% profit margin is a promising candidate for venture banker money.

Answer F   Page 430, Table 13.3

94. The biggest benefit of going public is the capital infusion the company receives.

Answer T   Page 431

95. It is easier for a start-up company to attract and retain quality employees than after a market emerges for a public company's stock.

Answer F   Page 432

96. Once a small business goes for a public stock offering, information that the owner used to keep private is not public information.

Answer T   Page 433

97. Small business owners, if they become a publicly-held company, can be sued by stockholders for management decisions that depress the price of the company stock.

Answer T   Page 434

98. In a public stock offering, the underwriter's primary role is in selling stock through an underwriting syndicate it assembles.
Answer T   Page 435

99. The typical letter of intent prevents an underwriter from withdrawing a company's stock offering before it is executed.
Answer F   Page 435

100. A firm commitment underwriting agreement essentially guarantees that the small company making the initial public offering will receive the funds it needs.
Answer T   Page 435

101. The reason Joe Falsetti couldn't get investors interested in an IPO for his ROM Tech was his unwillingness to disclose key financial information.
Answer T   Page 436

102. A lock-up agreement prevents the sale of "insider" shares for a specific time period—often 12 to 36 months—after an initial public offering.
Answer T   Page 437

103. The purpose of the road show coordinated by the underwriter of an initial public offering (IPO) is to promote interest in the IPO among potential syndicate members.
Answer T   Page 438

104. Form SB-1 registration is the SEC's basic filing statement and most small companies, especially start-ups, use it.
Answer F   Page 441

105. Filing the standardized disclosure statement for a Small Company Offering Registration (SCOR) is so simple that many small business owners do it on their own.
Answer T   Page 441

106. The capital ceiling on a Small Company Offering Registration (SCOR) is $1million, and the price of each share must be at least $5.
Answer T   Page

107. When a small company uses Regulation D - Rule 504 to make a stock offering, it sells its share directly to private investors without "going public", but it must still register with the SEC, albeit through an abbreviated form.
Answer F   Page 442

108. SCOR offerings have several disadvantages including a limited secondary market and it can't be used by partnerships.
Answer T   Page 442

109. Within Regulation D, Rule 506 has the least restrictive provisions and a $1 million limit in any 12-month ceiling on the amount that can be raised.
Answer F   Page 443

110. In a Rule 147 (intrastate) offering, a company may only sell its shares to investors in the state in which it is incorporated and does business.
Answer T   Page 443

111. Regulation A is not used often but it permits the raising of up to $5 million per 12-month period and costs between $80,000 and $120,000 to file.
Answer T   Page 443

112. While DPOs permit entrepreneurs to avoid the paperwork involved in traditional IPOs, these direct offerings do not save them any money because of the time and extra expense involved in doing all the work themselves.
Answer F   Page 444

113. An advantage of DPOs is that the cost is a little less than half that of a traditional stock underwriting effort.
Answer T   Page 445

114. A drawback of a DPO is that the company has to do its own matching of buyers and sellers of stock; they are not permitted to use a broker.
Answer F   Page 446

115. One of the fastest growing sources of capital for small businesses is the use of the Internet to offer stock to investors.
Answer T   Page 446–447

116. Experts feel that DPOs over the web are the wave of the future and say that research shows such offers always meet federal and state requirements for disclosure.
Answer F   Page 447

117. Foreign stock markets offer entrepreneurs easier access to equity funds than do U.S. markets.
Answer T   Page 447

118. The Alternative Investment Market is a subsidiary of the London Stock Exchange and most of the small business stock offerings raise between $1.6 and $16 million.
Answer T   Page 447

119. Michael Quinn used Regulation D, Rule 505 to do a DPO of his company's stock to investors and raised nearly $4.6 million.
Answer F   Page 448

120. Getting venture money from the United Kingdom has several advantages to it, including the fact that costs are lower and the offering prices tend to be higher than in the United States.
Answer T   Page 448

Essay Questions
121. Define and describe the importance of the following types of capital.
   - seed capital
   - fixed capital
   - working capital

- growth capital

Pages 412–414

122. Outline and briefly describe the common sources of equity capital.
Pages 415–434

123. What are the cardinal rules that an entrepreneur should follow when borrowing venture money from friends and relatives?
Pages 418–420

124. Discuss the role of "angels" in financing small companies, and what and how they tend to finance start-ups.
Pages 420–422

125. How can an entrepreneur avoid problems with his/her angel?
Pages 422–424

126. Venture capital companies are an important source of equity funding for small businesses. Discuss their policies, ownership, control, and investment preferences when it comes to funding small businesses.
Pages 425-429

127. Explain the advantages and disadvantages of a small company "going public."
Pages 432–434

128. Briefly review the steps involved in registering a small business for a public stock offering.
Pages 435–438

129. How are each of the following different from a traditional IPO?
- Regulation S-B
- Regulation D - Rule 504
- Regulation D - Rules 505 & 506
- Intrastate offerings - Rule 147
- Regulation A

Pages 438-443

130. What is a direct public offering, how is it done, and what are the disadvantages to using it?
Pages 444–446

Mini-Cases

Case 13-1: Bowden Brake Service
Jim Bowden has been operating his business for some time now and thinks it's time to grow and expand. To compute the cost of expanding his existing business, Jim Bowden makes the following estimates:

Adjacent lot	$ 40,000

Metal prefab building	25,000
Hydraulic lifts	15,000
Tools and equipment	9,000
Parts and inventory	5,000
Additional operating expenses	$ 55,000
Total	$149,000

Questions

1. Classify Jim's expansion estimates into the three categories of capital: (a) fixed capital requirements, (b) working capital requirements, and (c) growth capital requirements.

2. Explain to Jim the possible (and realistic) sources of capital for expansion. Where would you recommend that he go for the funds he needs? Why?

Chapter 14 –
Sources of Debt Financing

Multiple Choice Questions

1. Sometimes small businesses have to use debt financing instead of equity financing. When they do, they discover that:
    a) banks give them a lower interest rate because of their closeness to the customer and better management practices.
    b) finance companies are their primary source for debt funding.
    c) the cost of debt financing is often less than the cost of equity financing.
    d) there are fewer lenders than investors in the marketplace, but the money is easier to get from lenders.

Answer c   Page 454

2. Small business owners should consider borrowing money from a bank when:
    a) they need to refinance existing debt.
    b) they need start-up seed money for a new venture.
    c) 95
    d) 80

Answer a   Page 454

3. Studies suggest that ___% of the loans to operating small businesses comes from banks.
    a) 35
    b) 15
    c) 95
    d) 80

Answer d   Page 455

4. _____ are second only to _____ as a source of capital for launching businesses.
    a) Entrepreneurs' personal savings; banks
    b) Venture capitalists; SBA loans
    c) Bank loans; entrepreneurs' personal savings
    d) SBA loans; venture capitalists

Answer c   Page 455

5. For small businesses, _____ are the heart of the financial market.
    a) banks
    b) finance companies
    c) private placement
    d) insurance companies

Answer a   Page 455

6. As the providers of debt financing to small businesses, banks tend to:
    a) make only asset-based, long-term loans.
    b) be very conservative and lend primarily short-term capital.
    c) focus on either inventory or accounts receivable when evaluating a business's loan requests.
    d) be eager lenders to start-ups as these tend to be smaller loans at less risk.

Answer b   Page 456

7. The most common type of commercial bank loan granted to small businesses is:
   a) the short-term commercial loan.
   b) the lines of credit agreement.
   c) the floor plan.
   d) the unsecured term loan.
Answer a   Page 456

8. A _____ is an agreement with a bank that allows a small business to borrow up to a predetermined specified amount during the year without making an application each time.
   a) term loan
   b) factor
   c) line of credit
   d) floor plan
Answer c   Page 456

9. When a small business uses a line of credit:
   a) it tends to use it a great deal for day-to-day operating capital.
   b) it is permitted to borrow up to 50% of its present working capital.
   c) the business must keep a compensating balance in the bank.
   d) it must be repaid once per quarter.
Answer d   Page 457

10. Sunny Bright's, The Tanning Parlor, is in the middle of its busy season. The hiring of extra help, some unexpected repairs on equipment, etc., has led to a shortage of operating capital. What type of financing would Sunny most likely use in this situation?
    a) Line of credit
    b) Floor planning
    c) A discounted installment contract
    d) An asset-based loan
Answer a   Page 457

11. _____ is a method of financing frequently employed by retailers of "big ticket items"—autos and major appliances.
    a) Discounted installment contracts
    b) Trade credit
    c) Installment loans
    d) Floor planning
Answer d   Page 458

12. A small retail boat shop is most likely to rely on _____ to finance its inventory.
    a) discounted installment contracts
    b) floor planning
    c) installment loans
    d) trade credit
Answer b   Page 458

13. First Security Bank grants the owner of Sam's Appliance Store a loan primarily based on his past operating experience. As part of the loan agreement with the bank, Sam agrees to limit his salary to $39,000 per year. What type of loan is this?
    a) Installment loan
    b) Unsecured term loan
    c) Floor plan
    d) Commercial loan
Answer b   Page 459

14. A/An _____ loan is made available to small and medium-sized businesses due to government regulation. The loan is based not on creditworthiness, but on the borrower's reputation and reliability. The loan must be less than $900,000 and cannot exceed 3% of the bank's total capital.
    a) line of credit
    b) discounted installment contract
    c) character
    d) SBA
Answer c   Page 459

15. Entrepreneurs can manage their banking relationships by:
    a) sending their banker samples of new products.
    b) knowing as much about the bank and banker as they do about their own business.
    c) inviting the banker to lunch periodically.
    d) doing all these things.
Answer a   Page 460

16. Asset-based borrowing permits small businesses:
    a) to borrow up to 100% of the value of their inventory or their accounts receivable for the money they need for long-term goals.
    b) to use normally unproductive assets—accounts receivable and inventory.
    c) to obtain loans more easily but with less borrowing power than if they used an unsecured line of credit.
    d) access to a source of funds ideally suited for long-term financing needs.
Answer b   Page 461

17. In asset-based borrowing, the _____ is the percentage of an asset's value that a lender will lend.
    a) prime rate
    b) margin rate
    c) advance rate
    d) discounted rate
Answer c   Page 461

18. The most common form of secured credit is:
    a) accounts receivable financing.
    b) inventory financing.
    c) floor planning.
    d) discounted installment contracts.
Answer a   Page 461

19. ____ is/are an asset-based financing technique.
    a)   Discounted installment contracts
    b)   Inventory financing
    c)   Installment lending
    d)   Floor planning
Answer b   Page 462

20. A small business with accounts receivable of $2 million could borrow between _____ as an asset-based loan.
    a) $2 and $4 million
    b) $ 300,000 and $500,000
    c) $1.1 and $1.7 million
    d) $1 and $2.3 million
Answer c   Page 462

21. Asset-based financing:
    a)   is efficient since the small business borrows only the money it needs.
    b)   provides less borrowing capacity than inventory-based financing.
    c)   is less expensive than other types of financing.
    d)   is less desirable than inventory-only deals to bankers.
Answer c   Page 462

22. When a small business is refused a loan because it is not profitable and deemed a poor credit risk, the owner can usually turn to ____ as a source of short-term funds.
    a)   venture capital companies
    b)   trade credit
    c)   stockbrokers
    d)   loans from insurance companies
Answer b   Page 462–463

23. Janis Reardon is in the process of launching a craft shop. Her biggest supplier, Lothrop's Craft Supply, agrees to sell her the inventory she needs to stock her store on a delayed payment schedule. Janis is using what type of financing?
    a)   Line of credit
    b)   Floor planning
    c)   Trade credit
    d)   Asset-based borrowing
Answer c   Page 463

24. The most common method used by commercial finance companies to provide credit to small businesses is:
    a)   asset-based.
    b)   insurance–based.
    c)   unsecured lines of credit or "character loans."
    d)   balance-sheet based.
Answer a   Page 463

25. The loans of commercial finance companies to small businesses:
    a) tend to be for less than a commercial bank but at a lower interest rate.
    b) are offered based on the company's balance sheet.
    c) tend to be at a lower interest rate but are harder to get.
    d) are in many of the same forms as commercial bank offers.

Answer d   Page 464

26. Savings and loan associations typically specialize in loans for:
    a) equipment.
    b) inventory.
    c) real property.
    d) accounts receivable.

Answer c   Page 464

27. A loan from a stockbroker, based on the stocks and bonds in the customer's portfolio:
    a) tends to be at a higher rate than a bank but easier to obtain.
    b) can be "called" for payment in a matter of hours or days.
    c) is for a maximum of $50,000.
    d) has a fixed repayment schedule and must be paid within 90 days.

Answer b   Page 465

28. Insurance companies typically make two types of loans:
    a) policy loans and mortgage loans.
    b) asset-based, inventory and discounted accounts receivable.
    c) short-term and policy loans.
    d) mortgage loans and unsecured loans.

Answer a   Page 465

29. Entrepreneur Wally Wilton wants to build a colossal amusement park for kids of all ages. Wilton will need $48 million to get the first phase of "Wally World" into operation. Which of the following is the type of loan best suited for Wally?
    a) An asset-based loan, based on inventory or accounts receivable
    b) A mortgage loan from an insurance company
    c) A credit union loan
    d) A MESBIC loan

Answer b   Page 465

30. A/An _____ is a private nonprofit financial institution that will make small loans to its members for the purpose of starting a business.
    a) SBIC
    b) private placement
    c) credit union
    d) insurance company

Answer c   Page 466

31. A popular form of debt financing with large companies, a sort of corporate"IOU," which is becoming more accessible to a growing number of small companies is:
    a) stockbroker-based loans.
    b) bonds.
    c) commercial bank loans.
    d) SBICs.

Answer b   Page 466

32. Zero coupon bonds:
    a) are backed by collateral.
    b) are an excellent form of financing for almost all small businesses.
    c) are not subject to the same regulations that govern businesses making public stock offerings.
    d) are sold at deep discounts, do not require periodic interest payments, and repay the lender the full par value at maturity.

Answer d   Page 467

33. A/An ___ is a hybrid between a conventional loan and a bond; at its heart it is a bond, but its terms are tailored to the borrower's individual needs, as a loan would be.
    a) private placement
    b) industrial revenue bond
    c) 504 loan
    d) zero coupon bond

Answer a   Page 467

34. The typical private placement of debt is characterized by:
    a) a variable interest rate.
    b) a maturity shorter than most bank loans.
    c) more restrictions imposed on the borrower than with a comparable bank loan.
    d) a spreading of risk by the selling of the debt to one or more small investors.

Answer d   Page 467

35. SBICs:
    a) were chartered by the SBA to help start-up companies find private financing from commercial banks and finance companies.
    b) provide short-term debt-based capital to small businesses through the sale of the debt to private investors.
    c) cannot invest in or lend money to a business for more than five years.
    d) were created by the Small Business Investment Act to use a combination of private and federal guaranteed debt to provide long-term capital to small businesses.

Answer d   Page 468

36. Small Business Investment Companies (SBICs):
    a) prefer to finance companies in later stages rather than "raw start-ups."
    b) only provide long-term debt financing to small businesses.
    c) cannot make their own investment decisions, which are controlled by the SBA.
    d) loan money through debentures not requiring regular interest payments.

Answer a   Page 469

37. SBICs may lend up to _____% of their private capital to a single client.
    a) 10
    b) 20
    c) 30
    d) 40

Answer b   Page 469

38. A _____ makes only intermediate and long-term SBA guaranteed loans. It specializes in loans many banks would not consider.
    a) small business investment company
    b) local development company
    c) small business lending company
    d) MESBIC

Answer c   Page 469

39. A federally-sponsored program which offers loan guarantees to create and expand businesses in areas with below-average income and high unemployment is called:
    a) the Small Business Administration.
    b) the Economic Development Administration.
    c) SBIC.
    d) the Farmers Home Administration.

Answer b   Page 470

40. Grants to small businesses, made to strengthen the local economy in cities and towns that are considered economically distressed, are made by:
    a) the Department of Housing and Urban Development.
    b) a local development company.
    c) the Farmers Home Administration.
    d) the Economic Development Administration.

Answer a   Page 470

41. Malcolm wants to start a business in the prosperous little town of Grove City, a town of 10,000 about 65 miles from Pittsburgh, Pennsylvania. His business will create about 25 manufacturing jobs. What federal agency would most likely be interested in loaning Malcolm money?
    a) The Department of Housing and Urban Development
    b) A local development company
    c) The Farmers Home Administration
    d) The Economic Development Administration

Answer c   Page 471

42. Designed to operate as a profit or nonprofit business, this group consists of local residents who provide capital to local start-ups. The group must have at least 25 members and may seek additional funding from the SBA.
    a) a small business investment company
    b) a local development company
    c) a small business lending company
    d) the small business innovation and research program

Answer b   Page 471

43. A local development company is:
    a) a federal agency created by the Small Business Investment Act.
    b) a type of private offering arranged by stockbrokers.
    c) a nonprofit agency formed and funded by an SBA participating bank.
    d) a profit or nonprofit company that sells stock to residents and then obtains loans from the SBA and banks to help small businesses.

Answer d   Page 472

44. This program was started to encourage small businesses that wanted to expand their research and development efforts. It has made over 30,000 awards in excess of $4.5 billion.
    a) Small Business Technology Transfer Act
    b) Local development companies
    c) The SBA Capline program
    d) Small Business Innovation Research Program

Answer   Page 472

45. Which of the following businesses would be eligible for an SBA loan?
    a) A small computer manufacturer
    b) A nonprofit business
    c) A magazine publisher
    d) A casino

Answer a   Page 473

46. When a bank makes enough good SBA-guaranteed loans to become a _____ lender, the SBA promises a faster turnaround time for the loan decision—typically 3 to 10 business days.
    a) preferred
    b) qualified
    c) certified
    d) LDC

Answer c   Page 473

47. When a bank proves the quality of its loan decisions to the SBA and becomes a _____ lender, the bank makes the final lending decision itself, subject to SBA review for the guarantee.
    a) preferred
    b) qualified
    c) certified
    d) LDC

Answer a   Page 473

48. A process established to streamline the application process for SBA loans is called:
    a) the direct loan program.
    b) Capline.
    c) immediate participation loan program.
    d) FAS$TRAK.

Answer d   Page 474

49. The majority of loans provided by the SBA are:
    a) direct.
    b) preferred.
    c) guaranteed.
    d) immediate participation

Answer c   Page 474

50. About ___ % of all SBA-guaranteed loans go to business start-ups.
    a) 10
    b) 30
    c) 50
    d) 90

Answer b   Page 475

51. The average interest rates on SBA-guaranteed loans is:
    a) prime-minus-2-percent.
    b) 2 percent.
    c) prime-plus-2-percent.
    d) 7 percent.

Answer c   Page 475

52. The median loan through the SBA's guaranteed loan program is:
    a) $95,000.
    b) $175,000.
    c) $250,000.
    d) $450,000.

Answer b   Page 476

53. _____ provides short-term capital to finance seasonal needs in inventory and accounts receivable, basically providing a line of credit.
    a) A Capline program
    b) A Section 504 loan
    c) An LDC loan
    d) An export working capital program

Answer d   Page 477

54. A Section 504 program has three types of lenders involved:
    a) a local development company, the SBA, and a commercial finance company.
    b) a bank, the SBA, and a certified development company.
    c) the SBA, a private placement, and an SBIC.
    d) HUD, a bank, and an economic development company.

Answer b   Page 477

55. _____ were created by the SBA in 1992 to provide loans under $25,000 that are normally shunned by banks.
    a) Microloans
    b) Preferred loans
    c) Seasonal line of credits
    d) 8(a) program loans

Answer a   Page 478

56. What do ACCION International, Bangladesh's Grameen Bank, and Mountain Microenterprise all do for small businesses in their areas of the world?
    a) Provide business incubation centers for their growth
    b) Provide microloans from as little as $25 to as much as $8,000
    c) Assist in technology transfer from research and development to practical application
    d) Offer business start-up advice through a pool of experienced established small business owners

Answer b   Page 479

57. The _____ is designed to help minority-owned businesses get a fair share of federal government contracts.
    a) microloan
    b) preferred loan
    c) seasonal line of credit
    d) 8(a) program

Answer d   Page 479

58. If a minority business owner is able to convince the SBA that his/her business meets the appropriate criteria, the SBA finds a federal agency needing work to be done and matches the minority small business and that agency. This program is
    a) a bootstrap program.
    b) the 8(a) program.
    c) the minority and women's prequalified program.
    d) a Section 504 certified development company program.

Answer b   Page 480

59. A small business that uses factoring:
    a) pledges its accounts receivable as collateral to obtain a loan from a financial institution.
    b) relies on a third-party consultant to apply for SBA-guaranteed loans.
    c) sells its accounts receivable to a third party to get the capital it needs.
    d) borrows money from lenders by offering them the option to convert the loan into stock in the company.

Answer c   Page 481

60. Factoring:
    a) is a more expensive method of financing than borrowing from a bank.
    b) places the risk of uncollected accounts receivable on the small business owner.
    c) is best used as a long-term source of capital.
    d) is a type of trade credit.

Answer a   Page 481

True or False Questions

61. Generally speaking, all growing companies need to borrow money at some point.
Answer T   Page 453

62. A small business owner should avoid borrowing money when he/she see a downturn, in business or to refinance existing debt.

Answer F   Page 454

63. 47% of small business owners rely on banks as their source of start-up capital.
Answer F   Page 455

64. Commercial banks are lenders of last resort for small businesses.
Answer F   Page 455

65. Banks focus on a small business's ability to generate a positive cash flow when lending money.
Answer T   Page 455

66. Commercial banks are primarily lenders of short-term capital to small businesses.
Answer T   Page 456

67. The common short-term loan is for one year, often repaid sooner, and repaid in one lump sum.
Answer T   Page 456

68. A line of credit is usually secured by collateral.
Answer T   Page 457

69. A recent survey of small companies with lines of credit found that only 25% actually use them.
Answer F   Page 457

70. A boat retailer would most likely use a line of credit to finance the purchase of his inventory.
Answer F   Page 457

71. A business owner does not pay interest on a floor-planned item in inventory until it is sold.
Answer F   Page 458

72. Unsecured term loans typically involve very specific terms which may limit the owner's freedom to make financial decisions.
Answer T   Page 459

73. In an installment loan for equipment, the loan's amortization schedule would coincide with the equipment's useful life.
Answer T   Page 459

74. Banks may make "character loans" when the small business is able to pledge installment contracts as collateral.
Answer F   Page 459

75. It is important for the small business owner to stay in communication with his/her banker by visiting, sending customer mailings to him/her, and even sending samples of new products.
Answer T   Page 460

76. Even companies whose financial statements are too weak to produce other types of loans can get asset-based loans.
Answer T   Page 461

77. Typically, a commercial bank will lend a small business owner 100% of the value of accounts receivable pledged as collateral.
Answer F   Page 462

78. Inventory-only deals are the easiest form of asset-based financing to obtain because banks like to have "tangible" assets backing a loan.
Answer F   Page 462

79. Asset-based financing is an efficient means of borrowing because the business only pays for the capital it actually needs and uses.
Answer T   Page 462

80. Trade credit, while more difficult to obtain than bank financing, is a somewhat important source of financing to most established companies.
Answer F   Page 462

81. Start-up companies often use trade credit from suppliers to buy equipment and fixtures for their business.
Answer T   Page 463

82. Commercial finance companies are willing to take more risks in making loans, but they also charge a higher interest rate.
Answer T   Page 463

83. The majority of the loans a commercial finance company makes are unsecured by collateral.
Answer F   Page 463

84. Commercial finance companies offer many of the same types of loans as commercial banks, but they are willing to tolerate more risk in their loan portfolios.
Answer T   Page 464

85. Savings and loan associations specialize in loans for the purchase of and for working capital.
Answer F   Page 464

86. Loans from stockbrokers carry higher interest rates since the collateral—stocks and bonds in the borrower's portfolio—involve a high level of risk.
Answer F   Page 465

87. Loans from a stockbrokerage on the small business owner's portfolio can be "called" to be paid within a matter of days or even hours.
Answer T   Page 465
88. Insurance companies specialize in long-term loans.
Answer T   Page 465

89. Some credit unions are now extending personal loans to members, often without personal collateral, in order to start a business.
Answer T   Page 466

90. Zero coupon bonds are ideally suited for businesses with small capital requirements.

Answer F   Page 466

91. Unlike traditional bonds, zero coupon bonds require the issuing company to make periodic interest payments to bondholders.
Answer F   Page 466

92. Industrial revenue bonds are a relatively inexpensive source of funds for small manufacturers.
Answer T   Page 467

93. Private placement debt is a hybrid between a conventional loan and a bond.
Answer T   Page 467

94. Because private investors are willing to take greater risks than banks, they are more willing to finance deals through private placements than are banks.
Answer T   Page 467

95. SBICs are privately owned financial institutions that are licensed and regulated by the SBA.
Answer T   Page 467

96. Over the past 30 years, SBICs have provided over $13 billion in financing to some 80,000 small businesses.
Answer T   Page 468

97. An SBIC can lend up to 40% of its private capital to a single client.
Answer F   Page 469

98. SBICs provide only debt financing to small businesses.
Answer F   Page 469

99. Small Business Lending Companies (SBLCs) make only intermediate and long- term SBA-guaranteed loans.
Answer T   Page 469

100. The EDA makes low-interest loans to create new businesses in economically depressed areas with below-average incomes and high unemployment rates.
Answer T   Page 470

101. Urban Development Grants are used to construct buildings and plants for small businesses and have no ceilings or geographic limitations.
Answer T   Page 470

102. The Farmers Home Administration only makes loans to small farms.
Answer F   Page 471

103. The Farmers Home Administration makes direct loans to small businesses meeting the rural area criteria in order to create nonfarm employment.
Answer F   Page 471

104. Most LDCs are nonprofit, and only finance working capital or inventory costs.

Answer F   Page 471

105. LDCs finance only the fixed assets of a business and allow longer repayment periods—20 to 25 years.
Answer T   Page 472

106. The Small Business Innovation Research Program was started by the National Science Foundation and spread to 10 other federal agencies with an annual budget in excess of $100 million.
Answer T   Page 472

107. The Small Business Technology Transfer Act of 1992 supports the SBIR program by exploiting promising technological developments that come out of small businesses and funds and guides their practical application to the commercial world.
Answer F   Page 473

108. Certified and preferred lenders make nearly 60% of all SBA-guaranteed loans.
Answer F   Page 473

109. An entrepreneur seeking an SBA loan guarantee can cut out a tremendous amount of time and paperwork by working with a bank that is either a certified or a preferred lender.
Answer T   Page 473

110. The majority of loans provided by the SBA are direct.
Answer F   Page 474

111. The SBA's immediate participation loans are a mix of private and public funds, and the SBA is prohibited from financing more than 75% of the loan.
Answer T   Page 474

112. The average SBA loan guarantee is $150,000 and has an average duration of seven years.
Answer F   Page 474

113. Approximately 75% of SBA-guaranteed loans go to small businesses start-ups.
Answer F   Page 475

114. SBA loans do not carry special deals or interest rates and typically are set at prime plus 2.25% for loans under seven years in length.
Answer T   Page 475

115. The media loan in the SBA guarantee program is for $175,000 for 12 years.
Answer T   Page 476

116. The SBA's Section 504 program is designed to encourage small businesses to expand their facilities and to create jobs.
Answer T   Page 477

117. The Minority and Women's Prequalified Loan Program guarantees loans up to $250,000 to minorities and women if local commercial banks decline to lend to them.
Answer F   Page 478

118. In a factoring arrangement, the risk of uncollected accounts receivable falls on the small business owner.
Answer F   Page 481

119. Leasing is an effective way to reduce long-term capital requirements for a small business.
Answer T   Page 482

120. Jerry Turner and Michael Clarke needed money to buy equipment and weren't able to get either trade credit or a bank loan because they had no assets and didn't have the cash for a down payment.
Answer T   Page 483

Essay Questions

121. Under what circumstances should the small business owner consider borrowing money?
Page 454

122. Explain the role of commercial banks as source of debt capital for small businesses. What types of financing are available from commercial banks?
Pages 455–459

123. What is asset-based borrowing? Explain the two major types of asset-based borrowing, including the pros and cons of each type.
Pages 461–462

124. What is trade credit? How is it different from or the same as loans from equipment suppliers?
Pages 462–463

125. What role do commercial finance companies, savings and loan associations, stockbrokerages, and insurance companies play in providing debt-based loans to small businesses?
Pages 464–466

126. What is an SBIC? What is an SBLC? How important are they as sources of small business capital? How does do they operate?
Pages 467–470

127. How does the EDA, HUD, FHA, and RECD lend money to small businesses?
Pages 470–471

128. What are local development companies and the small business innovation research programs? How do they help small businesses?
Pages 471–473

129. Explain the different SBA loan programs. Explain how a typical SBA loan guarantee works. What interest rates do such loans normally carry?
Pages 474–480

130. Explain how a small business can use factoring to raise funds. What are the advantages and dangers of this type of financing?
Pages 481–482

Mini-Case

Case 14-1: "Where Do I Go Now...?

Christine Hernandez is in the process of launching a restaurant. Christine has never owned her own restaurant before, but she has worked for two of the best restaurants in town. Starting out as a hostess, Christine developed a special knack for the business and quickly worked her way up to the job of manager. Her 18 years of experience have given her a solid foundation for running her own restaurant.

Christine has worked with a counselor at a nearby Small Business Development Center and a counselor from the Service Corps of Retired Executives to prepare a business plan. She asked two other consultants and an accountant to review the plan and incorporated their suggestions into the finished product. Christine has personal savings of about $15,000, a paid life insurance policy worth $100,000—which her grandfather bought her when she was born—and a small rental property with no mortgage, worth about $75,000.

Christine is considering how to finance her business start-up. She needs $165,000 to start her restaurant. She has chosen a location in the center of a major city. The neighborhood is economically depressed but she thinks a "trendy" restaurant would draw regardless of location and her initial rent and utility expenses would be low.

Questions

1. Evaluate Christine's plan and current status and explain if a commercial bank would or would not loan her the money and why.

2. If Christine is turned down by commercial banks, what other sources of capital would you suggest that Christine explore? Offer the advantages and disadvantages of each.

3. There are several types of financial institutions formed under the Small Business Administration for helping businesses like Christine's find capital. Explain which of these institutions would be most helpful to Christine and what the criteria are for granting loans or loan guarantees.

Chapter 15 –
Location, Layout and Physical Facilities

Multiple Choice Questions

1. The secret to selecting the ideal location for a business is:
   a) the available labor pool for the business.
   b) knowing the customer and what is convenient to them.
   c) the tax rate of the local and state governments.
   d) the security of the area and the services provided by the site to the business owner.

Answer b Page 492

2. The first phase in determining where to locate a business is:
   a) choosing what state the business owner wants to move to.
   b) determining which city has the demographics that fit the business best.
   c) conducting an Internet search for information on the cities of choice and competitors in those cities.
   d) determining what regions in the country have what the new business needs to succeed.

Answer d Page 492

3. If an entrepreneur wanted census data updated on a monthly basis, he/she would read:
   a) *1990 Census Basics*.
   b) *Census and You!*
   c) *Census '90: Introduction to Products and Services.*
   d) *Practical Use of Government Statistics.*

Answer b Page 494

4. _____ is a publication that provides important data to aid entrepreneurs in their search for the best location.
   a) *Consumer Reports*
   b) Index of Retail Saturation
   c) *Sales and Marketing's Survey of Buying Power*
   d) Sales Conversion Index

Answer c Page 494

5. The publication that contains highlight and summary sections, analyses of changes in metro markets, projections for metro markets, etc, is called:
   a) *Topological Integrated Geographic Encoding Referencing.*
   b) *The Commercial Atlas and Marketing Guide.*
   c) *The Zip Code Atlas and Market Planner.*
   d) *Sales and Marketing Management's Survey of Buying Power.*

Answer d Page 494

6. A Geographic Information System (GIS):
   a) is a software package combining the ability to draw detailed maps with the power to search through databases.
   b) records data not available through the census and includes eleven indicators of economic growth.

    c) contains the name of every street in the country and detailed block statistics for 345 urban areas.

    d) breaks down the population, retail sales, etc., by census region.

Answer a   Page 495

7. TIGER:

    a) is a software package combining the ability to draw detailed maps with the power to search through databases.

    b) records data not available through the census and includes eleven indicators of economic growth.

    c) contains the names of every street in the country and detailed block statistics for 345 urban areas.

    d) breaks down the population, retail sales, etc. by census region.

Answer c   Page 495

8. When selecting a state in which to locate, one should consider:

    a) the financing options available to the small business owner.

    b) zoning laws.

    c) the compatibility of the business with the community.

    d) the proximity to one's markets.

Answer d   Page 495

9. Carlos owns a heavy equipment repair and maintenance business. Which of the following criteria for selecting a state in which to locate the business would be of greatest concern to Carlos?

    a) Labor supply

    b) Proximity to markets

    c) Tax laws and incentives

    d) Proximity to raw materials

Answer b   Page 495

10. A small brick manufacturer would be concerned most with which location criterion?

    a) Business climate

    b) Labor supply needs

    c) Wage rates

    d) Proximity to markets

Answer d   Page 496

11. A glass manufacturer that requires an extremely pure, very fine type of sand in its production process would be most concerned with which location criteria?

    a) Business climate

    b) Proximity to raw materials

    c) Proximity to markets

    d) Wage rates

Answer b   Page 496

12. When examining a state's available labor force, the potential business owner needs to know:

    a) the state's labor relations history.

    b) the demographics of the target customers.

    c) both the number and education of the available workforce.

d) the proximity of its customers.

Answer c   Page 496

13. _____ would be most important to someone wishing to locate a manufacturing facility for computers.
    a) Proximity of the target market
    b) Business climate
    c) Labor supply
    d) Proximity to raw materials

Answer c   Page 496

14. An interstate trucking firm would be most concerned with which selection criterion at the state level?
    a) Business climate
    b) Proximity to markets
    c) Proximity to raw materials
    d) Wage rates

Answer a   Page 496

15. Sonny Tilman relies on _____ to assist site selection for his franchise's restaurants because location is crucial to their success.
    a) TIGER
    b) *The Commercial Atlas and Marketing Guide*
    c) *The Zip Code Atlas and Market Planner*
    d) geographic information systems

Answer d   Page 497

16. A telemarketing customer service unit for the credit card business of an interstate bank would be most concerned about _____ in the choice of state.
    a) proximity to markets
    b) wage rates and labor supply
    c) competition and business climate
    d) population trends and competition

Answer b   Page 498

17. Which of the following characteristics for selecting a city would be of greatest interest to a retail store selling fine china and collectibles?
    a) Public services
    b) Transportation
    c) Zoning
    d) Population trends

Answer d   Page 499

18. The index of retail saturation is:
    a) retail expenditures times retail facilities divided by the number of customers.
    b) the ratio of a trading area's sales potential to its sales capacity.
    c) a buying power index.
    d) retail facilities times the number of customers divided by the retail expenditures.

Answer b   Page 500

Use the following information to answer questions 19 and 20.
An entrepreneur considering two sites for a men's and boys' shop determines that he needs sales of $158 per square foot to be profitable. Site #1 has 13,500 potential customers who spend an average of $160.20 per year on men's and boys' wear. Two competitors occupy 14,200 square feet of space. Site #2 has 10,800 potential customers spending an average of $152.10 per year on men's and boys' wear. One competitor has 10,000 square feet.

19. The index of retail saturation for site #1 is:
    a) $150.21.
    b) $168.51.
    c) $152.30.
    d) $166.19.
Answer c   Page 500–501

20. The index of retail saturation for site #2 is:
    a) $164.27.
    b) $140.83.
    c) $170.64.
    d) $146.30.
Answer a   Page 500–501

21. Based on the above calculations, what is the entrepreneur's best option?
    a) He should choose site #1.
    b) He should choose site #2.
    c) Neither site meets minimum criteria.
    d) Either site will work well since both meet minimum criteria.
Answer b   Page 501

22. _____ is a system that divides a county or a city into small cells or districts to control the use of land, buildings, and sites.
    a) An enterprise zone
    b) Zoning
    c) TIGER
    d) A central business district
Answer b   Page 502

23. Which of the following sets of city factors does an entrepreneur need to consider when choosing a location for his/her new business?
    a) The business growth potential
    b) Business climate and labor market
    c) Proximity to the target market and raw materials
    d) The availability of transportation, public services, and police and fire protection
Answer d   Page 502

24. A manufacturer or wholesaler would be most interested in which of the following criteria for the selection of a city location for a new business?
    a) Public services
    b) Transportation
    c) Reputation of the location
    d) Compatibility with the community
Answer b   Page 502

25. Carmen is starting a childcare center. One location, a former "biker bar" closed after a murder in the bar, is near several manufacturing plants where there are many single parents. What city site selection factor might give Carmen problems with her childcare center?
    a) Transportation
    b) Police and fire protection
    c) The reputation of the location
    d) Compatibility with the community
Answer c   Page 503

26. The area from which a small business expects to draw customers over a reasonable time span is its:
    a) trading area.
    b) metropolitan statistical area.
    c) enterprise zone.
    d) incubator.
Answer a   Page 504

27. The primary variable(s) that influence(s) the scope of a trading area is/are:
    a) the character of the transportation network.
    b) the nature of competing businesses.
    c) the type and size of the business operation.
    d) the racial and political barriers in the local community.
Answer c   Page 504

28. Which of the following factors influences the size of a retail store's trading area?
    a) The location of competitors
    b) The physical layout of the store
    c) Zoning regulations
    d) The nature of competing businesses
Answer d   Page 505

29. Shopping malls typically average ___ parking spaces per ____square feet of shopping space.
    a) 10; 1,000
    b) 5; 1,000
    c) 15; 5,000
    d) 3; 1,000
Answer b   Page 506

30. Ben was doing more business than his store could handle. Because there were stores on each side of his location, he had to open a second store. This expense cut into profits and didn't really double his business. Ben had neglected to keep which site selection criteria in mind?

a) What is the proximity of the business to the market?
b) Can customers easily see and locate the business?
c) Is there adequate parking?
d) Does the site have room for future expansion?

Answer d   Page 507

31. Mary's successful clothing store was located on the back edge of the parking lot of a large mall. She didn't pay mall rents since she wasn't part of the mall, but drew a lot of customers who parked at the mall and then noticed her store. The mall developers built a movie theater on the part of the parking lot directly in front of Mary's store, basically hiding her from most mall customers and her business dropped off so much she had to move. What retailer site selection criterion forced Mary to move?
a) Proximity of competitors
b) Visibility
c) Adequate parking
d) Room for expansion

Answer b   Page 507

32. A central business district is:
a) the traditional center of town.
b) a plan that contains 12 to 50 stores and has a department store as a leading tenant.
c) a type of "mall" that has experienced 1500 percent growth over the last 5 years.
d) a shopping area that draws its customers primarily from the immediate local area.

Answer a   Page 508

33. Central business districts:
a) provide ample parking in front of the stores.
b) are characterized by one-stop shopping.
c) tend to have better prices and selection than malls do.
d) are experiencing a resurgence in popularity.

Answer d   Page 508

34. Since 1960, the number of shopping malls and centers has:
a) declined by about 200 malls.
b) been stable with some signs of moderate growth.
c) grown by 1,500 %.
d) grown by about 150 %.

Answer c   Page 509

35. The _____ serves a large trading area (10 to 15 miles or more), contains from 50 to 100 stores, and has several major department stores as its anchors.
a) neighborhood shopping center
b) community shopping center
c) regional shopping mall
d) central business district

Answer c   Page 509

36. The type of business that does well when located near competitors is:
a) one that has a unique product line, dissimilar to that of its competitors.

   b)   one that sells high-priced products customers comparison shop for.
   c)   one whose location is part of its trademark.
   d)   one located in an incubator.
Answer b   Page 510

37. Generally speaking, the one location that most small businesses have difficulty surviving in and therefore should avoid is:
   a)   a power center.
   b)   among competitors.
   c)   in outlying areas.
   d)   a central business district.
Answer c   Page 510

38. Mall owners are trying to draw shoppers back to the malls by:
   a)   adding entertainment and attractions to draw and keep customers in the mall.
   b)   providing more parking and shuttle service from the parking lots.
   c)   adding more stores and more variety of stores.
   d)   increasing the number and variety of dining options for customers.
Answer a   Page 511

39. As the service economy has grown, a business location being used more and more by service businesses is:
   a)   the industrial park.
   b)   home.
   c)   central business districts.
   d)   outlying areas.
Answer b   Page 512

40. Some cities develop _____ in cooperation with private industry for the benefit of manufacturers.
   a)   incubators
   b)   central business districts
   c)   industrial parks
   d)   high visibility locations
Answer c   Page 513

41. Originally created to encourage companies to locate in economically depressed areas, _____ offer tax breaks and federal tax breaks for hiring workers living in the immediate area.
   a)   industrial parks
   b)   small business incubators
   c)   trade zones
   d)   empowerment zones
Answer d   Page 513

42. Incubator facilities are established in order to:
   a)   revitalize central business disricts.
   b)   enhance economic development and diversify the local economy.
   c)   centralize types of businesses and provide tax breaks to those businesses.
   d)   encourage businesses to locate in economically depressed areas of a city.

Answer b   Page 514

43. Firms that graduate from incubators have a/an _____% survival rate.
     a) 40
     b) 11
     c) 12
     d) 89
Answer d   Page 515

44. To ensure that a building will accommodate expansion plans, a new business should:
     a) plan space requirements for one to two years into the future and update the plans every six
         months.
     b) build, buy, or lease facilities that are 50–100% too big for their current operations.
     c) buy or lease facilities that had the same type of business in them previously.
     d) always build a new facility.
Answer a   Page 515

45. When evaluating existing buildings, retailers:
     a) need to find the lowest cost per-square-foot possible due to the need for maximum display
         space.
     b) should locate in store space previously occupied by a similar type of business.
     c) should recognize that the store's appearance and layout create an image for the customer of the
         business.
     d) can discount the interior appearance of the building if it has a strong exterior appeal.
Answer c   Page 516

46. Entrances should invite entry. The way to accomplish this is to:
     a) have large doors and attractive displays set back from the doorway that can lure customers into
         the store.
     b) offer discounts.
     c) have displays as close to the entry of the store as possible.
     d) have a big sign to attract customers.
Answer a   Page 517

47. The Americans with Disabilities Act of 1990 requires that:
     a) businesses with more than 25 employees comply fully with the Act by June 1993.
     b) all buildings be remodeled to accommodate any disabled customer or employee.
     c) all businesses must accommodate all disabled customers or job candidates, regardless of the
         cost.
     d) buildings occupied after January 23, 1993 must be designed to accommodate disabled
         customers and job candidates.
Answer d   Page 518

48. When it comes to compliance with the Americans with Disabilities Act:
     a) it is estimated that in 20% of the cases the changes could be made at no cost.
     b) companies with less than $1 million in annual revenues and less than 30 employees do not
         have to comply.

   c) companies may apply for exemption from the law if they can prove undue hardship in compliance.

   d) only manufacturing companies with at least 25 employees have to be in full compliance.

Answer a   Page 518

49. Signs are important to the small business owner because they:
   a) grow in effectiveness the longer they are in place.
   b) are easy to use and to change.
   c) provide the maximum space for relatively complex messages.
   d) are a medium that is not subject to regulation, thereby permitting maximum flexibility.

Answer b   Page 519

50. The science of adapting work and working conditions to complement employees and to suit customers is called:
   a) physiology.
   b) ergonomics.
   c) layout design.
   d) kinesiology.

Answer b   Page 519

51. If a small business owner installs a lighting system that turns itself off when people leave a room, a company can save as much as ___% on their lighting bill.
   a) 35
   b) 50
   c) 75
   d) 85

Answer c   Page 522

52. When evaluating the floors, walls, and ceilings in a retail store, the small business owner should:
   a) look for dark colored ceilings that both conserve energy and project a cool feeling.
   b) strive for a light and bright interior.
   c) look for bare functional walls that can be recovered at the owner's expense.
   d) emphasize function over attractiveness.

Answer b   Page 521

53. For retailers, lighting:
   a) is used to attract customers to a specific display.
   b) is an expensive investment.
   c) has little impact on the overall appearance of the business.
   d) requires the same considerations as for manufacturers.

Answer a   Page 521

54. The best way to determine where to place merchandise, what a store's "hot" and "cold" spots are, is to:
   a) conduct a kinesiology study.
   b) hire a market research firm to study your business.
   c) conduct focus groups with former customers.
   d) simply observe customers in the store.

Answer d   Page 522

55. A/An ____ layout arranges displays in a rectangular fashion with parallel aisle. It is a formal layout that controls the traffic flow through the store.
    a) free-form
    b) grid
    c) angled
    d) boutique
Answer b   Page 522

56. The typical grocery store uses a/an _____ layout.
    a) grid
    b) free-form
    c) boutique
    d) arcade
Answer a   Page 522

57. A/An ____ layout has the advantage of creating a relaxed, friendly shopping atmosphere encouraging shoppers to linger and increasing the number of impulse purchases.
    a) free-form
    b) grid
    c) angled
    d) boutique
Answer a   Page 523

58. A/An ____ layout divides a store into a series of individual shopping areas, each with its own theme. This layout can create a distinctive image for a business.
    a) free-form
    b) grid
    c) angled
    d) boutique
Answer d   Page 523

59. The boutique layout is commonly used in:
    a) supermarkets.
    b) self-service stores.
    c) small department stores.
    d) stores with a high number of impulse goods.
Answer c   Page 524

60. Accessibility is the key to the sale of impulse goods. The normal reach of an individual is about:
    a) 24 inches.
    b) 57 inches.
    c) 16 inches.
    d) 12 inches.
Answer c   Page 525

61. The value of the floor space in a retail store depends upon:

    a)   the merchandise in that area.
    b)   the type of store and customer.
    c)   the number of salespeople servicing the area.
    d)   its proximity to aisles and entrances.
Answer d   Page 525

62. Which of the following statements concerning store layout is true?
    a)   Most shoppers turn left upon entering the store and go around it in a clockwise fashion.
    b)   Most shoppers turn right upon entering a store and move around it in a counterclockwise fashion.
    c)   Most shoppers move directly to the back of the store and work their way to the front door.
    d)   There is no predominate pattern for shoppers viewing merchandise in a retail store.
Answer b   Page 526

63. Approximately ____ of a store's customers will go more than halfway into the store.
    a)   one-fourth
    b)   one-half
    c)   one-third
    d)   three-fourths
Answer a   Page 526

64. What is the 40-30-20-10 rule in retailing?
    a)   It is a formula for figuring who your best and worst customers are.
    b)   It is a formula for calculating the ratio of expenditures on signage, displays, advertising, and interior decorating.
    c)   It is an expression of the decline of the value of store space as you move front to back in the store.
    d)   It is the percentage of customers who move straight into a store, go right, go left, leave before fully entering.
Answer c   Page 527

65. Manufacturing layout decisions take into consideration:
    a)   customer buying behavior, the types of product sold, and the physical dimensions of the building.
    b)   the product, the process, the facility, and key economic considerations.
    c)   the status of the building; built, bought, or leased and the type of product sold.
    d)   the employees, the customer, and the mechanical process used to produce the product.
Answer b   Page 528

66. The manufacturing layout that arranges workers and equipment according to sequence of operation and is best suited for highly standardized or mass-produced products is called:
    a)   process layout.
    b)   fixed-position layout.
    c)   function layout.
    d)   product layout.
Answer d   Page 529

67. A product layout has the disadvantage of:

    a) a high fixed investment in specialized equipment.
    b) the highest materials costs with lower productivity.
    c) being harder to schedule and monitor.
    d) dividing the work area into separate operations that are highly independent with a duplication of equipment.

Answer a   Page 529

68. The manufacturing layout that groups workers and equipment according to the general function performed, and that works best with short production runs or when there are considerable variations in the finished product, is called:
    a) process layout.
    b) fixed-position layout.
    c) function layout.
    d) product layout.

Answer a   Page 530

69. A process layout would be best fitted to:
    a) an automobile assembly plant.
    b) an oil refinery.
    c) a manufacturer of handmade metal gifts.
    d) a textbook publishing plant.

Answer c   Page 530

70. When manufacturing large, bulky products, it is sometimes necessary to bring the materials to a specific spot and do the assembly in one place. This type of layout is know as a:
    a) process layout.
    b) fixed-position layout.
    c) function layout.
    d) product layout.

Answer b   Page 530

71. The starting point for designing a layout is:
    a) creating a detailed layout design showing the space relationships.
    b) discovering the single best flow for the manufacturing process.
    c) arranging the equipment and materials stocking areas in the proper sequence.
    d) determining how and in what sequence product parts or service tasks flow together.

Answer d   Page 530

72. Designing layouts ergonomically and seeking to automate product flows can result in:
    a) reducing the owner's initial capital outlay in starting the business.
    b) lowering the high initial fixed costs of starting a business.
    c) eliminating the need for a layout plan for the business.
    d) improving productivity and lowering material handling costs.

Answer d   Page 531

73. When considering building over buying or leasing, the small business owner:
    a) needs to weigh the facility's ability to attract sales and reduce operating costs against the high initial fixed investment.

b)   must remember that there is little savings in operating costs or utilities.

c)   should include the cost of building in the initial estimates of capital needs and the break-even point of the business.

d)   does not need to create a layout plan if he/she decides to build.

Answer c   Page 532

74.   The decision to buy a facility means that the small business owner:

a)   needs the same outline of facility requirements as he/she would if building.

b)   has greater mobility than leasing because it is easier to sell property than break a lease.

c)   will have a smaller initial capital outlay than leasing because the building will collaterize the construction loan, while a lease requires a large down payment.

d)   is limited in the amount and number of changes that can be made in the building.

Answer a   Page 532

75.   The major advantage of leasing is:

a)   unlimited ability to remodel.

b)   there is no large initial cash outlay required.

c)   more favorable consideration by lenders when seeking start-up capital.

d)   not needing a facility's requirement plan or a layout plan.

Answer b   Page 532

True or False Questions

76.   Site selection begins with considering what city in which to locate and then broadening the search to consider the region and state.

Answer F   Page 492

77.   The first phase in selecting a location is determining what regions of the country are experiencing substantial growth.

Answer T   Page 493

78.   Published annually, *The Survey of Buying Power* provides a detailed breakdown of population, retail sales, spendable income, etc., for various census regions, states, etc.

Answer T   Page 494

79.   *The Zip Code Atlas* and *Market Planner* provide detailed information on sales, spendable income, etc., by census region, county, and city.

Answer F   Page 494

80.   While GIS software allows a business owner to plot his/her existing customer base on a map, it does not provide zip code information.

Answer F   Page 495

81.   The U.S. Census Department's "TIGER" file is a computerized map of the entire United States that gives entrepreneurs the power to pinpoint existing and potential customers.

Answer T   Page 495

82.   The more specialized the firm, the greater the importance of proximity in the location decision.

Answer T   Page 495

83. When analyzing the labor supply, a small service business is only concerned with the level of education and training of the labor force in the area.
Answer F   Page 496

84. When selecting a city, a small business owner needs to ask questions about the wage rates, the business climate, and proximity to markets and raw materials, in order to properly analyze the city.
Answer F   Page 499

85. The trends or shifts in population components, such as population age, have more meaning for the small business owner than total population trends.
Answer T   Page 499

86. To calculate the IRS, a retailer needs to know the number of customers in the area, the retail expenditures for his/her product, and the total square feet of space allocated to selling his/her kind of product in the trading area.
Answer T   Page 500

87. For many businesses, especially manufacturers, cost is a primary force in choosing location.
Answer T   Page 501

88. Local laws, zoning regulations and building codes can affect the location to be chosen depending on the type of business and its particular requirements.
Answer T   Page 502

89. Criteria for a "good location" are universal and apply to all types of small businesses.
Answer F   Page 503

90. One element of the location decision common to all businesses is the need to locate where customers wish to do business.
Answer T   Page 504

91. The three factors that influence the size of the retail trading area are: type and price of products, type of the business, and the demographics of the area.
Answer F   Page 504

92. When doing a traffic count, the total number of shoppers passing by is the critical factor in evaluating the site.
Answer F   Page 505

93. Central business districts often lack convenient and safe parking.
Answer T   Page 508

94. When in doubt, shopping centers are always a wise location for a small business to choose.
Answer F   Page 509

95. The typical neighborhood shopping center contains from 3 to 12 stores, with a supermarket or drug store as its "anchor."
Answer T   Page 509

96. It is critical for all retail and service businesses to be located as far from competitors as possible.
Answer F   Page 510

97. Generally, it is not advisable for a small business to be "off the beaten path," but there are exceptions. Some do it and are still successful.
Answer T   Page 510

98. Home-based businesses represent nearly 50% of all newly created small businesses.
Answer F   Page 512

99. Zoning is a significant concern for the choice of location by manufacturers.
Answer T   Page 512

100. A foreign trade zone is a specially designed area that allows resident companies to import from foreign countries what they need to do their business and ship finished products out with minimal tariffs, etc.
Answer T   Page 513

101. An "incubator" is a facility with low rent that permits start-up small businesses to share resources.
Answer T   Page 514

102. The purpose for establishing incubators is enhancing economic development while grouping similar types of businesses into a consolidated economy.
Answer F   Page 514

103. Poorly planned layouts undermine employee productivity and create organizational chaos.
Answer T   Page 515

104. New businesses should only plan or buy the space for which they have immediate need, to conserve cash.
Answer F   Page 515

105. A store's external appearance plays an insignificant role in identifying its personality to customers.
Answer F   Page 516

106. The Americans with Disabilities Act requires all companies to make their facilities accessible to disabled customers and employees.
Answer F   Page 517

107. Any company with 15 or more employees and any buildings occupied after January 25, 1993 must comply with the Americans with Disabilities Act.
Answer T   Page 517

108. The key to determining what needs to be accessible is to determine what are the "primary function" areas of the business.
Answer T   Page 518

109. Buildings under three stories high or with less than 3,000 square feet per floor do not have to have elevators.
Answer T   Page 518

110. Signs are one of the most expensive and least effective ways available to small businesses for communicating with customers.
Answer F   Page 519

111. For a sign to be effective, its message must be complete and complex enough to be thought provoking.
Answer F   Page 519

112. The functional aspects of a building's interior are as important as exterior considerations.
Answer T   Page 519

113. Changes in office design have a direct impact on workers' job performance, job satisfaction, and ease of communication.
Answer T   Page 519–520

114. When evaluating an existing building's interior, the entrepreneur should pay particular attention to the building's structural components and the suitablity for his/her business.
Answer T   Page 520

115. Wall coverings are expensive but essential in almost any small business for employee job satisfaction and customer enjoyment.
Answer F   Page 520

116. Lighting is an inexpensive investment for improving employee performance and the overall appearance of the business.
Answer T   Page 520

117. Layout of any retail facility requires the owner's observation and understanding of customers' buying habits.
Answer T   Page 522

118. A grid layout is a formal layout that controls traffic flow through the store.
Answer T   Page 522

119. The boutique layout divides a store into a series of individual shopping areas, each with its own theme.
Answer F   Page 523

120. The primary advantage of a free-form layout is the relaxed, friendly shopping atmosphere it creates.
Answer T   Page 523

121. The free-form layout is the most efficient use of space; merchandise can be changed around freely.
Answer F   Page 523

122. Customers relate to displayed merchandise more easily than to merchandise on racks or shelves.
Answer T   Page 524

123. When planning the placement of impulse goods, it is important to remember that the average man's eye level is 62 inches off the ground and the average woman's is 57 inches.
Answer T   Page 525

124. The wise small retailer doesn't worry about separating selling and nonselling activities but focuses on the best placement of merchandises within the space available.
Answer F   Page 525

125. In small stores, every portion of the interior space is of equal value in generating sales.
Answer F   Page 525

126. The majority of a store's customers go more than halfway into the store.
Answer F   Page 526

127. The purpose of understanding the value of store space is to ensure proper placement of merchandise.
Answer T   Page 526

128. The farther away an area is from a store's entrance, the lower its value.
Answer T   Page 527

129. The most important issue in designing manufacturing is that of minimizing costs.
Answer F   Page 527

130. Mary Carol Garrity's success with her Nell Hill's antique and home decorating shop lies in its great location in a major city.
Answer F   Page 528

131. Product layouts have the advantage of maximum flexibility to do customer work and to enhance job satisfaction among employees.
Answer F   Page 529

132. The design of a product layout requires the fitting of equipment and work stations needed in the available facilities in the correct sequence.
Answer T   Page 529

133. Process layouts, unlike product layouts, require keeping the same operation in the same environment within the manufacturing facility.
Answer F   Page 530

134. Process layouts are used where the process flows in a straight line to enable high volume output.
Answer F   Page 530

135. The assembly of large products, such as ships or airplanes, is done most efficiently with a fixed position layout.

Answer T   Page 530

136. Generally speaking, there is one best layout for any manufacturer. The job of the small business owner is to do sufficient analysis of his/her product and processes to find it.
Answer F   Page 531

137. Lower operating costs can make new construction more economical in the long run than fixing up an existing facility.
Answer T   Page 532

138. One disadvantage of owning the building which houses a business is that the owner may feel tied to one location.
Answer T   Page 532

139. When leasing or buying an existing building, you must be very careful to see that the layout "as is" will suit your needs because modifications can't be made.
Answer F   Page 532

140. Buying a building has the advantage of ensuring a positive return on your investment since commercial real estate always appreciates in value.
Answer F   Page 532

141. Leasing is an attractive option to small businesses which are short on cash.
Answer T   Page 532

142. An entrepreneur can avoid lease nightmares by simply having an experienced attorney review the lease before signing it.
Answer T   Page 533

143. It is possible that as the leasee you will need insurance to cover any damage to the property not just to your inventory.
Answer T   Page 533

144. One disadvantage to leasing is that the building owner does not have to renew your lease when it expires.
Answer T   Page 534

145. Generally speaking most building owners welcome remodeling by the tenant because it will increase the value of the building and must remain once the tenant leaves.
Answer F   Page 534

Essay Questions

146. How does the entrepreneur choose the region of the country for his/her business?
Pages 492–495

147. Identify and explain the five criteria a small business owner should consider when selecting the state in which to operate his/her business.
Pages 495–498

148. What factors should the small business owner consider when selecting the city location for his/her small business? What is the index of retail saturation and how does it help a retailer in making this decision?

Pages 499–503

149. Joe wants to open a retail outlet. Discuss with him the factors he should consider in conducting a site selection analysis.

Pages 504–507

150. Outline the six areas from which the retailer and service business owner have to choose in locating their stores. What are the advantages and disadvantages of each?

Pages 508–512

151. What factors influence the choice of location for a manufacturer?

Pages 512–513

152. What is a business incubator? What can an incubator offer an entrepreneur just starting out?

Pages 514–515

153. List and briefly explain the fundamental considerations in evaluating a building.

Pages 515–522

154. What impact has the Americans with Disabilities Act had on small businesses in terms of building location and layout?

Pages 517–519

155. Discuss the functional aspects of a building's interior and lighting and their importance to the business.

Pages 519–522

156. What layout options are available to retailers? Explain why you would use each one and give an example of each.

Pages 522–527

157. Describe the basic types of layout available to manufacturers. Give the advantages and disadvantages of each and an example of each one.

Pages 527–531

158. Compare the advantages and disadvantages of building, buying, or leasing the facilities a new business may need.

Pages 531–532

Mini-Cases

Case 15-1: "It's a Great Location for a Bar"

Fred Stanford has just completed bartender's school in Los Angeles and is ready to build a life for himself. Sunday's paper has an ad in the business opportunities section for a bar in Mesa Verde, Colorado. Fred has heard that the West is a high growth area and the quality of life in Colorado is very good. Fred's best friend, Carl, begins to ask Fred some questions about his new idea. "To begin with, Fred, where is Mesa Verde, Colorado?"

Fred decides to call the telephone number in the ad and is put in touch with Ansel King, a business broker located in Pueblo, Colorado. When asked where in Colorado, Mesa Verde was, Ansel was prompt to point out that it was only 35 miles from Pueblo on the Interstate and has a population of nearly ten thousand. "Fred, this town is a great location for a bar, and I have just the kind of deal for a young man like you looking to get started."

Questions

1. What publications could Fred use to investigate whether or not this is a good region for his bar?
2. What city-related factors does Fred need to consider when evaluating if this community is a location for a bar?

Case 15-2: Customer Cars, Inc.

Al and Helen Wise have a love affair with cars. After collecting and restoring cars for a number of years, they decide to form their own "kit car" company. This type of company sells "kits" to people who want to build their own functioning replicate of a famous or collectable car. About 60% of their business is selling the kits, 10% is conducting classes and seminars on assembling the kits, and the remaining 40% is actually building the cars for the customers.

Their business has three distinct manufacturing issues. The production of the car kits, the assembly of the custom cars for owners who want them but don't have the time to do the work themselves, and the "assembling and selling" of the training seminars on how to put the cars together.

Questions

1. Explain what manufacturing layouts would be best for each of the three manufacturing issues they have.
2. Describe the advantages and disadvantages of each layout.

Case 15-3: Hungarian Heaven

Mike Pontya has operated a neighborhood restaurant in Cleveland for over 30 years. Mike is planning to move to Arizona because of his health, and has put the business up for sale. The restaurant, which caters to the local trade, is well known in the Hungarian community of Cleveland as having the best authentic Hungarian food in town, but it is not in a traditional restaurant district. The restaurant has parking for 10 cars. Most customers park on the street. In the past, this wasn't a problem as there was a great deal of walk-in business from the neighborhood. Now, however, a new four-lane highway passes by the front door of the restaurant. There is a stoplight on the corner the restaurant is on to improve access to the highway for drivers emerging from the neighborhood. The flight to the suburbs has taken a heavy toll on the neighborhood. However, the restaurant is still doing well financially.

Terry and Judy Kozma are brother and sister who share a love for cooking and a desire to be in the restaurant business. All of their relatives have encouraged them to quit their jobs and buy the restaurant. Terry and Judy were reared two blocks from the restaurant and both worked part-time for Mike Pontya while in college.

Questions

1. What site analysis criteria are relevant to Terry and Judy's evaluation the restaurant's location?
2.   What are the advantages and disadvantages of the restaurant's current location? Why?

Case 15-4: "We're Moving On Up"

Mike and Earl Moore, owners of College Men's Unlimited, have just signed a five-year lease in the new College Town Mall. The new mall is ideally located for their business—a short walk from campus and only two blocks from downtown. The far side of the mall is bounded by the most prestigious homes in the city. It will be opening in five weeks and Mike and Earl are lucky to have such a prime spot. Ray Thomas, their banker, called them last Wednesday with word that the store which had agreed to take the space they just leased had canceled. Eighteen months ago when the mall had put this location up for lease, they were not in financial condition to make a commitment. In the last 18 months, however, business has been exceptional. The city has grown and the college has experienced expanded enrollments. By next Monday morning, Mike and Earl must provide the mall developer with a complete layout for their new store so the developer can assign an emergency work crew to complete the store for the grand opening.

College Men's Unlimited is a full-line men's store offering middle- to upper-quality traditional men's wearing apparel. The present location is an old two-story house that Mike and Earl converted into their combination business and living area. The house has 4,000 square feet of area, 3,600 being used for the store, and the rest for a three-room apartment. The new store has a 40-foot front and is 70 feet deep. The mall developer is willing to put up walls for storage and office space wherever they wish.

Questions

1. Assuming that the new store space is 2,100 square feet (30'×70'), and that the shape is rectangular, draw a layout for the new men's store. What merchandise should be placed where? What size office space and storage is needed? Where should counters be placed?

2. What other considerations should be included in the layout?

Chapter 16 –
Purchasing, Quality Control and Vendor Analysis

Multiple Choice Questions

1. Purchasing is critical to the small business as it can amount for ___ to ___ of every $1.00 of sales revenue.
   a) $0.50; $0.75
   b) $0.25; $0.85
   c) $0.75; $0.90
   d) $0.65; $1.00

Answer b   Page 540

2. The primary objective of the purchasing function is to:
   a) acquire enough stock to ensure uninterrupted sales or production.
   b) ensure an adequate turnover of merchandise.
   c) determine the "best" possible price for both supplies and finished products.
   d) maximize carrying and set-up costs for the firm.

Answer a   Page 540

3. The small company's purchasing plan is closely linked to which of the other functional areas?
   a) Marketing and sales
   b) Finance and accounting
   c) Production and engineering
   d) All of the above

Answer d   Page 540

4. Managers have discovered that a quality approach to doing business:
   a) is much more expensive than a nonquality focus, but worth it.
   b) is easier to achieve than expected when TQM is implemented in an existing business.
   c) can lower employee turnover, increase market share, and decrease costs.
   d) works in manufacturing but is not applicable to the purchasing process.

Answer c   Page 541

5. A recent study of managers at mid-sized companies found that ___% had actually calculated the "cost of quality"—scrap, rework, inspections, etc.
   a) 83
   b) 31
   c) 47
   d) 13

Answer b   Page 541

6. Quality experts place the actual cost of bad quality at __% of sales.
   a) 5–10
   b) 10–15
   c) 20–30
   d) 30–40

Answer c   Page 541

7. Total Quality Management (TQM):
    a) defines world-class quality as 95% defect-free products and services.
    b) has been implemented by about 90% of all American manufacturers and is now moving into the service industry.
    c) relies on an army of quality inspectors to ensure that products and services meet quality targets.
    d) is a lifelong process of continuous improvement that focuses on doing the job right the first time.

Answer d   Page 542

8. As a solution to a company's quality problems, managers will find that TQM:
    a) may be implemented without significant training of employees.
    b) takes 3–4 years to bring about a significant change in quality.
    c) techniques can be implemented piecemeal, one-at-a-time.
    d) creates little turmoil or change in the way a company does most of its business.

Answer b   Page 542

9. Research on the implementation of TQM programs shows that it takes _____ to completely implement a TQM program.
    a) eight to ten years
    b) three to four years
    c) six months to two years
    d) one to three years

Answer a   Page 542

10. A small business owner needs to do which of the following well in order to successfully implement a TQM program?
    a) Focus on production and manufacturing.
    b) Set a "finishing line" for the quality effort.
    c) Move from a management-driven to team-driven company culture.
    d) Modify the rewards program to reward individual effort and innovation.

Answer c   Page 543

11. Successful Total Quality Management (TQM) requires:
    a) training employees in the use of the tools of statistical quality control.
    b) directive management, providing clear quality direction.
    c) thorough and complete quality inspections.
    d) holding middle management responsible for the results.

Answer a   Page 543

12. Quality improvement efforts must ultimately focus on:
    a) the product.
    b) the customer.
    c) the manufacturing process.
    d) the purchasing process.

Answer b   Page 544

13. TQM:
   a) instills the philosophy of 100% inspection of all products.
   b) provides a "finish line" for the race for quality.
   c) avoids placing blame and focuses on fixing mistakes.
   d) makes middle managers responsible for product quality.

Answer c   Page 544

14. Critical to TQM is:
   a) management competence.
   b) understanding the product.
   c) continual improvement.
   d) knowing your competition.

Answer b   Page 545

15. Deming's 14 Points include:
   a) awarding business to suppliers on the basis of the best price.
   b) correcting defects at the end of the production process.
   c) establishing production quotas.
   d) adopting a total quality philosophy.

Answer d   Page 545

16. The implementation of TQM can not succeed unless:
   a) the company is willing to undergo immediate radical transformation of all of its processes.
   b) the company has extensive market research on its markets, competitors, and customers.
   c) it is fully supported by upper management and has the involvement of the CEO.
   d) the lowest level of employees are willing to implement the program.from the very beginning.

Answer c   Page 545

17. Companies are seeking ISO 9000 certification because:
   a) it complements their TQM efforts.
   b) studies show following ISO 9000 standards increases profitability.
   c) it is the next generation, the next step in quality improvement beyond TQM.
   d) their business customers are pressuring them to become certified.

Answer d   Page 545

18. The average cost of ISO 9000 certification for the small business of under $11 million in sales is:
   a) $71,000.
   b) $110,000.
   c) $47,000.
   d) $138,000.

Answer a   Page 546

19. A danger of an excessive investment in inventory for the small business is:
   a) excessive inventory taxes by local and state government.
   b) minimizing reordering costs.
   c) creating too quick a turnover of inventory.
   d) tying up an excessive amount of the firm's capital.

Answer d   Page 547

20. Which of the following represents the cost of the units in the basic EOQ model?
    a) $Q/2 \times H$
    b) $D \times C$
    c) $D/Q \times S$
    d) $(L \times U) + S$
Answer b   Page 547

21. Holding or carrying costs include the costs of:
    a) ordering materials and inventory.
    b) receiving and inspecting items and all administrative costs.
    c) insurance, taxes, depreciation, etc.
    d) processing a purchase order.
Answer c   Page 548

22. The formula for calculating the cost of carrying inventory is:
    a) $Q/2 \times H$
    b) $D \times C$
    c) $D/Q \times S$
    d) $Q/H \times S$
Answer a   Page 548

23. _____ is one of the elements of the total inventory costs.
    a) Demand
    b) Set-up costs
    c) Standing costs
    d) Safety stock
Answer b   Page 549

24. Set-up or ordering cost is found by:
    a) multiplying the average inventory times the set-up costs per unit.
    b) multiplying annual demand times set-up costs for a single run.
    c) dividing annual demand by the quantity of the inventory ordered, times set-up costs for a single run.
    d) dividing the quantity of inventory ordered by holding costs, times set-up costs for a single run.
Answer c   Page 549

Use the following information to answer questions 25 through 27:
Albemarle Sprinkler Company purchases the sprinkler heads for its line of lawn sprinklers from a supplier. Albemarle's production manager wonders how many sprinkler heads she should order for the next six months. The company's marketing manager forecasts sales to be 29,400 units for the upcoming six months. The purchasing manager has negotiated a price of $6.47 per head. The production manager estimates that it costs $17.25 to place an order with the supplier and $2.97 to store a sprinkler head in inventory for six months.

25. What is Albemarle's Economic Order Quantity (EOQ) for the upcoming six months?
    a) 292 heads
    b) 358 heads
    c) 396 heads
    d) 584 heads

Answer d   Page 550

26. Approximately how many orders will Albemarle place over the next six months if it uses the EOQ point?
    a) 28
    b) 50
    c) 74
    d) 82

Answer b   Page 551

27. What is Albemarle's total inventory cost using the EOQ point?
    a) $191,954
    b) $192,388
    c) $192,166
    d) $192,087

Answer a   Page 552

28. The Economic Order Quantity assumes:
    a) a 30-day cycle in filling orders.
    b) orders are filled instantaneously.
    c) usage will impact delivery time.
    d) none of these things.

Answer b   Page 553

29. When shopping for a vendor, a small business owner should seek:
    a) the best transfer of risk possible.
    b) the lowest price.
    c) the best price at acceptable quality.
    d) to change vendors often in order to get the lowest price.

Answer c   Page 554

30. A key element to Deming's 14 Points is:
    a) ordering on the basis of price.
    b) changing suppliers frequently.
    c) conducting frequent quality inspections.
    d) developing long-term relationships with venders.

Answer d   Page 554

31. Trade discounts are offered on the basis of the:
    a) size of the order.
    b) position of the business in the distribution channel.
    c) time of payment.
    d) type of payment.

Answer b   Page 556

32. ____ discounts are normally set up on a graduated scale and are based on a firm's position in the channel of distribution and on the functions it performs in that channel.
    a) Trade
    b) Quantity
    c) Cash

    d) Cumulative
Answer a   Page 556

33. The table below is an example of a _____ discount.

Order Size	Price
1–1,000 units	List Price
1,001–5,000 units	List Price–3%
5,001–10,000 units	List Price–6%
10,001 & over	List Price–10%

    a) trade
    b) quantity
    c) cash
    d) cumulative
Answer b   Page 557

34. _____ discounts give customers an incentive to pay for merchandise promptly.
    a) Trade
    b) Quantity
    c) Cash
    d) Cumulative
Answer c   Page 557

35. Small business people need to remember that:
    a) there is an implicit cost of forgoing a cash discount.
    b) they should avoid cash discounts.
    c) by forgoing cash discounts they have more money for daily expenses.
    d) cash discounts have hidden annual interest rates.
Answer a   Page 557

36. If a supplier offers 3/10, net 30 terms on a $500 invoice and the small business owner forgoes the discount, she is paying an effective interest rate of:
    a) 3.8%.
    b) 22.27%.
    c) 36.18%.
    d) 55.67%.
Answer d   Page 558

37. You have received a $2,000 invoice from the Acme Swampwater Company for raw materials to use in your beer manufacturing plant. The terms are 3/10, net 60. If you fail to take advantage of this discount, you are paying what interest rate?
    a) 22.27%
    b) 36.735%
    c) 37.11%
    d) 55.67%
Answer a   Page 558

38. The reorder point model requires that the small business owner know:
    a) the usage rate, the minimum level of stock, the lead time, and the EOQ.
    b) who the supplier is, statistical process controls, and TQM.

c) the demand pattern for the product, reliability and proximity of the supplier, and who has title.

d) holding costs for the product, the usage rate, and the three "Cs" of the product.

Answer a   Page 559

39. The small business owner needs to know _____ in order to avoid stockouts and calculate safety stock.

a) the EOQ

b) the minimum level of stock allowable

c) the lead time

d) the usage rate

Answer b   Page 559

40. A firm's reorder point for an item takes into consideration its _____, which is the difference between the time an order is placed and the time it is actually received.

a) minimum level of stock allowable

b) EOQ

c) usage rate

d) lead time

Answer d   Page 559

41. Many small businesses build a/an _____, or cushion, into their inventories in case demand runs ahead of the anticipated usage rate.

a) lead time

b) EOQ

c) safety stock

d) stockout point

Answer c   Page 559

42. The formula for calculating the reorder point of a product is:

a) $Q/2 \times H$.

b) $D \times C$.

c) $D/Q \times S$.

d) $(L \times U) + S$.

Answer d   Page 560

43. The basic reorder point model assumes that:

a) the firm's inventory usage rate is constant.

b) the lead time varies.

c) safety stock is set at 5%.

d) the demand pattern is constant.

Answer a   Page 560

44. A company whose reorder point model includes a 95% desired service level will experience stockouts ____% of the time.

a) 1

b) 5

c) 50

d) 95

Answer b   Page 561

45. The consequences for the small business owner of a vendor certification program include:
    a) guaranteed quality and price for selected items.
    b) that the vendor will not supply components to competitors.
    c) using one supplier for the majority of their inventory needs.
    d) less government scrutiny and regulation of their business.

Answer c   Page 564

46. The creation of a vender certification program requires:
    a) a vendor rating scale developed by the company.
    b) a firm price list from the vendor, good for three years.
    c) membership in the SBA vendor certification program.
    d) understanding the firm's EOQ.

Answer a   Page 564

47. Softubs problem with faulty jet assemblies and other components was solved by:
    a) developing a list of several vendors and changing whenever a problem occurred with one of the vendors.
    b) the implementation of an ISO 9000 certification process.
    c) the utilization of self-managed work teams as part of a TQM effort at their plant.
    d) using a cross-functional team with a criteria checklist to evaluate vendors before ordering from them.

Answer d   Page 565

48. The first step in developing a vendor certification process is to:
    a) develop a grading scale for vendors.
    b) identify the most important criteria.
    c) create a list of vendors to be evaluated.
    d) weight the criteria used to evaluate the vendors.

Answer b   Page 565

49. The vendor certification process assumes:
    a) all vendors are charging the same prices.
    b) the use of a cross-functional team to conduct the evaluation.
    c) the business owner has detailed knowledge of the vendors.
    d) vendors are publicly owned so information can be gathered on each of them.

Answer c   Page 566

50. When seeking suppliers, a small business owner use which of the following sources?
    a) Competitors
    b) The local telephone directory
    c) The industry trade association
    d) All of these

Answer d   Page 567

51. If a small business owner wanted an international vendor, he/she could use:
    a) *MacRae's Blue Book.*
    b) *Kelly's Manufacturer and Merchant's Directory.*
    c) *Thomas Register.*
    d) *Sources of State Information and State Industrial Directories.*

Answer b   Page 568

52. The advantages resulting from concentrating purchases with a single supplier include:
    a) protection from fraudulent vendors and excess inventory.
    b) a longer lead time.
    c) lower usage rates.
    d) the ability to negotiate the best price package.
Answer d   Page 568

53. ____ is the right to ownership of property and, for a small business owner, determines who has responsibility for ownership.
    a) Identification
    b) Risk of loss
    c) Concept of title
    d) F.O.B.
Answer c   Page 570

54. The first rule governing transfer of title and risk of loss states that:
    a) title transfers to the buyer as soon as the goods are delivered.
    b) the buyer has both title and risk of loss as soon as the goods are paid for, regardless of their physical location.
    c) the supplier and small business may agree to a shift of the risk of loss at any time during the transaction between them.
    d) title transfers to the buyer as soon as the goods are in the hands of the carrier.
Answer c   Page 571

55. Newton orders 14 electric staplers for his office supply store from Home Office Suppliers. The contract specifies shipping terms as "F.O.B. Home Office Suppliers." Home Office Suppliers delivers the goods to Zippy Shippers and invoices Newton. The electric staplers never arrive, and Newton refuses to pay Home Office Suppliers. Home Office Suppliers sues Newton for the contract price of the staplers. Who wins?
    a) Newton, because it wasn't his fault that the staplers never arrived.
    b) Home Office Suppliers, because they were the last ones to touch the goods.
    c) Newton, because in an F.O.B. contract, the risk of loss does not shift to the buyer until the goods are actually delivered to the buyer.
    d) Home Office Suppliers, because in an F.O.B. seller contract, risk of loss shifts to the buyer when the seller delivers the goods to the carrier.
Answer d   Page 571

56. Buyer owns a retail shop in Baltimore. Seller is a manufacturer in San Diego. Buyer orders from seller to be shipped "F.O.B. San Diego." Risk of loss passes to the buyer when:
    a) the seller delivers the goods to the carrier.
    b) the goods are identified to the contract.
    c) the contract is made.
    d) the goods are delivered to the buyer's retail shop.
Answer a   Page 571

57. "F.O.B. seller" means that:
    a) title passes to the buyer when the seller delivers the goods to the buyer.

b) risk of loss transfers to the buyer when the seller delivers the goods to the carrier.

c) the seller pays all shipping and transportation costs.

d) the buyer has both title and risk of loss as soon as the goods are paid for, regardless of their physical location.

Answer b   Page 571

58. "F.O.B. buyer" means that:
  a) title passes to the buyer when the seller delivers the goods to the shipper.
  b) risk of loss passes to the buyer when the seller delivers the goods to the buyer's place of business.
  c) the buyer pays all shipping and transportation costs.
  d) both title and risk of loss pass to the buyer immediately upon payment of the contract regardless of location of the goods.

Answer b   Page 571

59. The responsibility for verifying the identity and condition of merchandise:
  a) is the seller's.
  b) is the carrier's.
  c) depends on the nature of the contract between buyer and seller.
  d) is the buyer's.

Answer d   Page 572

60. The small business gains what advantage by selling on consignment?
  a) Shorter lead time when reordering than with standard contracts
  b) Better customer service
  c) Not bearing the risk of loss for the consigned goods
  d) Receiving absolute title to the goods prior to paying for them

Answer c   Page 572

True or False Questions

61. Most entrepreneurs can neglect the purchasing function because they buy so little from vendors they don't gain anything by spending time working on improving it.

Answer F   Page 539

62. Savings of 5% in the purchasing bill can add 3% to the net profit.

Answer T   Page 540

63. The purchasing plan should identify a company's quality requirements, its cost targets, and the criteria for determining the supplier.

Answer T   Page 540

64. The purchasing plan is developed independently from other functional areas of a business.

Answer F   Page 540

65. The quality message is getting out, 85% of managers in mid-sized companies calculate the cost of quality for their business.

Answer F   Page 541

66. Most executives estimate the cost of bad quality to be just 5% or less of sales but others estimate it is really 20–30% of sales.
Answer T   Page 541

67. Total Quality Management (TQM) defines world-class quality at a 99.1% level of quality.
Answer F   Page 542

68. The implementation of TQM is relatively simple in that other than training managers and employees little else needs to be changed in the company.
Answer F   Page 543

69. Statistical process control is central to the success of Total Quality Management efforts.
Answer T   Page 543

70. Implementing TQM means a radical change in the management of information in that much more information must be shared with workers.
Answer T   Page 544

71. Another process central to the successful implementation of TQM is identifying the individual(s) responsible for any mistakes as part of fixing the immediate quality problems.
Answer F   Page 544

72. Successful Total Quality Management (TQM) requires leadership from the top.
Answer T   Page 545

73. ISO 9000 certification simply verifies that a company has established a quality control process and follows it; it does not certify the quality of the company's products.
Answer T   Page 546

74. When implementing TQM, managers should remember that change and turmoil are essential elements of the implementation.
Answer T   Page 547

75. The inventory investment is usually the largest single investment for a small firm.
Answer T   Page 547

76. It is better to maintain too little rather than too much inventory because there are significant storage costs for excess inventory, but few if any costs associated with understocking inventory.
Answer F   Page 547

77. The cost of units is simply the typical costs involved in having units in storage.
Answer F   Page 547

78. Although there are many costs associated with carrying large levels of inventory, the opportunity costs of large inventories are virtually nonexistent.
Answer F   Page 548

79. Depreciation costs of holding inventory represent the reduced value of inventory over time.
Answer T   Page 548

80. Spoilage, obsolescence, and pilferage are all part of the set-up costs of inventory.
Answer F   Page 548

81. When thinking about inventory holding costs, remember that the greater the quantity ordered, the greater the inventory carrying costs.
Answer T   Page 549

82. Set-up costs are the expenses incurred in the actual ordering of materials and inventory, or in setting up the manufacturing line.
Answer T   Page 549

83. In the basic EOQ model, the higher the economic order quantity, the greater the number of orders placed.
Answer F   Page 550

84. The EOQ solution balances the ordering costs and the carrying costs of an inventory item so that total costs are minimized.
Answer T   Page 551

85. The best way to minimize carrying costs is to order as many units as possible in each order.
Answer F   Page 551

86. To minimize ordering costs, the small business should place as few and as large orders as possible.
Answer T   Page 551

87. The advantage of the EOQ with usage calculation is that it takes into consideration that the inventory order does not arrive at the same time.
Answer T   Page 553

88. The best purchase price is the lowest price at which one can obtain goods and services.
Answer F   Page 554

89. The problem with the shoes thrown into the container from China was one of miscalculating the correct EOQ with usage point.
Answer F   Page 555

90. As the shoe shipment from China shows, sometimes understanding of the language used is as important as all the quantitative methods used when shipping the product.
Answer T   Page 555

91. Selling terms are as important to the small business as the actual price of the goods and services being purchased.
Answer T   Page 556

92. Trade discounts are offered within the distribution channel and are on a graduated scale.
Answer T   Page 556

93. A noncumulative quantity discount grants a discount if a large enough volume of merchandise is purchased in a single order.
Answer T   Page 556

94. Cumulative quantity discounts are provided to members of the distribution channel in recognition of the services they provide the manufacturer.
Answer F   Page 556

95. Cash discounts are offered to customers as an incentive to pay for merchandise promptly.
Answer T   Page 557

96. "3/10, EOM" means a 3% discount can be taken if the bill is paid by the tenth day of the month after the purchase.
Answer T   Page 557

97. Generally, business owners should not be lured into taking cash discounts vendors offer; that cash could be put to better use elsewhere.
Answer F   Page 557

98. As it is a good idea to take advantage of discounts from vendors, small business owners ought to stretch accounts payable to at least the first notice of past due.
Answer F   Page 558

99. If a vendor offers a firm 2/10, net 30, and the firm doesn't take it, the firm is paying an interest rate of over 36% on an annual basis.
Answer T   Page 558

100. The time gap between placing an order and receiving is called lead time.
Answer T   Page 559

101. The cushion owners build into their inventory to prevent stockouts is called demand stock.
Answer F   Page 559

102. The simple reorder technique assumes that the rate of usage is constant and that lead time is constant.
Answer T   Page 560

103. Because of its assumptions, the simplest reorder model is no longer valid or useful to the small business owner in today's dynamic business environment.
Answer F   Page 560

104. The formula for calculating safety stock is: safety stock = $SLF \times SD_L$.
Answer T   Page 561

105. The appropriate service level factor in the safety stock calculation is called the Z score.
Answer T   Page 562

106. The vendor certification program is an effort by the SBA to protect small businesses from unscrupulous vendors.
Answer F   Page 564

107. The purpose of a vendor certification program is to create a list of acceptable vendors that the small business owner can spread his/her orders among to avoid stocking out due to delays in shipments.

Answer F   Page 564

108. A small business owner seeking suppliers can find lists of products and services, along with the names, addresses, telephone numbers, and ratings of manufacturers, in either *Thomas Register of American Manufacturers* or *MacRae's Blue Book*.
Answer T   Page 567

109. The small business owner should concentrate purchases at a single supplier.
Answer T   Page 568

110. Industrial Supply began to explore making its inventory ordering process more efficient when the owner's son, Miles, showed him how to calculate the EOQ and reorder points for several items.
Answer F   Page 569

111. "Identification" is the designation of goods as the subject matter of the sales contract.
Answer T   Page 570

112. Risk of loss always passes with title to the goods.
Answer F   Page 570

113. Under the Uniform Commercial Code, the party who has title to goods also has the risk of loss if those goods are lost, damaged, or destroyed.
Answer F   Page 570

114. Seller and buyer can agree to the terms under which title and risk of loss shift in a business transaction.
Answer T   Page 571

115. In an "F.O.B. seller" (shipment) contract, both title and risk of loss transfer to the buyer when the seller delivers the goods to the carrier or shipper.
Answer T   Page 571

116. A sales contract designated F.O.B. buyer requires the seller to deliver the goods to the buyer's place of business (or some other designated location), and risk of loss does not pass to the buyer until the goods are so delivered.
Answer T   Page 571

117. A buyer gets an insurable interest in goods once they are identified as the goods pertaining to the contract.
Answer T   Page 572

118. Both a buyer and a seller cannot have an insurable interest in the same goods.
Answer F   Page 572

119. A consignment contract means that the supplier (i.e., the consignor) retains title and risk of loss for the consigned merchandise.
Answer T   Page 572

120. Selling through a consignment contract allows the small business owner to delay payment to the consignor until an item is sold.
Answer T   Page 572

Essay Questions

121. Discuss the purchasing plan, briefly describing each of the five key elements of the plan.
Pages 540–541

122. Explain the philosophy of Total Quality Management, naming the ten things a small business owner should do to successfully implement a TQM program.
Pages 542–544

123. Outline Deming's 14 Points.
Page 545

124. Discuss the concept of the economic order quantity. What is its value to the small business owner and what are the three principal elements needed to calculate it? Offer an example calculation.
Pages 547–552

125. How does the EOQ with usage differ from the standard EOQ? Why is this difference important to the small business owner?
Pages 553–554

126. What should the role of price be as an element of the purchasing process?
Pages 554–556

127. Identify and briefly describe the types of discounts a small business might receive from a manufacturer.
Pages 556–558

128. What does the small business owner give up if he/she doesn't take advantage of a vendor's discount? Demonstrate by calculating the interest rate on a $12,000 invoice that is 3/10 net 30.
Pages 557–558 and Table 16.7

129. Timing is a critical element of the purchasing process. Explain the various elements of the timing of purchases: usage rate, stockouts, safety stock, reorder points, and demand patterns.
Pages 559–564

130. Compute the reorder point for a small business owner using the following data.
   - Lead time   =   7 days
   - Usage rate   =   28 units/day
   - Safety stock   =   56 units
   - EOQ   =   740 units
Page 560

131. What is a vendor certification program and why would a small business owner use it?
Pages 564–566

132. Discuss finding a vendor, including both sources of information and the primary criteria for selecting a vendor.
Pages 567–570

133. It is important to understand transfer of title and the risk of loss when discussing purchasing. Discuss the three concepts that explain the concept of title, including the rules that affect the passage of title and risk.
Pages 570–573

Mini-Cases

Case 16-1: Victoria Valves

Victoria Valves, located near the Gulf of Mexico in Southern Texas, manufactures specialty valves for many small wildcatters and the major companies engaged in oil exploration. Victoria Valves purchases several component parts from suppliers to use in the manufacture of its valves. One part in particular, a pressure-sensitive locking device, has caused the manufacturer all sorts of problems. Says one manager, "Sometimes I go back into the storage area and the place is overflowing with locking devices. Other times our production process is delayed because we've run out of them."

Management has decided to use EOQ analysis to try to control the purchase of this locking device. Sales forecasts show that Victoria Valves will require 60,000 of the locking devices in the upcoming year. Each unit costs $3.40. Managers estimate that it costs $3.12 to hold one unit in inventory for one year and that it costs $2.25 to place an order.

Questions

1. What is the Economic Order Quantity for the locking devices?

2. How many orders will Victoria Valves have to place in the next quarter?

3. What is the total cost of ordering that many units?

Case 16-2: Art's Cash

Art's Pro Shop has just received an invoice for $1,180 for the purchase of golfing supplies and equipment. The credit terms are 3/10, net 40. Art consults his checkbook and his cash budget and sees that he will not have enough cash to take advantage of the cash discount, but Art does have a line of credit with the First State Bank. Art wonders if he should borrow to take advantage of the cash discount.

Questions

1. If Art fails to take advantage of the cash discount, what effective interest rate would he be paying?

2. Would you recommend that Art take advantage of the cash discount? Under what circumstances?

Chapter 17 –
Managing Inventory

Multiple Choice Questions

1. For most retailers and wholesalers, the investment in _____ is the largest capital outlay next to payroll.
    a) office equipment, computers, etc.
    b) vehicles, automobiles and trucks
    c) inventory
    d) taxes and licensing fees
    Answer c   Page 576

2. Effective management of inventory begins with:
    a) developing an accurate sales forecast.
    b) setting realistic inventory turnover objectives.
    c) determining what level of safety stock to maintain.
    d) establishing purchasing procedures.
    Answer a   Page 577

3. A firm can increase its profitability _____ by careful management of inventory.
    a) 10–15%
    b) 20–50%
    c) 100%
    d) 60–75%
    Answer b   Page 577

4. The 80/20 rule suggests that business owners:
    a) try to exercise control 80% of the time over 20% of their inventory.
    b) identify those inventory items that represent the greatest value to the business and focus inventory control efforts on them.
    c) focus on the 80% of their inventory that only produces 20% of their results in order to improve performance.
    d) try to earn 20% more out of the 80% of their inventory that isn't producing.
    Answer b   Page 578

5. If a small business carries 10,000 items in stock, approximately ____ of them will account for about 80% of the company's sales volume.
    a) 2,000
    b) 4,000
    c) 8,000
    d) 16,000
    Answer a   Page 577

6. _____ inventory systems are designed to maintain a running count of the items in inventory.
    a) Partial
    b) Physical
    c) Perpetual
    d) ABC

Answer c   Page 578

7. Which of the following would most likely use a perpetual inventory system?
    a) A hardware store
    b) A department store
    c) A landscaping/greenhouse operation
    d) A retailer of large appliances

Answer d   Page 578

8. Perpetual inventory systems:
    a) are relatively inexpensive to use and therefore quite popular among discount retailers.
    b) are not particularly effective for keeping accurate track of large, expensive items.
    c) require consistent use of the inventory sheets in order to provide accurate results.
    d) are the simplest and quickest to use of all inventory systems.

Answer c   Page 578

9. The computerization of cash registers has:
    a) completely eliminated the need for perpetual inventory systems.
    b) overcome many of the disadvantages of perpetual inventory systems.
    c) eliminated the need for physical inventories.
    d) overcome the disadvantages of ABC inventory systems but is too expensive for most small businesses.

Answer b   Page 578

10. Which of the following functions will the typical point-of-sale system perform?
    a) Computing the annual dollar usage value of every item in the inventory
    b) Allowing the owner to check on the inventory level of any item listed in the database
    c) Reconciling actual inventory levels with inventory levels reported by the system
    d) Calculating the EOQ on any item in inventory

Answer b   Page 579

11. Combining _____ with a POS system gives a small business owner a state-of-the-art checkout system and further extends the abilities of the POS system in the information it provides the owner.
    a) TQM
    b) an EDI system
    c) universal product code labels and scanners
    d) an ABC system

Answer c   Page 579

12. A common perpetual inventory control system that provides both the customer and the business owner with a record of the purchase is a:
    a) sales stub method.
    b) floor sample method.
    c) sales ticket method.
    d) punched card method.

Answer a   Page 579

13. The _____ method of inventory control is commonly used by businesses selling "big ticket items" with high cost.
   a) ABC
   b) floor sample
   c) visual
   d) punch card
Answer b   Page 579

14. The _____ inventory control system, used with large expensive items, keeps a pad of numbered pages on a sample in the store. Each time an item is sold, a numbered page corresponding to the sold item is removed and the sale is logged into inventory.
   a) floor sample
   b) two-bin system
   c) partial
   d) visual
Answer a   Page 580

15. The most common method of controlling inventory in a small business is the ____ system.
   a) floor sample
   b) two-bin system
   c) partial
   d) visual
Answer d   Page 581

16. The _____ method of inventory control is the least effective for ensuring accuracy and reliability and often leads to stockouts.
   a) perpetual
   b) ABC
   c) partial
   d) visual
Answer d   Page 581

17. The _____ inventory control system relies on the validity of the 80/20 rule.
   a) partial
   b) perpetual
   c) visual
   d) ABC
Answer a   Page 581

18. The purpose of ABC inventory analysis is:
   a) to help retail stores control their inventories to prevent shoplifting and employee theft.
   b) to save time by only inventorying those items that produce the majority of a firm's sales.
   c) to focus inventory control efforts on items that account for the majority of sales.
   d) a system to facilitate the computerization of a firm's perpetual inventory system.
Answer c   Page 581

19. In an ABC system of inventory control, _____ is/are the measure of the relative importance of an item in the company's inventory.
    a) dollar usage value
    b) carrying costs
    c) set-up costs
    d) optimum inventory level

Answer a   Page 581–582

20. In ABC analysis, the dollar usage value of an item is determined by:
    a) its price per unit times its shrinkage rate.
    b) a statistical application of the 80/20 rule.
    c) POS systems.
    d) its cost per unit and its sales volume.

Answer d   Page 582

21. Items classified as "A" in ABC analysis should be controlled by a/an _____ inventory system.
    a) periodic
    b) perpetual
    c) visual
    d) ABC

Answer b   Page 583

22. A _____ inventory control system is best suited for controlling merchandise classified as "B" items.
    a) partial
    b) perpetual
    c) visual
    d) periodic

Answer d   Page 583

23. The ABC inventory control system causes managers to:
    a) not keep a large safety stock on "A" items because it ties up too much cash.
    b) keep a large safety stock on "C" items because they generate the greatest revenue.
    c) keep a large safety stock on "A" items.
    d) keep small levels of safety stock for "C" items because they are of relatively little value.

Answer a   Page 583

24. "C" items, in an ABC analysis:
    a) are those items that account for a moderate dollar usage volume.
    b) are those that are low-cost and high-volume by nature.
    c) do not require detailed recordkeeping or inventory control.
    d) should be tracked with analytical tools and frequent counts.

Answer c   Page 583

25. By their very nature, "C" items give a firm the opportunity to:
    a) keep little safety stock.
    b) use minimal inventory control procedures.
    c) justify the latest POS or product bar coding systems.
    d) use basic analytical tools like EOQ and reorder point analysis.

Answer b   Page 583

26. The two-bin system and the tag system of inventory control are best suited for items classified as ___ in ABC analysis.
    a) "A" items
    b) perishable items
    c) "C" items
    d) "B" items

Answer c   Page 583

27. An alternative to a two-bin system, wherever space or the type of item doesn't fit the system, would be a:
    a) tag system.
    b) punch card system.
    c) physical inventory system.
    d) POS system.

Answer a   Page 584

28. A physical inventory count should be taken at least:
    a) once a week.
    b) once a year.
    c) every six months.
    d) daily.

Answer b   Page 585

29. A periodic physical inventory count:
    a) is not necessary if the business owner uses a perpetual inventory control system or has a computerized point of sale (POS) terminal.
    b) typically involves one employee and is done weekly.
    c) allows the owner to evaluate the effectiveness and the accuracy of his/her inventory control system.
    d) is not necessary if the business owner uses an ABC inventory system.

Answer c   Page 585

30. Armand Schaubroeck's House of Guitars is successful partially because of:
    a) the close management of a lean inventory.
    b) the ability to find whatever the customer wants through an electronic database.
    c) the extensive use of POS terminals and information databases.
    d) its large inventory and great memory of the owner.

Answer d   Page 586

31. Which of the following is a part of the "Just-In-Time" inventory control philosophy?
    a) Job tasks should be highly specialized.
    b) Machinery must produce a large number of items to justify long set-up times and high costs.
    c) The lower the level of inventory a manufacturer maintains, the more efficient is the production system.
    d) Long production runs of standard items are ideal.

Answer c   Page 587

32. According to your authors:
    a) JIT involves the consolidation of manufacturing processes.
    b) almost any change leading to more efficient inventory use can be considered a part of JIT.
    c) only large companies with long manufacturing runs can benefit from the implementation of JIT.
    d) manufacturing runs need to be large to justify set-up costs in a JIT environment.

Answer b   Page 587

33. "Just-In-Time" inventory control techniques are most successful in what type of environment?
    a) Repetitive manufacturing operations where inventory levels are significant at the outset
    b) Where product requirements are customized for each customer
    c) Where a company changes suppliers regularly and those suppliers are independent of the manufacturer
    d) Where inventory levels have been reduced to safety stock levels

Answer a   Page 588

34. Companies experience a number of benefits from JIT including:
    a) better customer acceptance of their products and services.
    b) increased job satisfaction among employees.
    c) a reduction of inventory and handling costs.
    d) longer equipment life and lower maintenance costs.

Answer c   Page 588

35. JIT systems need two significant human elements to be successful: mutual trust and teamwork, and:
    a) an individual incentive/rewards program.
    b) staff training.
    c) a benefits program.
    d) empowerment.

Answer d   Page 588

36. A form of inventory management used in manufacturing that stresses a harmonious relationship with suppliers is:
    a) kaban.
    b) TQM.
    c) efficient consumer response.
    d) JIT II.

Answer d   Page 589

37. JIT II differs from other production improvement methods in that:
    a) it requires the close cooperation of companies and their suppliers.
    b) it uses teams.
    c) it empowers through extensive training of employees.
    d) it makes heavy use of computer technology.

Answer a   Page 589

38. A retail version of Just-In-Time inventory control is called:
    a) kaban.
    b) TQM.
    c) efficient consumer response.
    d) JIT II.
Answer c   Page 589

39. A firm's ____ expresses the number of times per year the business sells all of its inventory.
    a) liquidity ratio
    b) inventory turnover ratio
    c) operating ratio
    d) quick ratio
Answer b   Page 590

40. Typically, the small business owner's response to slow-moving inventory is to:
    a) hold a one-day sale.
    b) mark it down to move it out and put the cash generated into fresh inventory.
    c) set up bargain tables or place it in a middle-of-the-aisle display.
    d) postpone marking it down until its too late.
Answer d   Page 590

41. The most common method of liquidating slow-moving merchandise is:
    a) a markdown.
    b) the one-day only sale.
    c) quantity discounts for volume purchases.
    d) an advertising blitz.
Answer a   Page 590

42. When it comes to losses due to crime, companies lose nearly:
    a) $1 billion annually.
    b) $100 billion annually.
    c) $250 million annually.
    d) $400 billion annually.
Answer d   Page 591

43. Retail theft in America occurs every ___ and costs the average American household _____ a year in increased prices.
    a) 10 minutes, $1,000
    b) 5 seconds, $200
    c) 3 minutes, $350
    d) 25 seconds, $1,500
Answer b   Page 591

44. A Justice Department study shows that ___ of employees are hard-core pilferers.
    a) 5%
    b) 10%
    c) 30%
    d) 50%
Answer c   Page 591

45. Most employee theft:
    a) involves values in excess of $1,000.
    b) is expensive merchandise.
    c) is small amounts of cash.
    d) is the equivalent of nickel and dime items.
Answer d   Page 591

46. Harvey's Hardware makes use of what type of inventory strategy to succeed as a retail business?
    a) having a wild mass of excess inventory
    b) efficient customer response
    c) JIT II
    d) a computerized database linked to hundreds of suppliers
Answer a   Page 592

47. Harvery's Hardware is a success because of his inventory strategy and:
    a) his low prices.
    b) his location.
    c) customer service.
    d) computer automation.
Answer c   Page 592

48. The median loss due to fraud for small businesses was:
    a) larger than for large companies.
    b) $120,000.
    c) very small due to the close working relationships in the company.
    d) $13,000.
Answer b   Page 593

49. In 90% of the cases of significant employee theft:
    a) the employee would be described as trustworthy.
    b) the owner was suspicious of the thief prior to the theft.
    c) the employee would have a record of absenteeism and poor work habits.
    d) the owner would have disciplined the employee within the last 48 hours.
Answer a   Page 594

50. A number of organizational factors encourage employee theft including:
    a) being permitted to manage their own work and time schedules.
    b) working with one-of-a-kind items the employee could never afford to buy.
    c) having too elaborate of financial and inventory controls in place.
    d) a low probability of getting caught.
Answer d   Page 594

51. Employee theft can be caused or encouraged by a number of factors including:
    a) physical breakdowns of security.
    b) improper cash controls.
    c) organizational atmosphere.
    d) all of these.
Answer d   Page 595

52. Employers can reduce employee theft through:
    a) careful screening of employees during hiring.
    b) only hiring relatives and the friends of current employees.
    c) the use of metal detectors and random strip searches of employees.
    d) searching employees' lockers and cars during work hours.
Answer a   Page 595

53. One way to reduce employee theft is:
    a) hire private investigators to do background checks on prospective employees.
    b) install audio surveillance equipment at key locations in the facility.
    c) monitor employees at work and on breaks by having supervisors walk by periodically.
    d) to have a strict company policy about theft and to prosecute when someone is caught.
Answer d   Page 596

54. Powell's Books had an employee theft. The consequence of this theft was:
    a) a loss of the sense of trust built up in the company.
    b) a revision of the operation of a number of business systems.
    c) making Powell's Books stronger in many ways.
    d) all of these.
Answer d   Page 597

55. Nearly half of all shoplifters are:
    a) professionals.
    b) impulse shoplifters.
    c) juveniles.
    d) none of these.
Answer c   Page 598

56. U.S. businesses lose ____ to shoplifters every year.
    a) $10–12 billion
    b) $17–20 billion
    c) $25–35 billion
    d) more than $50 billion
Answer b   Page 598

57. The ____ shoplifter is often a regular customer, well-respected individual, etc.
    a) juvenile
    b) kleptomaniac
    c) professional
    d) impulse
Answer d   Page 599

58. Professional shoplifters account for about ___ percent of all shoplifters though they steal much more than that.
    a) 5
    b) 10
    c) 15
    d) 20
Answer c   Page 599

59. When it comes to catching and prosecuting shoplifters:
    a) there is only a 1 in 100 chance a shoplifter will go before a judge.
    b) nearly ½ of all shoplifters are caught and prosecuted.
    c) women and juveniles are most frequently caught, nearly 98% of the time.
    d) the store owner or employees must catch the shoplifter in the store to make the charges stick.

Answer a   Page 602

60. Store owners and employees may apprehend and charge a shoplifter:
    a) merely on the suspicion that they have stolen something.
    b) if the individual puts something in their bag or pocket without paying for it but hasn't left the store.
    c) only if the theft amounts to more than $25.
    d) only if they see the theft and can prove the merchandise belongs to the store and wasn't paid for.

Answer d   Page 603

True or False Questions

61. Businesses in the United States spend more than $700 billion dollars on inventory every year.

Answer T   Page 576

62. Your relationship with your suppliers is relatively unimportant to the actual management of your inventory.

Answer F   Page 577

63. It is not possible to accurately compute an optimum inventory level without an accurate cost of carrying inventory.

Answer T   Page 577

64. The goal of inventory management is to reduce the costs of holding and maintaining inventory with meeting customer demands for merchandise.

Answer T   Page 578

65. The 80/20 rule states that 80% of each sales dollar should be spent on purchases, and the remaining 20% should go towards covering costs and making a profit.

Answer F   Page 578

66. Perpetual inventory systems keep a continuous tally of each item added to or subtracted from the company's stock of merchandise.

Answer F   Page 578

67. Because of their relatively inexpensive nature, perpetual inventory systems are used most frequently and successfully in controlling low-dollar, high-volume items.

Answer F   Page 579

68. Computerized point-of-sale systems have given small business owners the ability to use perpetual inventory control systems across a larger portion of their inventories.

Answer T   Page 579

69. Point-of-sale systems can be programmed to alert the business owner when key items drop below the reorder point.
Answer T   Page 579

70. The sales ticket method of inventory management is a type of physical inventory control.
Answer F   Page 579

71. The key to the management of the auto parts inventory at Ron Sturgeon's AAA Small Car World was his sales ticket method of inventory control.
Answer F   Page 580

72. The most common method of controlling inventory in a small business is the perpetual system.
Answer F   Page 581

73. Visual inventory control systems work best with firms that have strong variations in their sales.
Answer F   Page 581

74. ABC inventory systems are designed to maintain a running count of the items in inventory.
Answer F   Page 581

75. The dollar usage volume of an item is how the importance of the item to inventory is measured in an ABC inventory system.
Answer T   Page 581

76. The basic principle of ABC analysis is that inventory costs are reduced when the small business owner spends time and effort controlling items representing the greatest inventory value.
Answer T   Page 582

77. In an ABC inventory system, approximately 50% of the inventory usually are counted as C category items.
Answer T   Page 582

78. In an ABC system, A items are those that account for a low dollar usage volume.
Answer F   Page 582

79. The purpose of classifying items according to their value in ABC analysis is to establish the proper degree of control over each inventory item.
Answer T   Page 582

80. "C" items typically comprise a minor proportion of the small firm's inventory value.
Answer T   Page 583

81. "A" items should be controlled under a perpetual inventory system with as much detail as necessary.
Answer T   Page 583

82. In a two-bin system, the amount of stock in the second bin should equal the quantity ordered.
Answer F   Page 583

83. The tag system of inventory management is the equivalent of the two-bin system but is used by retail, wholesale, and service businesses.
Answer T   Page 584

84. Total inventory costs are reduced when the small business manager spends her time and effort controlling items that represent the greatest inventory value.
Answer T   Page 584

85. Choosing the most appropriate system of inventory control eliminates the need for the small business owner to conduct a periodic physical inventory count.
Answer F   Page 585

86. Small business owners using the ABC system of inventory control need not worry about conducting a physical inventory count.
Answer F   Page 585

87. Because they keep continuous track on each item added to or taken from inventory, perpetual inventory control systems eliminate the need for a physical inventory count.
Answer F   Page 585

88. Simon counts a few items of his inventory every week, working his way through the entire inventory during the year. Simon is using cycle counting to control his inventory.
Answer T   Page 585

89. Electronic data interchange (EDI) is an ordering system used by owners to submit their inventory orders directly to suppliers using bar codes and scanning wands.
Answer T   Page 585

90. The description of Armand Schaubroeck's House of Guitars inventory makes it sound like if he were using an ABC inventory system he would have a high percentage of "A" items in his inventory.
Answer T   Page 586

91. For changes in inventory management to be considered consistent with a "Just-In-Time" philosophy they must use both EDI and POS technology to manage the inventories.
Answer F   Page 587

92. "Just-In-Time" inventory control techniques are best suited for manufacturing operations where there are significant inventory levels and where the manufacturing operations are unique and varied, producing custom items.
Answer F   Page 588

93. One force driving the move to JIT inventory management is competition among companies to provide excellent customer service.
Answer T   Page 588

94. The radical change involved in JIT II is that suppliers' employees work onsite with the customer's plant and there is a sharing of what is normally confidential information.
Answer T   Page 589

95. JIT II in the retail and service industries is more commonly called efficient customer response.
Answer T   Page 589

96. Small business owners should avoid cutting prices on slow-moving items since it is better to hold onto them and try to sell them later at normal prices.
Answer F   Page 590

97. Carrying unsold inventory from one year to the next is senseless since it represents an investment earning no return and it ties up working capital that could be put to more productive uses.
Answer T   Page 590

98. Research shows that the nature of the business contributes to its vulnerability to crime.
Answer T   Page 591

99. The greatest criminal threat to small business is from professional crooks in the form of shoplifters, fraudulent insurance sales, and computer scams.
Answer F   Page 591

100. One consequence of Harvey's Hardware's large inventory strategy is a low inventory turnover ratio but a higher than normal profit per item, offsetting the slow inventory turnover.
Answer F   Page 592

101. Participants in a study on fraud losses estimate that they lose about 6% of their annual revenues to employee theft and fraud.
Answer T   Page 593

102. Generally speaking, it is not the "workaholic" employee but the one who seems to be hanging around a lot who is a risk factor for employee theft.
Answer F   Page 593

103. If an owner or his/her relatives take the product home without properly logging it out, employees will perceive that it is okay and will be more likely to "steal" from the company in this way.
Answer T   Page 594

104. Both unreasonable rules and unenforced rules are equally harmful to small business security.
Answer T   Page 594

105. Small businesses have had employees steal by putting merchandise in the trash, take it out, and then return to the dumpster and remove it after their shift is over.
Answer T   Page 595

106. Doing daily inspections of the cash register tape to check for employee theft are of little value since the theft would have already taken place and it would be difficult to trace and prove at that point..
Answer F   Page 595

107. Keeping internal records current is a simple but effective deterrent to employee theft.
Answer T   Page 596

108. The theft at Powell's Books was noted by an employee who noticed an unusually large number of cash payouts by one employee for used books.
Answer T   Page 597

109. Approximately 6% of the average price tag in a small business is there due to shoplifting losses.
Answer F   Page 598

110. Owners do not need to prosecute juvenile shoplifters when they are caught, as the scare of getting caught is often enough to make them stop.
Answer F   Page 598

111. Surprisingly, kleptomaniacs account for nearly 9% of all small business retail losses.
Answer F   Page 599

112. When watching for shoplifters, owners should remember that impulse shoplifters tend to work alone while juveniles and professionals work in groups.
Answer T   Page 599

113. The best way to deal with shoplifting is to take steps to prevent it rather than stress catching the shoplifter in the act.
Answer T   Page 600

114. A valuable shoplifting reduction technique is to train employees on what to watch for in potential shoplifters.
Answer T   Page 601

115. Generally, training employees is more expensive than the losses to shoplifting but if employees are trained shoplifters will eventually leave your store alone.
Answer F   Page 601

116. How the store is laid out has little impact on shoplifting unless video cameras are installed as well.
Answer F   Page 602

117. 98% of the time, shoplifters are successful in their thefts.
Answer T   Page 602

118. The mistakes the store made in apprehending Patricia Caldwell as a probable shoplifter included losing sight of her and not letting her go when nothing was found in her bag.
Answer T   Page 603

119. To make shoplifting charges stick, two of the things the owner/employee needs to be able to do is to identify the merchandise as belonging to the store and that it was not paid for.
Answer T   Page 603

120. Small business owners should always prosecute and not worry about negative publicity or legal entanglements.
Answer T   Page 604

Essay Questions

121. Inventory management involves seven other interrelated steps. Identify each and explain their importance to inventory management.
Page 577

122. Briefly explain each of the three primary inventory systems.
Pages 578–582

123. What is a perpetual inventory control system? Explain its advantages and disadvantages.
Pages 578–580

124. Discuss the ABC method of inventory control, offering its strengths and weaknesses.
Pages 581–582

125. What is the value of a physical inventory count? In what ways can it be done?
Pages 585–587

126. Explain the concept of the "Just-In-Time" inventory control technique. Under what circumstances would JIT be most appropriate?
Pages 587–588

127. What is JIT II? How does it differ from JIT? What is the importance of those differences?
Pages 589–590

128. How can a small business owner turn slow-moving inventory items into cash?
Pages 590–591

129. Why do employees steal?
Pages 591–595

130. How can a small business owner prevent employee theft?
Pages 595–596

131. Who are the people who shoplift and what can the small business owner do to deter shoplifting?
Pages 598–602

Mini-Case

Case 17-1: The ABC's of Inventory Control

H.M.W., Inc. is conducting an ABC analysis of its present inventory. The owner has gathered the following data from inventory records:

Item	Annual $ Usage	% of total value
Paragon	37,500	5.00
Electromite	232,500	31.00
Datamatic	6,000	0.80
MicroReader	37,500	5.00

Compustat	1,500	0.20
Insofar	292,500	39.00
Visceral	5,000	0.67
Autostart	52,500	7.00
Macropack	7,500	1.00
Starbuck	67,500	9.00
Mobil	2,500	0.33
Astropak	7,500	1.00
	$750,000	100.00%

Questions

1. Categorize the above list of items into "A" items, "B" items, and "C" items.

2. What control system would you recommend for each class of items? "A" items, "B" items, "C" items?

Chapter 18 –
Using Technology to Gain a Competitive Edge

Multiple Choice Questions

1. Technology:
   a) has had a significant impact on large companies but passed by small companies.
   b) has transformed the way small companies do business.
   c) will radically change small business but not for another five years, until prices come down more.
   d) has had little, if any, real effect on business other than in the management of numeric data.

   Answer b   Page 608

2. The area of business most positively affected by technology has been:
   a) accounting.
   b) managing people.
   c) sales and marketing.
   d) inventory management.

   Answer c   Page 609

3. The relationship between information technology and the developing of a competitive advantage in the small business is best expressed as:
   a) information technology being the foundation of future competitive advantage.
   b) a hoped-for but as yet unrealized synergy.
   c) not existing as all businesses have access to the same technology therefore they can not turn it into a competitive advantage.
   d) a function of budget; those companies with sufficient excess revenue will be able to integrate information technology into their competitive advantage.

   Answer a   Page 610

4. More small businesses are discovering the ability to create a techno-edge, which is:
   a) the ability to manipulate data faster and more efficiently than competitors can.
   b) using computers to give customers more of what they want, such as speed and convenience.
   c) conducting market research on their own without the aid of market research firms.
   d) the use of software programs like TIGER to better segment their markets.

   Answer c   Page 611

5. When it comes to technology giving the small business an edge, the benefit comes from:
   a) the technology itself.
   b) the type of product and needs of the customer interfacing with the technology.
   c) the way technology is reducing overhead by eliminating jobs and reducing necessary inventories.
   d) the creative way the owner uses technology to foster relationships with customers.

   Answer d   Page 611

6. A recent study by Yankelovich Partners shows that when it comes to technology, small businesses:
   a) are 3–5 years behind larger companies.
   b) have the greatest potential for improvements through technology.

    c) are almost ten years ahead of Fortune 500 companies in its use because of the closeness to the customer.

    d) are spending the same percentage of their revenues as large companies for technology.

Answer b   Page 611

7. When developing a technology plan, the small business owner needs to begin by:
    a) choosing the technology he/she wants to use.
    b) creating a budget for purchasing of technology.
    c) deciding what he/she wants the technology to be able to do.
    d) conducting a technology audit.

Answer c   Page 612

8. When choosing the technology needed to accomplish what the small business owner wants, it is very helpful to:
    a) talk with other entrepreneurs about their experiences.
    b) develop a technology budget first.
    c) buy a personal computer and work with it first.
    d) survey customers to see what they think and need.

Answer a   Page 612

9. Cassandra is studying what computers her company has, what each is capable of doing, and what software is on hand. Cassandra is:
    a) creating a technology budget.
    b) conducting a technology audit.
    c) outlining what is needed for a peer-to-peer LAN.
    d) working on creating a techno-edge.

Answer b   Page 613

10. Before developing the technology budget but after conducting the technology audit, the small business owner needs to:
    a) decide what he/she wants the technology to do.
    b) determine what equipment to buy.
    c) set goals and objectives for the technology plan.
    d) match existing goals with existing equipment.

Answer d   Page 613

11. After the cost barrier, the number two barrier to small businesses using technology is:
    a) time.
    b) getting the right equipment.
    c) learning to use the technology.
    d) keeping the technology current.

Answer c   Page 614

12. Technology in the small business:
    a) permits a drastic reduction in the number of customer service employees required.
    b) provides managers with the additional information needed to make better decisions.
    c) requires the owner and employees to perform more mundane routine tasks, reducing the time available to perform critical tasks.
    d) gives the owner the ability to use and act on information just as quickly as larger competitors.

Answer d   Page 615

13. The two forces in computer technology that have given small business owners unprecedented access to computers are:
    a) a more highly educated and more experienced workforce.
    b) the dramatic increase in computing power and flexibility and the equally dramatic decline in prices.
    c) the development of the minicomputer and graphical interface software.
    d) the significant decline in computing time and the development of character-based software.
Answer b   Page 615

14. Moore's law states that:
    a) computing power will double every 18 months, while prices will remain the same.
    b) computing power will triple every year, while prices will decline by 50% in the same time frame.
    c) computer prices will decline by half, while computing power will double every two years.
    d) none of these are true.
Answer a   Page 615

15. The key to successful computerization of the small business is:
    a) getting adequate technical support.
    b) buying as much power as cheaply as possible.
    c) making sure the technology fits the company's needs.
    d) involving both customers and suppliers in the technology purchasing decisions.
Answer c   Page 615

16. The key to making a wise computer system purchase is to:
    a) let price be the driving force behind the decision.
    b) translate what the owner knows about the business into computer criteria.
    c) buy used equipment and inexpensive software.
    d) train your employees.
Answer b   Page 615

17. The first step in computerizing your business is:
    a) deciding how much and which areas of the business to computerize.
    b) defining the informational needs of the business functions to be computerized.
    c) shopping for computer hardware.
    d) developing a list of current activities and ranking them from "least" to "most" important.
Answer d   Page 616

18. The small business manager starting to computerize his/her business operations should:
    a) start by computerizing a smooth, well-functioning system.
    b) start by computerizing a problem area that needs to be fixed.
    c) begin with a low-priority area first, so if anything goes wrong it has minimum impact.
    d) start by computerizing the company's financial operations.
Answer a   Page 616

19. In computerizing a business, managers should always:
    a) repair company weaknesses first.

b) leverage their strengths.

c) place cost considerations over function.

d) experiment with a personal PC at home first.

Answer b   Page 616

20. In the technology revolution, experts argue that computers are in the:

a) substitution stage.

b) adaptation stage.

c) revolution stage.

d) innovation stage.

Answer b   Page 617

21. Which of the following costs of computerizing is the greatest?

a) Hardware

b) Software

c) Training and support

d) Supplies

Answer c   Page 616–618

22. According to a recent study, the out-of-pocket costs of computer hardware comprise _____% of the total cost of owning a computer.

a) 15

b) 25

c) 33

d) 50

Answer a   Page 618

23. The purchase price of software equals about ___ % of the TCO.

a) 10

b) 20

c) 30

d) 50

Answer b   Page 618

24. If a business owner plans to computerize the inventory control system, the owner should begin by:

a) choosing a system of hardware on which to run inventory control software.

b) studying the flow of information through the manual inventory recordkeeping system to determine information needs.

c) selecting the software—the set of programs—which will drive the inventory control system.

d) hiring a consultant to identify computer needs.

Answer b   Page 618

25. Keemo is studying his company's computer network needs. They have a powerful server, a need to share software to reduce costs, and the ability to share work among the stations. Keemo's company would be best served by a:

a) wide area network.

b) peer-to-peer local area network.

c) client/server local area network.

d) computer interface narrow band network.

Answer c   Page 618

26. A firm can lower the total cost of owning a computer by taking a number of steps such as:
    a) buying individual software packages and sharing the software among employees.
    b) buying new technology as soon as it comes out to keep systems current.
    c) upgrading technology only once every three years.
    d) hiring freelance computer technicians.
Answer d   Page 619

27. Which of the following strategies will help a company hold down the total costs of ownership of their computers?
    a) standardizing hardware and software purchases
    b) buying new technology as soon as it comes out to keep systems current
    c) upgrading technology only once every three years
    d) staffing their company with full-time employee technicians
Answer a   Page 619

28. Before buying a computer network, entrepreneurs should consider:
    a) how many PCs they have.
    b) how will they use the network.
    c) how important the network is to the business.
    d) all of these.
Answer d   Page 620

29. Each year, computer users spend about ___ on software for every $1 they spend on hardware.
    a) 50 cents
    b) $1
    c) $3
    d) $5
Answer c   Page 620

30. The first phase of evaluating software packages is to:
    a) buy a "demo" and try it out.
    b) collect information on those in which the owner is interested.
    c) run the software on the computer to be used and try some sample examples.
    d) choose the hardware on which to run the software.
Answer b   Page 621

31. A/An _____ is an information source whose members use a similar type of computer and who swap information on relevant software and its applications.
    a) user's group
    b) trade association
    c) customers
    d) software assessment group
Answer a   Page 621

32. The best way to integrate a computer system into a business is:
    a) to do it in a matter of a few weeks.

  b) shut down the existing system and run the new system by itself.
  c) to do it overnight.
  d) through a gradual phasing in.
Answer d   Page 621

33. When converting a computer system and integrating it into the business, it is best to:
  a) "wean" employees from the other system as quickly as possible.
  b) run both systems parallel and compare them for at least a month or two.
  c) shut the old system down as the new system is started.
  d) keep the old system for 2–3 years as a backup.
Answer b   Page 622

34. The two most common software packages used by businesses are:
  a) spreadsheets and inventory management.
  b) database management and communication.
  c) word processing and accounting.
  d) presentation graphics and communication.
Answer c   Page 623

35. _____ is/are the primary use of 75% of all computer systems.
  a) Spreadsheet applications
  b) Word processing
  c) Accounting
  d) Database applications
Answer b   Page 623

36. Word processing software that prints out just what you see on your computer screen is called:
  a) graphical interface software.
  b) character-based software.
  c) WYSIWYG software.
  d) format software.
Answer c   Page 623

37. _____ programs are built around a specific application and can be used with other specific applications.
  a) Modular
  b) Character-based
  c) Integrated
  d) Graphical interface
Answer a   Page 623

38. Database managers and file managers record information into _____, which are accumulated into _____, which, in turn, are compiled into _____.
  a) files; records; fields
  b) records; fields; files
  c) fields; records; files
  d) fields; files; records
Answer c   Page 624

39. Examples of database management programs would be:

   a) Lotus Approach, Microsoft Access.
   b) Excel, Lotus 1-2-3.
   c) Wordstar, WordPerfect.
   d) QuickBooks, Business Works PC.
Answer a   Page 624

40. In a/an _____ accounting software package, an owner enters transactions into a general ledger and the package automatically posts them to the appropriate subprogram.
   a) modular
   b) integrated
   c) character-based
   d) graphical interface
Answer b   Page 624

41. The ability to answer important "what if" questions is a primary advantage of:
   a) database managers.
   b) spreadsheets.
   c) word processors.
   d) integrated software.
Answer b   Page 625

42. Excel for Windows, Lotus 1-2-3, and Quattro Pro are examples of which type of computer application?
   a) Word processing
   b) Project management
   c) Database management
   d) Spreadsheets
Answer d   Page 625

43. Entrepreneurs can use the world wide web for a number of purposes including:
   a) conducting market research.
   b) managing their company's cash.
   c) studying their competitors.
   d) all of these.
Answer d   Page 626

44. Approximately _____ small businesses are doing business online.
   a) 10,000
   b) 25,000
   c) 37,000
   d) 70,000
Answer d   Page 627

45. Online shoppers are:
   a) very different from instore shoppers and seek different products.
   b) becoming more like instore shoppers and are looking for a broader range of products.
   c) largely female, white, and 42–61 in age.
   d) actually in decline in terms of real numbers.

Answer b   Page 627

46. If a building contractor wanted a software package to help plan and control the construction of a water purification plant, he/she would purchase a/an _____ program.
    a) spreadsheet
    b) project management
    c) accounting
    d) database

Answer b   Page 628

47. Software suites account for ___ of word processing and ____ of spreadsheet sales of software.
    a) α, 2
    b) 18%, 67%
    c) 75%,85%
    d) 3, β

Answer c   Page 628

48. When building his web site, Bill Knight Wine House, he ____ to increase its visibility.
    a) offered live action video
    b) had music play while being browsed
    c) offered an online lottery
    d) built links to other wine-related sites

Answer d   Page 629

49. Wine House experienced a number of benefits from its web page, including:
    a) being able to expand the mailing list.
    b) lowering the inventory costs.
    c) national recognition by several Internet magazines.
    d) needing fewer telephone customer service representatives.

Answer a   Page 629

50. When buying computers, the small business owner should:
    a) buy the hardware first and then the software.
    b) always buy more speed and power than is currently needed.
    c) buy the very best, top-of-the line machine that he/she can afford.
    d) do all of these things.

Answer b   Page 631

51. When buying computer hardware, more and more entrepreneurs are buying:
    a) laptop computers.
    b) PDAs for their on-the-road computing needs.
    c) desktop machines with at least 19" monitors.
    d) a variety of things, with no clear pattern.

Answer a   Page 631

52. When buying a computer, the small business owner should set as <u>minimum</u> standard:
    a) Pentium, 200 MHz processor, 32 MB of RAM, 2.5 GB hard drive, etc.
    b) Pentium II, 500 MHz processor, 128 MB of RAM, 12 GB hard drive, etc.

    c) Pentium, 166 MHz processor, 48 MB of RAM, 6 GB hard drive, etc.

    d) Pentium II, 300 MHz processor, 96 MB of RAM, 8 GB hard drive, etc.

Answer d   Page 632

53. The brain of a personal computer is the _____ and the "power" that runs it—where programs are stored when you are working with them—is:
    a) motherboard, hard-disk drive
    b) central processing unit, RAM
    c) LAN, floppy-disk drive
    d) Pentium processor, CD-ROM drive

Answer b   Page 633

54. The first line of defense against electronic disasters with computers is:
    a) purchasing a good technical support package when you buy the computer.
    b) to not have an Internet connection so outsiders cannot gain access to your computer.
    c) to back up your data frequently.
    d) none of these; you cannot protect against electronic disasters.

Answer c   Page 634

55. One study found that _____% of the computer crimes reported result in criminal prosecution.
    a) 6
    b) 2
    c) 21
    d) 43

Answer a   Page 635

56. The FBI estimates that a computer thief nets about _____ in the average "job."
    a) $1,000,000
    b) less than $10,000
    c) $600,000
    d) $40 to $50,000

Answer c   Page 635

57. The number one computer problem leading to financial loss among companies is:
    a) unauthorized computer use.
    b) sabotage.
    c) theft of the laptop or computer.
    d) virus infection of the system or computer.

Answer d   Page 636

58. Carmen needs a printer that will print color, and is inexpensive to buy and use in a low volume printing situation. Her best choice of printer would be:
    a) an inkjet.
    b) monochrome laser.
    c) color laser.
    d) network.

Answer a   Page 637

59. _____ were once used strictly for graphics and are now used for text and have become common tools for making digital copies of images or documents.
    a) Printers
    b) Digital cameras
    c) Scanners
    d) Facsimile machines

Answer c   Page 638

60. The tool of the '90s that often combines the features of a portable computer, appointment book, pager, fax machine, etc. is the:
    a) digital fax machine.
    b) personal digital assistant.
    c) modern pager with text capability.
    d) combination of e-mail and voice-mail on new phone systems.

Answer b   Page 639

True or False Questions

61. The most common use of technology in terms of payoff to business is in the area of inventory management.

Answer F   Page 609

62. Small companies that do not use computers to collect and process information about their operations can still maintain a competitive edge over their rivals.

Answer F   Page 610

63. The most successful small businesses use technology to focus on their financial and inventory management.

Answer F   Page 611

64. More and more small businesses are learning how to develop a techno-edge: the use of technology to give customers what they want.

Answer T   Page 611

65. A recent study showed that most small businesses are using technology plans to build significant competitive advantages over their much larger rivals.

Answer F   Page 611

66. The major impact of technology on small business has been in helping the small company perform faster and more efficiently.

Answer T   Page 612

67. The area where technology has had the lowest or least impact on small business has been in increases in profitability and sales.

Answer T   Page 612

68. A technology audit is when the small business owner tries to match his/her goals and objectives for technology to the existing equipment he/she has.

Answer F   Page 613

69. When creating a technology budget, one should project 2–3 years into the future.
Answer T   Page 613

70. When it comes to the barriers that keep small businesses from implementing technology, time is the least of their problems.
Answer T   Page 614

71. The number one barrier to the implementation of technology in the small business is deciding which is the right technology to buy.
Answer F   Page 614

72. The process of choosing the right computer starts with the hiring of an outside consultant to assess the business and its technological needs.
Answer F   Page 615

73. It is important to include the employees in the process of developing a current list of activities that might be computerized.
Answer T   Page 616

74. The best use of the personal computer is to fix those processes and programs that weren't working properly prior to the computerization. This provides maximum quick return on the technology investment.
Answer F   Page 616

75. A computer budget should only be developed after a decision has been made about what and how much to computerize in the small business.
Answer T   Page 616

76. Jar Jar's company is in the process of computerizing. They are replacing existing tools with computers and doing the same things they did before, just faster. Jar Jar's company is in Stage II of the computer revolution.
Answer F   Page 617

77. Training and support costs for computerization often run 40–60% of the total cost of the project.
Answer T   Page 618

78. It is estimated that the five-year cost of a PC for the small business is about $40,000.
Answer T   Page 618

79. Research shows that employees waste one hour a week on personal tasks on their computer.
Answer T   Page 619

80. It is important to keep a computer as long as possible, for the longer you have it the less it costs the small business to operate.
Answer F   Page 619

81. The small business owner should select computer hardware before selecting computer software.

Answer F   Page 620

82. When buying computer hardware, price should be the driving factor.
Answer F   Page 621

83. The best way to integrate a computer system into a business is to "take the plunge" by introducing it quickly and getting it on line as soon as possible.
Answer F   Page 621

84. It is the choice of software that ultimately determines the success of a computerization effort.
Answer T   Page 622

85. The most popular business application of computer software is word processing.
Answer T   Page 623

86. When an owner enters transactions into the general ledger of an integrated accounting package, it automatically posts them to the appropriate subprograms in the system.
Answer T   Page 624

87. Integrated software packages tie together several software applications in one, helping managers perform more work in less time.
Answer T   Page 624

88. File managers differ from database managers in that file managers allow a manager to create and work with numerous files simultaneously.
Answer F   Page 624

89. Communications software help the entrepreneur turn his/her computer into a professional slide presentation platform that looks like Madison Avenue put it together.
Answer F   Page 625

90. The two most popular web browser programs available are NetScape and Microsoft Explorer.
Answer T   Page 626

91. Research shows that nearly 52 million people are currently on the Internet.
Answer T   Page 627

92. The largest number of people on the web is from the Baby Boomer generation.
Answer F   Page 627

93. The advantage of using project management software is that if the manager outlines the basic steps and prioritizes them, the software will calculate the necessary dates for each item and the whole project.
Answer T   Page 628

94. Software suites traditionally only include word processing, accounting, and web browser software programs.
Answer F   Page 628

95. Bill Knight's Wine House experienced a 100% increase in orders and revenues after it went online.
Answer F   Page 629

96. While Bill Knight is receiving over 20,000 hits a month on the Wine House web site, it is difficult to measure any direct gains to his business.
Answer T   Page 629

97. The use of industry specific software is in decline due to the increasing versatility of software suites and the increased number of individual software programs now included in each suite.
Answer F   Page 630

98. Today for the small business owner, buying a computer system for the business is akin to buying a toaster— easy, inexpensive, and commonplace.
Answer F   Page 631

99. It is important when buying a computer to plan for future expansion through adding memory, upgrading memory, etc.
Answer T   Page 631

100. Today, a basic computer system for a small business not only includes the computer but also a color printer and flatbed scanner.
Answer T   Page 632

101. In terms of computer technology, there is now little difference between a desktop computer and a laptop except for size and portability.
Answer T   Page 632

102. The key component of the computer in terms of upgrading it with additional components, memory, etc., is the central processing unit.
Answer F   Page 633

103. The easiest and least expensive way to back up hard drive program data is on a tape-backup drive.
Answer T   Page 633

104. Most companies are ill-prepared to handle an electronic/computer disaster.
Answer T   Page 634

105. The reliability of modern computers is such that the small business owner does not need a backup system.
Answer F   Page 634

106. The greatest threat to a small business's computer system is from external hackers.
Answer F   Page 635

107. Surveys estimate that only about 3 of all small companies have been victims of some type of computer crime within the past year.
Answer F   Page 635

108. A computer virus is a set of instructions that copies itself into a program it is not authorized to enter and then destroys data and programs.
Answer T   Page 636

109. In reality, there is less network break-in than any other high-tech crime in the computer world.
Answer T   Page 636

110. Experts argue that the key to computer security is having the best encryption software available and not permitting external access to your company's computer systems.
Answer F   Page 636

111. The workhorse printer for most small businesses is the networked color laser printer.
Answer F   Page 637

112. The least expensive type of printer a small business can buy is the inkjet.
Answer T   Page 637

113. The minimum acceptable resolution for a business computer printer is 300 dpi.
Answer F   Page 638

114. The most important criteria to consider when buying a flatbed scanner is the resolution of its scan.
Answer T   Page 638

115. The minimum acceptable quality for a digital camera depends on the entrepreneur's plans for its use but should not be below 640 by 480 resolution.
Answer T   Page 639

116. The personal digital assistant is making a significant dent in the laptop computer market as it begins to replace many of these machines due to their smaller size and versatility.
Answer F   Page 639

117. Mel wants Tia to let him build a web site for Tie One On, so they can begin processing online sales for her ties.
Answer T   Page 640

118. Pagers are being replaced by PDAs because the price of pagers has not come down below $250 and they can receive but not transmit messages.
Answer F   Page 641

119. There are more than 43 million people using cell phones in the United States with another 30,000 a day joining their ranks.
Answer T   Page 641

120. The average user of e-mail is currently receiving more than 25 messages a day.
Answer F   Page 642

Essay Questions
121. Discuss how information technology helps small businesses develop a competitive edge.
Pages 610–611

122. Outline the necessary components to a technology plan, briefly explaining each of the six steps.
Pages 611–613

123. How are computers changing the face of business? What is Moore's law and why is it important to the small business owner?
Pages 614–615

124. Computerizing a small business can be challenging. Explain the seven steps a small business owner should follow when computerizing his/her business.
Pages 615–622

125. In defining the informational needs of the various functions to be computerized, the small business needs to set up a number of local area networks. Identify and explain each type of LAN and what it takes to establish it.
Pages 618–619

126. Discuss the software decisions that face a small business that is computerizing, identifying the major categories of software choices the owner has to make.
Pages 622–630

127. A friend is computerizing his business. He's chosen his software and now he's trying to decide where to buy his hardware. Explain to him the four key guidelines he should follow in making his choices.
Pages 630–631

128. The dark side of computers covers both crime and mishaps. How can a small business owner protect the business from mishaps? What type of computer crime could a small business be exposed to and how can it be prevented?
Pages 634–636

129. Aside from information services and computers, what other technological choices does the small business owner need to make? Enumerate those choices, briefly explaining the key issues involved.
Pages 637-640

130. What part are the telephone, voice mail, and e-mail playing in the technological revolution that is impacting small business?
Pages 641–642

Mini-Case

Case 18-1: "A Computer Could Fix It"

Alan Leopard stood in the storage room of his auto parts store looking at the mess scattered all about him. Parts and boxes were strewn everywhere, and invoices and shipping receipts were scattered about. "No wonder we never know what we've got in stock or where it is," he muttered to himself. "In this mess, it's a wonder anyone can find the door." As he stood there pondering this problem, he saw the box containing a special order he'd made for one of his best customers. Earlier today, the customer had come in to pick up the parts, but no one could find it. The customer stormed out angrily. Alan knew he'd lost that customer forever. "And the parts were here the whole time!"

Just then, Burt, a long-term employee, came by and said "we got a real problem back here! But I've been doing some reading, and I think a computer could fix it. Whaddya' say we buy one and see?"

Questions

1. Do you agree with Burt? Could a computer fix Alan's problem? Why or why not?

2. Assume that Alan gets a computer. What software could Alan use in managing his business?

3. Given that Alan's employees are not the most computer literate, what advice would you give Burt if he implements a computer system in the business?

Chapter 19 –
Staffing and Leading a Growing Company

Multiple Choice Questions

1. The process of influencing and inspiring others to work to achieve a common goal and then giving them the power and freedom to achieve it is called:
   a) management.
   b) goal or objective setting.
   c) performance appraisal.
   d) leadership.

   Answer d   Page 647

2. Today's leader is different than leaders in the past in that he/she:
   a) is now like an orchestra conductor, guiding the members through the proper use of power.
   b) is like a referee in a TV wrestling match, running about, yelling directions, and keeping the organization's members from killing themselves.
   c) is like the leader of a jazz band, guiding individual and group creativity and innovation.
   d) is in tight control of resources and authority but delegating responsibility and opportunity.

   Answer c   Page 648

3. Effective leaders are noted for their:
   a) ability to get their followers to do what they themselves can't or won't do.
   b) ability to provide guidance based on values for making decisions.
   c) willingness to assign responsibility while retaining authority so they can monitor employee success.
   d) focused seriousness in achieving goals, working hard and then harder.

   Answer b   Page 648

4. If you were evaluating your college administration for effective leadership behaviors, you need to look for:
   a) their ability to husband and protect resources from misuse.
   b) their short-term focus, their ability to see the detail needing to be accomplished.
   c) the ability to encourage creativity in employees.
   d) all of these things.

   Answer c   Page 649

5. The primary reason managers/leaders evaluate their leadership skills more highly than employees do is:
   a) employees rate leaders on what they do, not what they say.
   b) that most managers/leaders are self-deluded about their leadership abilities.
   c) because managers/leaders have to make decisions that are unpopular, so naturally employees will rate them lower.
   d) employees don't understand what leadership is.

   Answer a   Page 649

6. If a company is to succeed, a leader must create six conditions which include:
   a) a sense of hope.
   b) helping employees know what, how, and why they are doing what they are doing.

    c)   a dependency on the leader for direction and help.

    d)   a feedback-free environment where employees are not corrected for their mistakes.

Answer b   Page 650

7.   Studies show that managers spend about ___ of their communication time talking, about ____ listening, and about ___ reading and writing.

    a)   80, 10, 10

    b)   15, 60, 25

    c)   75, 20, 5

    d)   30, 25, 25

Answer d   Page 650

8.   Sometimes effective communication is blocked between leaders and followers by:

    a)   information overload or ambiguity in the communication.

    b)   the followers' use of the grapevine.

    c)   the lack of nonverbal signals in an e-mail message.

    d)   the leader being too empathetic when talking with followers.

Answer a   Page 651

9.   Miguel and Jamie are talking. Miguel keeps using baseball metaphors as he is giving instructions to Jamie. Not having any experience with baseball, Jamie is only understanding about half of what Miguel is saying. Miguel and Jamie are experiencing ineffective communication because of:

    a)   information overload.

    b)   Miguel not expressing his feelings.

    c)   ambiguity in the communication.

    d)   the conflicting verbal and nonverbal messages Jamie is giving to Miguel.

Answer c   Page 652

10.   To increase the effectiveness of communication between the small business owner and his/her employees, he/she should practice:

    a)   selective listening.

    b)   being more sympathetic when listening.

    c)   giving as much information as possible in each communication.

    d)   telling the truth and encouraging feedback.

Answer d   Page 652

11.   Tom is counseling an employee who is facing corrective discipline for a serious error in judgment on the job. The employee is very upset. Tom is trying to understand how the employee feels and strives to tell the employee he knows that this is a tough time and that the employee is upset. Tom is using ___ to improve his communication with the employee.

    a)   feedback

    b)   empathy

    c)   clear organization in his thoughts

    d)   ambiguity

Answer b   Page 652

12.   The grapevine in most organizations is:

    a)   almost always incorrect in its content.

    b)   nonexistent in organizations where management communicates face to face and by memo.

    c) the first place employees hear about major organizational changes.

    d) generally only used by troublemakers and gossips within the organization.

Answer c   Page 653

13. When it comes to hiring in the small business:

    a) each hire is very important because bad hires are very expensive.

    b) it is only moderately expensive because bad hires can be quickly fixed due to the small businesses flexibility.

    c) they tend to be in full compliance of EEOC and HRM laws, more so than large companies because the hiring process is done by very few individuals.

    d) the small business owner is almost always in violation of some federal regulation due to the lack of an HRM professional on staff.

Answer a   Page 653

14. Which of the following is true about the use of the world wide web to recruit job applicants?

    a) While highly effective, it is more expensive than more traditional methods of recruiting.

    b) The web site should ask candidates to make an initial submission of a resume and a complete credential package.

    c) It is most effective when used for high-tech jobs but other types of jobs are becoming more common.

    d) All of these are true.

Answer c   Page 654

15. Experts estimate that, of every three employees hired by a small company:

    a) generally all three will become productive employees.

    b) only one employee with become fully productive.

    c) two of them will be terminated for cause within one year.

    d) two will become marginal workers and one will be a star worker.

Answer b   Page 655

16. Kim, the human resources manager, is conducting an orderly and systematic evaluation all of the facts about a new position in order to determine what kind of employee to hire and how to compensate the position. This is called a:

    a) job description.

    b) human resource plan.

    c) job specification.

    d) job analysis.

Answer d   Page 655

17. When conducting a job analysis, an employer needs to focus on questions about:

    a) duties and tasks to be performed daily.

    b) the skill, experience, and education necessary to perform the job.

    c) when certain people will be needed by the company due to growth.

    d) employee work habits.

Answer a   Page 655

18. A _____ outlines the duties and responsibilities associated with a job and the working conditions involved.

a) job analysis
b) job description
c) job specification
d) human resource plan

Answer b   Page 655

19. Lusia, the director of human resources, is discussing the duties and responsibilities of a new position and its working conditions with Delmar, the manager over the position. Lusia and Delmar are discussing the:
a) job description.
b) human resource plan.
c) job specification.
d) job analysis.

Answer a   Page 655

20. Gustavo is writing up a _____ in order to describe the best job candidate in terms of skills, education, experience, and other personal job-related characteristics.
a) job specification
b) human resource plan
c) job description
d) job analysis

Answer a   Page 656

21. A job specification:
a) determines when certain people will be needed by the company due to growth.
b) evaluates employee work habits.
c) translates the duties of the position into qualifications.
d) identifies the skill, experience, and education necessary to perform the job.

Answer c   Page 656

22. To conduct an effective interview, the manager or small business owner should:
a) only make minimal preparations to permit spontaneity in the interview.
b) use close-ended questions in order to maintain control of the interview.
c) not allow employees to spend time with the candidate to avoid them asking illegal questions.
d) ask candidates for examples of both successes and failures.

Answer d   Page 657

23. When conducting the job interview, the small business owner should:
a) begin by explaining the job and the company and asking low key questions.
b) talk as much as he/she listens.
c) never use hypothetical questions.
d) focus on the candidate's verbal responses, largely ignoring the nonverbals.

Answer a   Page 658

24. When it comes to enforcing employment laws and the job interviewing process, the EEOC:
a) flatly outlaws certain specific questions.
b) watches for questions that can lead to employment discrimination.
c) provides an interviewing guide with approved questions for use by the entrepreneur.

    d) is largely unconcerned about job interviews in small businesses unless someone files a complaint.

Answer b   Page 659

25. When checking references, the small business owner:
    a) can largely ignore the references of professional job candidates.
    b) should also talk with previous employers, not just the references provided.
    c) may only ask for confirmation of employment dates, job title, and salary information.
    d) is able to ask any question of the reference to find about things he/she could not ask the candidate.

Answer b   Page 660

26. Because the small business often can't compete on the basis of salary offers with larger companies, small business owners:
    a) generally have to settle for less qualified candidates.
    b) should not waste their time trying to attract the best and the brightest employees.
    c) can make use of temps to "test-drive" employees and/or hire older retired workers returning to the workplace.
    d) can do all of these.

Answer c   Page 661

27. Experienced business owners who make effective hires:
    a) know that everyone they hire will eventually move on.
    b) understand that a hire is the beginning of a long-term relationship.
    c) treat the hiring process as a single event that has a beginning, middle, and end.
    d) rely heavily on a human resource professional to guide them through the process.

Answer b   Page 662

28. A company's culture:
    a) plays an important part in the development of the company's competitive advantage.
    b) generally has little effect on employee behavior due to the more powerful influence of national culture.
    c) is relatively easy to change and adapt to changing company strategies.
    d) arises more from the employees than from the founder, emphasizing the importance of the hiring process.

Answer a   Page 662

29. A "cool" company culture:
    a) provides clear guidance through strong, top down leadership.
    b) stands apart from the world.
    c) uses a strong sense of purpose to connect employees to the company.
    d) focuses on working at work and playing when off work.

Answer b   Page 663

30. One of the primary characteristics of a "cool" company is:
    a) an average return on investment of 24%.
    b) it tends to be under 100 employees and still has the founder as CEO.
    c) that it practices participative management.

   d) that it has an organic ad hoc organizational structure.

Answer c   Page 664

31. When it comes to small companies and growth:
   a) their growth often leads to dramatic change in management, processes, etc.
   b) they tend to handle it better than large companies because of their flexibility.
   c) unlike large companies, growth has little effect on the culture of a small company.
   d) the founder is generally able to take the small company through growth into a large publicly held company.

Answer a   Page 665

32. Michele is growing her small garden supply business. She's at the point where she needs the help of other people to grow the company. She is hiring staff but does not delegate much authority, keeping all critical tasks under her direct supervision. Michele is using the _____ style of management.
   a) craftsman
   b) classic
   c) coordinator
   d) small partnership

Answer b   Page 666

33. Mac is hiring staff to help grow his company. He is delegating authority to key people but retains final decision-making authority. Mac is using the _____ style of management.
   a) craftsman
   b) coordinator
   c) entrepreneur-plus-employee team
   d) small partnership

Answer c   Page 666

34. If the small business owner begins to share managerial responsibility equally with others due to the complexity of the business, using other's complementary skills, the owner is using the ___ style of management.
   a) team-based
   b) coordinator
   c) entrepreneur-plus-employee team
   d) small partnership

Answer d   Page 667

35. If a business owner goes to self-directed work teams, he/she is most likely using the _____ style of management.
   a) team-based
   b) big-team venture
   c) entrepreneur-plus-employee team
   d) small partnership

Answer a   Page 667

36. The implementation of teams fails sometimes because:
   a) too many high performers are placed on one team and they compete with each other.

b) the implementation of team-based pay inhibits individual achievement and the whole team suffers.
c) the team leader and team members do not receive adequate training.
d) of all of these things.

Answer c   Page 668

37. Teams can be helped to succeed by:
a) placing a few underperformers on the team to minimize internal conflict.
b) forming teams around natural work flows, giving them specific tasks.
c) keeping pay based on individual effort.
d) not permitting teams' involvement in the assessment of their own performance.

Answer b   Page 669

38. In the stages of team development, a team is at the performance stage when it:
a) has its highest expectations.
b) recognizes fully the time and effort that will be involved.
c) begins to reset its goals and roles.
d) achieves commitment to the process and task.

Answer d   Page 670

39. _____ is the degree of effort an employee exerts to accomplish a task.
a) Empowerment
b) Job performance
c) Motivation
d) Open book management

Answer c   Page 670

40. When workers are empowered:
a) there tends to be increased confusion over specific responsibilities.
b) they are more successful on the job.
c) they initially experience significant anxiety of using their skills.
d) the company will lose about 20% of its workforce that doesn't want the responsibility.

Answer b   Page 671

41. When empowerment is implemented in a company:
a) 75% will accept and thrive under it.
b) about 20% of employees quit.
c) about 5% of employees eagerly embrace the opportunity.
d) 12% of managers will quit because they can't make the transition.

Answer a   Page 671

42. Empowerment works best in work environments where:
a) mistakes are quickly identified and punished.
b) authority and responsibility are given out incremental to the most trusted employees.
c) managers function as coaches not as bosses.
d) there is minimal training.

Answer c   Page 671

43. Open book management is one technique that supports:
    a) a job redesign strategy.
    b) the empowering of employees.
    c) job enrichment.
    d) effective job hiring.
Answer b   Page 672

44. Jasmine is cross-training employees so they can move among several different jobs in order to provide more challenging work for them and to make better use of their skills for the company. Jasmine is involved in:
    a) job simplification.
    b) job enlargement.
    c) job enrichment.
    d) job rotation.
Answer d   Page 673

45. When a small business owner increases the variety of skills needed on a job, permits the worker to complete an entire job rather than a portion of it, and gives the worker more freedom of decision on how to perform the job, the owner is using:
    a) job simplification.
    b) job enrichment.
    c) job enlargement.
    d) job rotation.
Answer b   Page 673

46. When employees can set their own work hours within certain guidelines, they are involved in:
    a) flextime.
    b) flexplace.
    c) job sharing.
    d) hoteling.
Answer a   Page 674

47. Approximately ___ American workers currently are involved in telecommuting.
    a) 1 million
    b) 7 million
    c) 12 million
    d) 25 million
Answer c   Page 675

48. Research shows that nearly ___ of workers are involved in some sort of bonuses or performance-related pay.
    a) 40%
    b) 50%
    c) 60%
    d) 70%
Answer a   Page 676

49. For a pay-for-performance system to work, it should:

  a) be exclusive; only the best performers may be part of the plan.
  b) make sure that pay and performance are clearly and closely linked.
  c) be complex enough to include all elements that affect performance.
  d) be administered by an outside agency on a contract basis to avoid bias.
Answer b   Page 676

50. When seeking to motivate Generation X employees, the small business owner:
  a) can use the same incentives as he/she does with older employees.
  b) should treat them as a group to ensure fairness.
  c) may use titles and more pay.
  d) should trust them and offer them varied assignments.
Answer a   Page 677

51. Companies with younger employees, especially Generation Xers, find that these types of employees respond best to:
  a) monetary rewards.
  b) intangible rewards.
  c) fancy titles and bigger offices.
  d) bonuses and raises for working long hours.
Answer b   Page 677

52. When motivating employees, small business owners need to know that:
  a) money always motivates and never loses its power to motivate.
  b) today's workers are more materialistic than in the past.
  c) today's workers are far more concerned about job security than money.
  d) some of the greatest motivators are the simplest—praise, recognition, etc.
Answer d   Page 678–679

53. A motivational tool that also helps to guide performance and lets the owner know that his/her company is accomplishing its operational goals is:
  a) benchmarking.
  b) feedback.
  c) job redesign.
  d) a human resource audit.
Answer b   Page 680

54. The first step in establishing a feedback loop is deciding:
  a) who will be responsible for the measurement of performance.
  b) how to measure performance criteria.
  c) what will be measured.
  d) why it will be measured.
Answer c   Page 681

55. Anuar is comparing this month's operational costs, productivity, accident rate, etc., to the goals his boss set with him at the beginning of the year. Anuar is at what point in the feedback loop?
  a) Comparing performance against standards
  b) Deciding what to measure
  c) Deciding how to measure performance

    d) Conducting a performance appraisal

Answer a   Page 682

56. In the feedback loop, the final and most important step is when the manager/small business owner:
    a) compares actual performance against the standards.
    b) takes action to improve performance.
    c) finds who is responsible for either shortfalls or surpassing of standards.
    d) plans for the future.

Answer b   Page 682

57. A _____ is used by the owner of a small business to determine wage and salary increases, need for training, overall job progress, etc., among other things.
    a) human resource plan
    b) job redesign
    c) compensation plan
    d) performance evaluation

Answer d   Page 683

58. Employees' biggest complaint about performance appraisals tends to be:
    a) they are unfair and do not measure what they actually do.
    b) that they only happen periodically, generally once a year.
    c) that they are more demotivating than motivating.
    d) most managers don't know how to conduct them.

Answer b   Page 683

59. An effective performance appraisal system:
    a) focuses on behavior, action, and results.
    b) focuses on fixing employee weaknesses.
    c) is both personal and general in terms of the comments made.
    d) is dominated by the manager giving feedback and asking if he/she is understood.

Answer a   Page 684

60. Research suggests that about ____ of U.S. companies have gone to 360-degree feedback systems.
    a) 5%
    b) 15%
    c) 20%
    d) 30%

Answer d   Page 684

True or False Questions

61. The most important role the entrepreneur can play in his/her company is that of manager.
Answer F   Page 647

62. Management skills keep the leader under some degree of control.
Answer T   Page 648

63. An effective leader helps employees focus their efforts on goals and keeps them driving to accomplish them.
Answer T   Page 648

64. An important part of effective leadership is not only communicating with employees but also providing them with the resources necessary to achieve their goals.
Answer T   Page 649

65. The small business leader performs four vital tasks; communicating the vision, finding the necessary resources to accomplish the vision, finding the external expertise to help accomplish the vision, and the ability to motivate his/her own workers to achieve the vision.
Answer F   Page 650

66. Leadership is like management in that it maintains order and structure in the accomplishment of goals.
Answer F   Page 650

67. The common element in all of the reasons generally offered as to why employees don't do what they are asked to do is poor communication.
Answer T   Page 651

68. Sometimes personal defense mechanisms and confusing verbal and nonverbal messages interfere with leader/follower communication.
Answer T   Page 651

69. To improve communication, leaders should use written means, e-mail, memos, notes, etc., to ensure clarity and to be able to track that instructions were given.
Answer F   Page 652

70. Listening is the entrepreneur's most important communication skill.
Answer T   Page 652

71. Hiring is very important for the small company, because the typical entry-level hire that quits in six months costs the company about $5,000 besides the wages and benefits paid.
Answer F   Page 653

72. Research shows that ^{3} of CEOs of growing companies say that finding skilled workers is the number one threat to the growth of their company.
Answer T   Page 653

73. When Jean West of Salestar used a web-based recruiting ad, she discovered that it cost $^\alpha$ of a newspaper ad and generated better results.
Answer T   Page 654

74. Experts say that when hiring employees, 2 out of every 3 hires turn out very well.
Answer F   Page 655

75. A job analysis describes what the job is, what its duties and responsibilities are, and what working conditions are involved.
Answer F   Page 655

76. Information gathered during a job analysis provides the foundation for creating job descriptions and job specifications.

Answer T   Page 655

77. A job description sets forth duties; a job specification translates these duties into qualifications for that job.
Answer T   Page 655–656

78. The job specification outlines the duties and responsibilities of a job and its working conditions.
Answer T   Page 656

79. It is important during the job interview to get the candidate to discuss actual situations in which he/she has used the skill or knowledge you are seeking.
Answer T   Page 657

80. The most effective job interviews are unplanned, unstructured interactions between the small business owner and the job applicant.
Answer F   Page 657

81. The small business owner should open an interview with a major question.
Answer F   Page 658

82. Effective interviewers spend about 75% of their time listening to the candidate.
Answer T   Page 658

83. It is legal and appropriate for the entrepreneur to ask a job candidate if they have children or have been arrested.
Answer F   Page 659

84. During an interview, an employer may not ask job candidates if they are a U.S. citizen or if they have any physical or mental infirmities that would interfere with performing the job.
Answer T   Page 659

85. It is estimated that at least 25% of all applications and resumes contain at least one major fabrication.
Answer T   Page 660

86. If an employment test measures what it is intended to measure, then the test is reliable.
Answer F   Page 660

87. Small companies can compete for the best and the brightest job applicants by hiring older retired people, offering "psychic income when they can't match a larger company's offer," and by making the work place a fun place to be.
Answer T   Page 661

88. The experienced business owner knows that either his/her interview or his current employees' reaction to the job candidate is the best determinant if this individual should be hired.
Answer F   Page 662

89. An organization's culture is largely formed by the founder/entrepreneur who started the company.
Answer T   Page 662

90. A "cool" company culture holds individual employees responsible for their own professional development, education, and learning.
Answer F   Page 664

91. The first management style that most entrepreneurs use when starting their companies is that of the classic.
Answer F   Page 665

92. The best management style for the entrepreneur when he/she wants to grow a company to be fairly large but only has a few employees is the coordinator style.
Answer T   Page 666

93. Once an entrepreneur has grown the company to a large size and implemented self-managed teams, he/she needs to adopt the entrepreneur-plus-employee team management style.
Answer F   Page 667

94. The use of teams in a small business can fail for a number of reasons including not providing the members or leader adequate training.
Answer T   Page 668

95. If the entrepreneur forms teams around the natural work flow and/or involves teams in deciding how to measure their own performance, the probability of success is significantly improved.
Answer T   Page 669

96. When a team is committed to the process and task and is monitoring its own behavior and providing members feedback, then the team is most likely in the realization stage of team development.
Answer F   Page 670, Figure 19.1

97. When a small business owner moves to an empowering management style, he/she should expect to lose about 5% of the workforce because that represents the number of workers who do not want to work in that type of environment.
Answer T   Page 671

98. Open book management is a management style where the owner provides employees with access to all the company's records, including financial statements.
Answer T   Page 672

99. When an entrepreneur wants to motivate his/her employees by giving them more responsibility in their jobs and more control over all the elements of the job, he/she would use job enlargement.
Answer F   Page 673

100. Tina is dismantling her assembly-line operation and giving her workers responsibility for the entire job of creating the arc welders her company sells. By doing this, Tina is using a job enrichment strategy by specifically increasing task identity.
Answer T   Page 673

101. Flextime is an arrangement where the employees both share responsibility for a single job and may choose where and when they accomplish the assigned tasks.
Answer F   Page 674

102. Workers who telecommute have lower productivity but increased job satisfaction.
Answer F   Page 675

103. When employees who spend a great deal of time away from the office share the same office space, just using it at different times, the company is practicing hoteling.
Answer T   Page 676

104. A survey of small companies shows that nearly half reward their workers with bonuses or other performance-related compensation.
Answer T   Page 676

105. When motivating Generation X employees, it is important to remember that the same things motivate them as older workers; most of the stuff written about their different value structure is media mythology. Besides, federal law requires you to manage all employees the same way.
Answer F   Page 677

106. Generation X employees are motivated by having varied assignments, being trusted, and being treated as individuals.
Answer T   Page 677

107. For pay-for-performance systems to work, there needs to be frequent payouts to the employees.
Answer T   Page 678

108. To effectively recognize good performance in a way that motivates employees, the small business owner is forced to use financial rewards.
Answer F   Page 679

109. To be effective, any reward system used must be tailored to the tastes and interests of the employees.
Answer T   Page 680

110. The first step in establishing a feedback or performance appraisal process is to decide what performance to measure.
Answer T   Page 681

111. The goal of providing feedback is to uncover the reasons for any deficiencies in performance, not merely blame or scold the employee.
Answer T   Page 682

112. When the feedback session is done the employer should leave any corrective action up to the employee, letting them decide what to do and when to improve their performance.
Answer F   Page 682

113. The biggest complaint heard about performance appraisals is that they only happen periodically, generally once a year, and most employees don't receive ongoing feedback on the job.

Answer T   Page 683
114. Effective performance appraisals link the employee's performance to his/her specific job description.
Answer T   Page 683

115. Most of the time of a performance evaluation should be spent discussing the future and what can be done to improve performance.
Answer T   Page 684

Essay Questions

116. What is the entrepreneur's role as a leader in the small business?
Pages 647–648

117. Outline and briefly explain the key behaviors that an effective leader of a small business should demonstrate.
Pages 648–649

118. What are the barriers to effective communication that the small business owner needs to be aware of and to overcome?
Pages 651–652

119. Why is the hiring decision so important to the small business?
Pages 653–654

120. Discuss the roles that job analysis, job descriptions, and job specifications play in the human resource planning process.
Pages 654–655

121. Review the process for planning an effective interview.
Pages 656–658

122. Outline the steps in conducting an interview, explaining the important aspects of each step.
Pages 658–660

123. Explain the use of employment tests and reference checking in the hiring process.
Pages 660–662

124. What is company culture and how does it influence the staffing and leading of a growing company?
Pages 662–665

125. Name and briefly explain the six management styles an entrepreneur can adopt in leading his/her small business.
Pages 665–667

126. When using team-based management style, what errors does the manager have to be careful to avoid? How can he/she ensure the teams' success?
Pages 667-669

127. What is the role of empowerment in motivating workers? What does the small business owner need to do to help empowerment to work in his/her company?
Pages 670–672

128. How can job design serve as a motivational tool for the small business owner? What are the various elements of job design the entrepreneur needs to consider when seeking to motivate employees?
Pages 673–676

129. What is pay-for-performance and how does it motivate workers to greater and more effective work efforts?
Pages 676–680

130. How is feedback motivational to employees?
Pages 680–681

131. What are the four key elements of the feedback loop? Briefly explain each.
Pages 581–682

132. Outline the necessary guidelines for establishing a performance appraisal system.
Pages 683–684

Mini-Cases

Case 19-1: The Pride of Vicksburg

Wallace Fry had been a lover of good food from the time he was a child. The only son of wealthy Southern parents, he spent hours with his mother watching her prepare meals for the family and friends. By the time Wallace was in high school, he had already won a number of awards for his original recipes. After leaving Vicksburg, Mississippi to attend college in the Midwest, Wallace returned home to what must have been an unbelievable graduation present. His relatives had purchased an old paddlewheel riverboat and had begun initial preparations to have it moored permanently at the foot of the Vicksburg landing on the Mississippi River. Wallace was presented with a 50% interest in the restaurant named "The Pride of Vicksburg."

The complete renovation and restoration of the beautiful old riverboat took an additional four months. Wallace was planning to have his new restaurant open for the spring tourist season. A number of regional magazines had already run feature stories on the project. With the opening one month away, Wallace decided it was time to staff the restaurant.

Questions
1. Choose five positions he needs to fill and create a job description and job specification for each.

2. Wallace needs to interview a number of candidates. Create a ten-question interview guide for two of the positions for which he needs to interview applicants.

Case 19-2: Moore Construction

Agnes Moore was a good person to work for. She permitted her crews to make on-site decisions as they were needed and then communicate to her what they did. Employees were accountable for what they did, but they appreciated Agnes' trust. Whenever she brought a new employee on the payroll, she had one of the experienced hands work with the new employee for several months, advising, guiding, and helping the new employee adjust to Moore Construction. As a consequence, when Agnes asked for an "extra effort" when money was tight, employees understood and didn't complain.

Questions

1   What form of management style is Agnes using? Do you think it's effective? Why or why not?

2   If Agnes decided to go to a team-based management style, which style would be most effective in this business and how would she go about implementing it?

Chapter 20 –
Management Succession and Risk Management
in the Family Business

Multiple Choice Questions

1. In the United States, family businesses:
   a) are in decline due to mergers and acquisitions by middle-sized companies.
   b) generate 30% of the nation's GNP.
   c) employ more than 100 million people.
   d) account for about 80% of all businesses.

Answer d   Page 689

2. Family businesses in the United States contribute as much as _____ of the gross domestic product.
   a) 25%
   b) 50%
   c) 75%
   d) 90%

Answer b   Page 689

3. _____ of the Fortune 500 companies are family businesses.
   a) One third
   b) One quarter
   c) One half
   d) One in ten

Answer a   Page 689

4. Approximately _____ of all family businesses do not survive into the second generation.
   a) 25%
   b) 50%
   c) 70%
   d) 85%

Answer c   Page 690

5. Almost _____ % of business founders intend to pass their companies on to their children.
   a) 80
   b) 25
   c) 75
   d) 60

Answer a   Page 690

6. More than _____ of family businesses do not have a formal management succession plan.
   a) 25%
   b) 50%
   c) 70%
   d) 85%

Answer b   Page 690

7. An often overlooked quality that is essential to a successful family business is:
    a) an exit strategy for the founder/owner.
    b) common market share and customer service goals.
    c) shared values and vision for the business.
    d) a tax plan for retaining as much of the company profits as possible.
Answer c   Page 690

8. The essential quality for a family business that shows a recognition that decisions should be left to the person with the greatest talent in that area is the quality of:
    a) shared power.
    b) shared values.
    c) tradition.
    d) strong family ties.
Answer a   Page 690

9. Amanda and William run a retail clothing store together. Amanda is a CPA with great financial analysis skills. William has the sense of style and strong negotiating skills. Financial decisions are largely left to Amanda, while buying and display decisions are left to William. This is an example of the essential quality of:
    a) shared power.
    b) a willingness to learn and grow.
    c) tradition.
    d) shared values and vision.
Answer a   Page 690

10. _____ is an essential quality for a successful family business but it can also become a barrier to change. When it provides a foundation it works well, when it restricts the future it becomes a barrier.
    a) Shared power
    b) Shared values
    c) Tradition
    d) Family behavior
Answer c   Page 691

11. The use of a formal family counsel with an open discussion of all ideas is a way to demonstrate the essential quality of:
    a) shared power.
    b) a willingness to learn and grow.
    c) shared values.
    d) family behavior.
Answer b   Page 691

12. While it is an essential quality for a successful family business, this quality is the one that cannot be imposed or forced. If family members refuse to embrace it, they can still be part of the business.
    a) shared power
    b) a willingness to learn and grow
    c) shared values
    d) family behavior

Answer d   Page 691

13. Alicia has decided to retire and sell her business. She wants to walk away from the business and enjoy her retirement without having to think about the business. She has no children or employees who want to buy it. Her best choice of an exit strategy is:
    a) a sale for cash plus a note.
    b) a leveraged buyout.
    c) a straight sale.
    d) an ESOP.

Answer c   Page 692

14. The employees of Martin's Cleaners, a small retail chain of dry cleaner stores and laundromats, are buying the business from the owner, who is retiring. They are offering the owner ^{2} of the asking price in cash plus quarterly payments on the balance, with payoff complete in three years. This is an example of:
    a) a sale for cash plus a note.
    b) a leveraged buyout.
    c) a straight sale.
    d) an ESOP.

Answer a   Page 693

15. Ted is retiring in five years and is thinking of selling the business. Ramon, his general manager, tells him that he, the other managers, and the employees want to buy the business from him. Ted sets up a process where all the managers and employees "buy" stock in the company each month through payroll deductions, so that in five years the employees hold 100% of the company. This is an example of:
    a) a sale for cash plus a note.
    b) a leveraged buyout.
    c) a straight sale.
    d) an ESOP.

Answer d   Page 693

16. ____ of all small business owners expect to transfer ownership of their business to their children within.
    a) 50%, 10 years
    b) 15%, the next year
    c) 40%+, 5 years
    d) 25%, 3 years

Answer c   Page 694

17. While a large percentage of business founders plan to pass on their businesses, few create a management succession plans because:
    a) they don't know how to do it.
    b) they are reluctant to let go of the business.
    c) they can't afford the attorneys' and accountants' fees.
    d) they don't feel they need one because they know which child will assume management of the business.

Answer b   Page 694

18. In ____ of the management succession process, the successor is allowed to rotate through a variety of jobs to broaden the base understanding of the business as well as to have his/her skills evaluated.
    a) Stage I
    b) Stage II
    c) Stage III
    d) Stage IV
Answer b   Page 695

19. A formal mentoring program should be established in ____, using both internal and external people. As the successor develops his/her skills and performance, he/she will transition to the next stage.
    a) Stage I
    b) Stage II
    c) Stage III
    d) Stage IV
Answer c   Page 695

20. In ____ of the management succession process, the successor's real decision-making power grows rapidly. The final assessment of the individual's abilities is determined.
    a) Stage I
    b) Stage II
    c) Stage III
    d) Stage IV
Answer d   Page 696

21. When Marshall Paisner decided to pass his Scrub-A-Dub car wash chain on to his children, he violated one of the cardinal rules of the transfer of power, but it worked. What he did was:
    a) made a quick transition in about 30 days and walked away.
    b) made both of his sons co-presidents and had them share power and the company.
    c) named his youngest son to the presidency of the company but retained all final decision control.
    d) sold the company to an outsider through a cash payment of 10% and a note for 90% of the value of the business.
Answer b   Page 697

22. Small business owners can make a number of mistakes in their management succession plan including:
    a) naming a successor too early.
    b) having another manager in the company mentor the successor.
    c) assuming his/her children want control of the business.
    d) all of these.
Answer c   Page 698

23. When transferring power in a management succession, the small business owner should:
    a) select the successor as close to his/her retirement as possible.
    b) provide the successor with a list of advisers, people who have given you good advice in the past.

c) not let the successor make any changes initially.
d) transfer power quickly and step back, letting the successor run the business without interference.

Answer b   Page 699

24. During the transfer of power, when the successor makes mistakes, the owner should:
    a) use them as a means for teaching.
    b) step in and fix them him/herself, to prevent damage to the company.
    c) explain how the owner would have handled it and insist it be done that way in the future.
    d) retake control of the company.

Answer a   Page 700

25. Current law permits the transfer of up to _____ to heirs without estate taxes.
    a) $10,000
    b) $150,000
    c) $600,000
    d) $1.3 million

Answer d   Page 701

26. The most common and popular estate planning tool for small business owners is the:
    a) buy/sell agreement.
    b) irrevocable trust.
    c) family limited partnership.
    d) estate freeze.

Answer a   Page 701

27. A/An _____ gives the surviving owner or heir of a family business the right to purchase the stock of the deceased owner at a price established by a predetermined formula.
    a) grantor-retained annuity trust
    b) estate freeze
    c) Unified Transfer Credit
    d) buy/sell agreement

Answer d   Page 701

28. A business founder relying on a lifetime giving strategy to minimize the taxes on the estate she is passing on to her son can give him a maximum gift of _____ in company stock each year, tax exempt.
    a) $5,000
    b) $10,000
    c) $25,000
    d) $100,000

Answer b   Page 702

29. A/An _____ is an agreement between a grantor and a trustee where the trustee holds legal title to property for the beneficiaries of the trust.
    a) grantor-retained annuity trust
    b) family limited partnership
    c) trust
    d) estate freeze

Answer c   Page 702

30. A/An _____ attempts to minimize taxes on a family business passed from one generation to the next by creating two classes of stock—one for the parents (preferred stock), whose value is locked in, and another for the children (common stock), whose value reflects the market value of the business.
    a) grantor-retained annuity trust
    b) estate freeze
    c) trust
    d) buy/sell agreement

Answer b   Page 703

31. In a grantor-retained annuity trust:
    a) there is an attempt to minimize taxes on a family by creating two classes of stock—preferred stock, whose value is locked in, and common stock, whose value reflects the market value of the business.
    b) a business owner can pass on up to $10,000 annually, which is exempt from federal gift taxes.
    c) the grantor retains the voting power and interest income from the stock in the trust for up to ten years.
    d) the surviving owner or heir of a family business has the right to purchase the stock of the deceased owner at a price established by a predetermined formula.

Answer c   Page 703

32. The _____ is a transfer of ownership strategy for an owner to transfer the company to his/her children while retaining control over it him/herself.
    a) grantor-retained annuity trust
    b) family limited partnership
    c) revocable trust
    d) estate freeze

Answer b   Page 703

33. Pyrrhic Revenge is the phenomenon in management succession when:
    a) an outside buyer fails to succeed and defaults on the purchase agreement.
    b) the founder/owner reneges on the transfer of power and reassumes control of the company.
    c) the succession turf battle between siblings destroys the company.
    d) the family limited partnership agreement is invalidated by the state government.

Answer c   Page 704

34. A small fireworks manufacturer that shuts its plant down permanently because the risk of fire and the resulting losses are too great is relying on a risk _____ strategy.
    a) avoidance
    b) reduction
    c) anticipation
    d) transfer

Answer a   Page 705

35. A company using a risk avoidance strategy would:
    a) buy an insurance policy to cover the risk.
    b) cease the process or function that constituted the risk.
    c) educate employees as to the risks and dangers of the problem process.

d)   set resources aside to deal with the problem when it arose.

Answer b   Page 705

36.   A company that installs a sprinkler system in its corrugated box factory is using a risk _____ strategy.
   a)   avoidance
   b)   reduction
   c)   anticipation
   d)   transfer

Answer b   Page 706

37.   A company using a risk reduction strategy would:
   a)   buy an insurance policy to cover the risk.
   b)   cease the process or function that constituted the risk.
   c)   educate employees as to the risks and dangers of the problem process.
   d)   set resources aside to deal with the problem when it arose.

Answer c   Page 706

38.   A small business that puts aside a specific amount of money into a special fund each month to cover the cost of replacing its highly specialized manufacturing equipment is using a risk _____ strategy.
   a)   avoidance
   b)   reduction
   c)   anticipation
   d)   transfer

Answer c   Page 707

39.   A company using a risk anticipation strategy would do which of the following?
   a)   Buy an insurance policy to cover the risk.
   b)   Cease the process or function that constituted the risk.
   c)   Educate employees as to the risks and dangers of the problem process.
   d)   Set resources aside to deal with the problem when it arose.

Answer d   Page 707

40.   A small business that buys a fire insurance policy on the equipment in its corrugated box factory is relying on a risk _____ strategy.
   a)   avoidance
   b)   reduction
   c)   anticipation
   d)   transfer

Answer d   Page 708

41.   A company using a risk transfer strategy would do which of the following?
   a)   Buy an insurance policy to cover the risk.
   b)   Cease the process or function that constituted the risk.
   c)   Educate employees as to the risks and dangers of the problem process.
   d)   Set resources aside to deal with the problem when it arose.

Answer a   Page 708

42. Insurance companies are able to assume so much risk because:
    a) they are stock-based companies with deep pockets.
    b) they are "gamblers" who bet they are going to make money before they have to pay off any claims.
    c) they share the risk among numerous policy holders.
    d) they are backed by the government and will be "bailed out" if they get into trouble.

Answer c   Page 709

43. There are specific requirements for insurability which include:
    a) the value of the actual loss must be possible to determine.
    b) the risk cannot be selected.
    c) the risk must be within a single geographical area.
    d) there must a pool of insurers who will accept the risk.

Answer a   Page 709

44. When a risk is evaluated in terms of how much it could affect a company's ability to operate, the risk is being assessed in terms of:
    a) probability.
    b) cost.
    c) actuality.
    d) severity.

Answer d   Page 709

45. If a risk is rated ADB, this means that:
    a) it is high in probability, low in severity, and above average in loss.
    b) it is high in severity, low in probability, and above average in loss.
    c) it is low in loss, high in severity, and average in probability.
    d) it is low in severity, high in loss, and above average in probability.

Answer b   Page 710

46. The business owner's policy (BOP) typically includes only:
    a) theft and crime.
    b) pensions and annuities, and health.
    c) property and casualty, and liability.
    d) disability and hospitalization.

Answer c   Page 711

47. _____ insurance is protection from loss, theft, or destruction applied to vehicles, buildings, etc. It can be written with a broad coverage or to cover a specific item or items.
    a) Life and health
    b) Pensions and annuities
    c) Workers' compensation
    d) Property insurance

Answer d   Page 711

48. When a business owner purchases protection for losses occurring when a contract is not completed on time or is performed incorrectly, it is buying _____ insurance.
    a) casualty
    b) surety

   c)   liability
   d)   comprehensive
Answer b   Page 712

49.   Life insurance differs from all other types of insurance in that:
   a)   it cannot be purchased by the one who benefits from the loss.
   b)   it does not pertain to risk.
   c)   it is federally insured.
   d)   it doesn't pay unless there is a loss.
Answer b   Page 712

50.   Bill is the CEO of a small company. Recently his board suggested he get _____ insurance. The board had come to realize that if Bill died or left the company, they would lose most of their major customers. It also would be a long and expensive process to find another CEO. This insurance would cover those losses.
   a)   business interruption
   b)   hospitalization and medical
   c)   key person
   d)   professional liability
Answer c   Page 712

51.   _____ is a form of disability insurance.
   a)   Life insurance
   b)   Surety insurance
   c)   Pension and annuities
   d)   Hospitalization and medical insurance
Answer d   Page 713

52.   A dentist or an attorney would buy malpractice insurance to transfer the risk of lawsuits. This is a type of _____ insurance.
   a)   casualty
   b)   surety
   c)   liability
   d)   comprehensive
Answer c   Page 714

53.   When a doctor or other health care provider claims payment for nonexistent or unnecessary treatments in relationship to a worker's compensation claim, the employer has a case of:
   a)   provider fraud.
   b)   insurer fraud.
   c)   premium fraud.
   d)   claimant fraud.
Answer a   Page 715

54.   _____ protects against damage a business causes clients due to a mistake on their part.
   a)   worker's compensation.
   b)   professional liability insurance.
   c)   surety insurance.
   d)   employment practices liability insurance.

Answer b   Page 716

55. One of the fastest growing forms of insurance that protects companies against claims due to suits on grounds of the Americans with Disabilities Act and the Medical Leave Act, etc., is:
    a) Worker's compensation
    b) Professional liability insurance
    c) Surety insurance
    d) Employment practices liability insurance
Answer d   Page 717

56. The most successful type of suit by employees against employers is for:
    a) race discrimination.
    b) age discrimination.
    c) sexual harassment.
    d) breach of contract.
Answer d   Page 717

57. There are a number of ways to control insurance costs in the property and casualty insurance area, including:
    a) increase policy deductibles.
    b) conduct a safety audit.
    c) conduct a yearly utilization review.
    d) increase the dollar amount of employee contributions.
Answer a   Page 718

58. Small business owners have a number of options for controlling health care costs, such as:
    a) increase policy deductibles.
    b) conduct a safety audit.
    c) pursue a loss-control program.
    d) decrease the dollar amount of employee contributions.
Answer b   Page 719

59. The creation of a safety team, conduct of a safety audit, and creation of a safety manual are all techniques for controlling:
    a) property and casualty insurance costs.
    b) professional liability insurance costs.
    c) health care insurance costs.
    d) worker's compensation insurance costs.
Answer c   Page 719–720

True or False Questions

60. 80% of all businesses in America are family-owned businesses.
Answer T   Page 689

61. Family businesses generate nearly 40% of the United States' gross domestic product and employ more than 60 million people.
Answer F   Page 689

62. One-third of the Fortune 500 companies are family businesses.

Answer T   Page 689

63. The majority of first-generation family businesses do not survive into the second generation.
Answer T   Page 690

64. Most business founders intend to pass their companies on to their children, and have a formal management succession plan for doing so.
Answer F   Page 690

65. Key to a successful family business is shared values.
Answer T   Page 690

66. The nice thing about a family business is that there is always a guaranteed successor within the family whenever the owner decides to step down.
Answer F   Page 690

67. It may be valuable for family members to work outside of the business for the purpose of learning how others conduct business.
Answer T   Page 690

68. The concept of shared power in the family business means that family members allow those with the greatest expertise in a particular area of the business to make decisions for that area.
Answer T   Page 690

69. Tradition, while important, is not essential to a successful family business.
Answer F   Page 691

70. A willingness to learn is not as important to a family business as a nonfamily business because the variety of talents and personalities within the family minimize the importance of new ideas and techniques from the outside.
Answer F   Page 691

71. "Playing together" at leisure activities makes it easier for family members to cooperate at work activities in the family business.
Answer T   Page 691

72. Playing together is so important to the success of a family business that family members should be forced to play together even when they don't want to.
Answer F   Page 691

73. A straight sale of the family business to outsiders is best for the founder because it is quick, easy, and has minimal tax consequences to the owner.
Answer F   Page 692

74. It is important for entrepreneurs to look beyond the financial aspects of buying a business and into the character and competence of the buyer.
Answer T   Page 693

75. ESOPs are simply another version of LBOs, used to buy companies from their owners.

Answer F   Page 693

76. Experts estimate that nearly $4.8 trillion dollars in wealth will be transferred from one generation to another in the twenty years from 1993 and 2013.
Answer T   Page 694

77. One barrier to management succession planning is that the founder often becomes so identified with the business it is difficult for him/her to let go.
Answer T   Page 694

78. It is important to remember that the succession planning process inevitably creates tension and distrust as family members envy the "chosen one."
Answer F   Page 695

79. Succession planning should begin when the children reach college age.
Answer F   Page 695

80. At Stage II, when the successor graduates from college, real decision-making authority begins to grow rapidly.
Answer F   Page 695

81. The successor to the business owner needs to have both technical ability—knowledge of the business and financial ability—and understanding of the financial aspects of the business for the transition to succeed.
Answer T   Page 696

82. Whenever a business has shared leadership, such as co-presidents, it is critical that the board of advisers have members on it from outside the family.
Answer T   Page 697

83. It is generally safe for the small business owner to assume that his/her children will succeed him/her into the business.
Answer F   Page 698

84. You should never keep your decision as to your successor a secret.
Answer T   Page 698

85. The preparation of a successor is a two-way process, showing the direction of the business and what led to its success, but also learning and listening.
Answer T   Page 699

86. Even though the owner has stepped aside, he/she should always jump back in to fix problems as they occur.
Answer F   Page 700

87. The process of transferring power should be quick and absolute.
Answer F   Page 700

88. Nearly $^\alpha$ of business owners think that their heirs will need to sell part or all of the business to satisfy estate taxes.
Answer T   Page 701

89. A buy/sell agreement often also uses life and disability insurance to ensure the surviving co-owners have the means to buy the business.
Answer T   Page 701

90. A bypass trust allows the business owner to keep life insurance proceeds out of his/her estate as long as the owner doesn't die within three years of establishing the trust.
Answer F   Page 702

91. An irrevocable asset trust is designated to pass insurance proceeds on to the small business owner's heirs without them having to pass through probate or be subject to estate taxes.
Answer F   Page 702

92. A trust is a contract between a grantor and a trustee which shields all assets from any federal tax and permits the small business owner to pass on his/her business without tax loss.
Answer F   Page 702

93. An estate freeze minimizes estate taxes by creating two classes of stock, preferred and nonvoting common stock, and only allowing the preferred stock, which the owner holds, to appreciate.
Answer T   Page 703

94. Insurance shields the small business owner from risk.
Answer F   Page 705

95. Risk management is deciding what type of insurance or other precautions need to be implemented to decrease a business's exposure to loss.
Answer T   Page 705

96. Anti-theft and anti-shoplifting equipment are risk avoidance devices.
Answer F   Page 705

97. Part of risk-reducing strategies is taking steps to build some safety into a situation.
Answer T   Page 706

98. Credit checking customers is an example of a risk reduction strategy.
Answer F   Page 706

99. Installing a sprinkler system to minimize the threat of fire would be a risk reduction strategy.
Answer T   Page 706

100. Risk anticipation strategies promote self-insurance.
Answer T   Page 707

101. Self-insurance is entirely a large business phenomenon.
Answer F   Page 707

102. A small business establishing a self-insurance fund is following a risk transferring strategy.
Answer F   Page 708

103. The risk behind self-insurance is that if there aren't sufficient funds set aside, the business will suffer losses.
Answer T   Page 708

104. Insurance coverage is an example of risk transfer.
Answer T   Page 709

105. Every risk can be insured.
Answer F   Page 709

106. A company with a CAB risk assessment would pay a higher premium that a company with a BAC risk assessment.
Answer F   Page 710

107. The lowest risk assessment rating on the risk management pyramid would be an ADB rating.
Answer T   Page 710

108. Automobile insurance is a form of property insurance.
Answer T   Page 711

109. Losses incurred by noncompliance with a contract are covered by surety insurance.
Answer T   Page 712

110. Goods in transit are insured by surety insurance.
Answer F   Page 712

111. Crime insurance covers for loss due to dishonesty, disappearance, and destruction.
Answer T   Page 712

112. Pensions and annuities are special forms of liability insurance.
Answer F   Page 713

113. When buying disability insurance, the primary criterion is the cost of the policy and any exclusionary clauses.
Answer F   Page 713

114. Every state in the Unites States requires an employer to subscribe to the worker's compensation program of their state.
Answer F   Page 714

115. Most BOPs do not include any liability coverage.
Answer F   Page 714

116. Due to the crackdown on fraud by employers, insurers, and states, the cost of worker's compensation insurance has actually gone down.

Answer T   Page 715

117. The highest median of compensatory awards due to lawsuits has been in the area of sex discrimination and sexual harassment.
Answer F   Page 716

118. One way to control health insurance costs has been for companies to switch to HMOs or PPOs from their traditional health care plans.
Answer T   Page 719

119. The key to controlling insurance costs for the small business owner is aggressive prevention.
Answer T   Page 720

Essay Questions

120. Identify and explain the essential qualities to a successful family business.
Pages 690–692

121. Describe the exit strategies available to the founder of the small business; if he/she wants to sell the company to insiders, and if he/she is willing to sell it to outsiders.
Pages 692–694

122. Why should the small business owner have a succession plan? Identify the five stages the owner needs to take his/her successor through in preparation for the succession.
Pages 694–698

123. Discuss the five steps involved in developing a management succession plan.
Pages 698–701

124. A friend wants to ensure that his succession plan succeeds. Explain how a "survival kit" can help the management plan succeed.
Pages 699–700

125. Name and outline the characteristics of the six strategies for reducing estate taxes in a family business.
Pages 701–704

126. Differentiate among the three risk management strategies: risk avoidance, risk anticipation, and risk transfer. Offer an example of each.
Pages 705–708

127. Explain the nature and purpose of insurance in relationship to the small business.
Pages 709–710

128. Outline the major types of insurance protection the typical small business needs.
Pages 710–717

129. What can a small business owner do to keep insurance costs under control?
Pages 718–720

Mini-Case

Case 20-1: Passing the Baton

Carol Wingard has worked hard building the small jewelry manufacturing company she started when she was in her late 20s into a highly successful family business. Now, 40 years later, she was "ready to step down and enjoy life." Seven family members, including her two sons, Ralph and Cooper, work in the business. Ralph, with 30 years of experience, and Cooper, with 22 years of experience, are both vice-presidents of the company.

Carol has always intended to pass the business on to her sons, who together own 20% of the company's stock. However, she has always been too busy running the business to put together a formal management succession plan. For the past decade, many of the employees have whispered among themselves about who would be named president it Mrs. Wingard stepped down and exactly what would happen to the business.

Now that she has decided to retire, Carol wants to begin developing a management succession plan.

Questions

1. Carol calls you and announces her plans to retire within a year. What advice would you offer her about a management succession plan?
2. What tools would you suggest to Carol to minimize the estate taxes involved in passing the business on to Ralph and Cooper? Explain the advantages and disadvantages of at least three choices and explain why you make the final recommendation that you do.

Chapter 21 –
Ethics, Social Responsibility and the Entrepreneur

Multiple Choice Questions

1. In a poll of Americans regarding business's role in society, nearly ___ rejected the idea that a company's only role in society was to make money.
   a) 55%
   b) 75%
   c) 95%
   d) 25%

Answer c   Page 723

2. The moral values and behavioral standards business people employ daily when making decisions and solving problems are known as:
   a) social responsibility.
   b) business ethics.
   c) the corporate culture.
   d) the company policies and procedures.

Answer b   Page 724

3. The various groups who affect and are affected by the decisions and actions of a small business are called:
   a) suppliers.
   b) stakeholders.
   c) minorities.
   d) intermediaries.

Answer b   Page 724

4. Small businesses are especially susceptible to ethically- charged issues because:
   a) of the limited resources inherently available to small businesses.
   b) of the regulatory environment in which they must operate.
   c) their owners lack knowledge of business law.
   d) of the lower standard of ethics most small business people have.

Answer a   Page 725

5. A small business's reputation in the business world is:
   a) very hardy and will withstand minor and occasional ethical lapses.
   b) built quickly and is lost just as quickly.
   c) hard to lose but also hard and slow to build up.
   d) fragile and precious, easily damaged and hard to regain.

Answer d   Page 725

6. The honor codes established by many colleges and universities are an example of which of the following ethical standards?
   a) The law
   b) The policies and procedures of the organization
   c) The moral stance of the individual
   d) A manager's code of conduct

Answer b   Page 726

7. Business ethics is a practical skill and:
   a) one that does not require development or practice.
   b) one under constant pressure, as over 75% managers have felt a conflict between profit considerations and ethical concerns.
   c) one that is seldom exercised for small business managers because there is little pressure to take ethical "shortcuts."
   d) less than 10% of all managers have felt any need or concern to exercise it.

Answer b   Page 726

8. Brauer software ran into trouble marketing their products on the web because they didn't consider the reaction of which stakeholder group?
   a) investors
   b) employees
   c) the government
   d) the community

Answer d   Page 727

9. Once a manager recognizes the ethical dimensions involved in a dilemma or decision, his/her next step in establishing a workable ethical framework to guide him/her would be to:
   a) identify key stakeholders and assess how the decision will affect them.
   b) generate alternative choices.
   c) distinguish between ethical and unethical responses to the situation.
   d) determine who is most responsible for making and implementing the decision.

Answer a   Page 728

10. The ultimate decision on whether to abide by ethical principles in any given situation rests with:
   a) the manager.
   b) the business owner.
   c) the individual.
   d) stakeholders.

Answer c   Page 728

11. Those who can most influence individual behavior within a small company and set the moral and ethical tone of a company are its:
   a) customers.
   b) managers or owners.
   c) employees.
   d) human resource managers.

Answer b   Page 728

12. The practice of moral management by the small business generally results in:
   a) a stronger competitive position.
   b) a weaker competitive position.
   c) increased governmental scrutiny of the company's business practices.
   d) lower operating costs and increased employee satisfaction.

Answer a   Page 729

13. Muhammad is considering an ethical dilemma. He is pondering how he would feel if he were on the other side of the issue and if the decision distributes benefits justly. Muhammad is considering the ethical dimension of:
    a) moral rights.
    b) justice.
    c) consequences and outcomes.
    d) public justification.

Answer b   Page 729

14. A/An _____ manager does not consider the impact his/her decisions will have on others.
    a) immoral
    b) amoral
    c) moral
    d) socially responsible

Answer b   Page 730

15. Ricardo disapproves of an advertising campaign featuring scantily clad models in suggestive poses with his company's product. Ricardo is practicing ___ ethical management.
    a) immoral
    b) amoral
    c) moral
    d) socially irresponsible

Answer c   Page 730

16. Ethical lapses happen for a number of reasons. Joan made an unethical decision. When confronted with it by her boss, she couldn't understand why he was upset because "Everyone does it." This is an example of an ethical lapse due to:
    a) a "bad apple."
    b) a "bad barrel."
    c) opportunity pressures.
    d) competitive pressures.

Answer a   Page 731

17. Ethical lapses caused by a chance to "get ahead" by taking some unethical action come about because of:
    a) a "bad apple."
    b) a "bad barrel."
    c) opportunity pressures.
    d) competitive pressures.

Answer c   Page 732

18. There are a number of "tests" of ethical behavior in business. The one that prioritizes choosing the option that results in the greatest good for the greatest number of people is known as:
    a) the utilitarian principle.
    b) the professional ethic.
    c) the Golden Rule.
    d) Kant's categorical imperative.

Answer a   Page 733

19. If your ethical conduct is based on treating other people the way you expect them to treat you, you are using:
    a) the family test.
    b) the professional ethic.
    c) the Golden Rule.
    d) Kant's categorical imperative.
Answer c   Page 733

20. The ethical standards test of ethical behavior in businesses that prioritizes acting in such a way that the action taken under the circumstances could be a universal law or rule of behavior is called:
    a) the family test.
    b) the professional ethic.
    c) the Golden Rule.
    d) Kant's categorical imperative.
Answer d   Page 733

21. A company "Code of Ethics" refers to:
    a) the awareness of a company's management of the social, environmental, political, and human, as well as the financial, consequences that its actions produce.
    b) the moral values and behavioral standards business people employ daily when making decisions and solving problems.
    c) a formal statement of the standards of behavior and ethical principles a company expects its employees to abide by.
    d) the process of bringing land, labor, and capital together, and of assuming the risks involved in producing a good or service in the hope of making a profit.
Answer c   Page 734

22. Robin works hard at acting on principle and conviction and striving to do the honorable thing. Robin is guided by the ethical principle of:
    a) honesty.
    b) integrity.
    c) fidelity.
    d) fairness.
Answer b   Page 734

23. A number of things can be done in order to integrate ethical principles into a company, such as:
    a) limiting diversity in their hiring.
    b) establishing a legalistic and rigid set of rules and ensuring obedience to them.
    c) creating a one-way communication culture, clearly communicating expectations.
    d) the conduct of top managers setting impeccable ethical examples.
Answer d   Page 735

24. The entrepreneur can implement and maintain ethical standards by:
    a) performing periodic ethical audits.
    b) making examples of clearly visible violators.
    c) handing down a strict code of ethics established by upper management.
    d) doing all of these.
Answer a   Page 735

25. Survey research shows that ____ of consumers would buy on the basis of a company's social responsibility if price, service, and quality were equal among products.
    a) 25%
    b) 50%
    c) 70%
    d) 90%

Answer d   Page 736

26. This term denotes the awareness of a company's management of the social, environmental, political, human, and financial consequences that its actions produce:
    a) company polices and procedures.
    b) the corporate culture.
    c) social responsibility.
    d) business ethics.

Answer c   Page 736

27. Perhaps the best way to deal with the environmental challenges we face would be to:
    a) create redesigned, "clean" manufacturing systems.
    b) conduct corporate education programs on the issues for employees.
    c) revert society to a simpler, more environmentally friendly economy.
    d) enhance efforts at recycling existing waste.

Answer a   Page 737

28. Ray Anderson improved his company's response to the environment by:
    a) creating a clean manufacturing environment.
    b) reusing materials.
    c) recycling materials in his plant.
    d) increasing cultural diversity in his company.

Answer a   Page 738

29. If the small business owner wants to demonstrate that the company is serious about its responsibility toward employees, he/she should:
    a) focus on creating the maximum return on investment.
    b) listen to employees and involve them in decision making.
    c) begin a reengineering effort to improve productivity.
    d) decrease the cultural diversity in his/her company.

Answer b   Page 738

30. It is estimated that by the year 2005, ____% of the workforce will be women and minorities.
    a) 85
    b) 43
    c) 62
    d) 37

Answer c   Page 739

31. Cultural diversity in the small business brings several benefits to its owner, including:
    a) less government scrutiny of his/her business practices.
    b) local and state tax breaks.
    c) a smaller but better educated and skilled labor force from which to hire new employees.
    d) a rich blend of perspectives, skills, and talents.

Answer d   Page 739

32. Managing diversity in the workforce means managers need to:
    a) hire more minorities and fewer non-minorities.
    b) create an environment in which all types of workers can flourish.
    c) establish affirmative action programs.
    d) strive for more homogeneity in the workforce.

Answer b   Page 740

33. Managing diversity begins with:
    a) concentrating on communication.
    b) recognizing your own biases and stereotypes.
    c) valuing diversity as a core company value.
    d) assessing your company's diversity needs.

Answer d   Page 741

34. The small business owner can successfully manage diversity in his/her business by:
    a) avoiding invalid assumptions.
    b) placing managers of the same gender or ethnic origin over workers.
    c) treating all employees the same regardless of their cultural background.
    d) setting quotas or goals for how many individuals from different groups should work in the company.

Answer a   Page 741

35. Experts estimate drug abuse costs U.S. businesses _____ a year because almost _____ of all drug abusers are employed.
    a) $100 million, 34%
    b) $250 million, 63%
    c) $1 billion, 74%
    d) $3.2 billion, 82%

Answer c   Page 742

36. Experts estimate that _____% of all American workers use drugs on the job.
    a) 23
    b) 56
    c) 37
    d) 64

Answer a   Page 742

37. Companies can avoid drug and other related problems by including several key elements in the company drug program.
    a) Drug testing all employees periodically regardless of need
    b) Having a written substance abuse policy

c) Turning supervisors into "drug police" by having them watch employees for signs of substance abuse

d) By including all of these in the drug program

Answer b   Page 742

38. What is an EAP?
a) It is a drug testing program for small businesses.
b) It is a program to help employees with substance abuse and other types of personal and family problems.
c) It is an HIV screening process used in the recruiting process.
d) It is a type of diversity management program.

Answer b   Page 743

39. AIDS is becoming a serious problem in the workplace, as it is the leading cause of death for Americans aged:
a) one month to 7 years.
b) 17–20.
c) 25–44.
d) 45–57.

Answer d   Page 743

40. When it comes to small businesses and AIDS:
a) businesses with 50 or more employees are subject to the Sherman Act which classifies AIDS as a disease.
b) they will be bankrupted by HIV-positive employees if they don't fire them prior to the onset of AIDS.
c) any company with 15 or more employees is subject to the Americans with Disabilities Act which classifies AIDS as a disability.
d) they are far less impacted by AIDS issues than large companies.

Answer c   Page 743

41. One of the great dangers of AIDS in the workplace is:
a) the risk of infection for other employees.
b) its potential for destroying relationships at work.
c) the probability that it will bankrupt small businesses.
d) that it is likely to make it more expensive and difficult to get health care insurance.

Answer b   Page 744

42. When dealing with AIDS in the workplace, small business owners should:
a) Treat AIDS positive employees as they would any other employees with life threatening illnesses.
b) make certain their employment policies comply with local regulations but not worry about federal regulations.
c) require HIV screening as part of the hiring process.
d) inform all employees when someone tests HIV positive.

Answer a   Page 745

43. A company's AIDS policy should include:

a) an open communication policy where all employees will be informed if someone becomes ill.
b) a continuation of employee benefits as any other employee would have.
c) process for dismissal of the affected employee.
d) all of these.

Answer b   Page 745

44. Sexual harassment is a serious problem in the workplace and:
a) about 40% of all sexual harassment in the workplace is done by females to males.
b) is especially bad in small businesses.
c) employers are only liable as the sexual harassment is "quid pro quo."
d) 90% of the charges are brought by women.

Answer d   Page 745

45. Marian works in an office where the male employees constantly tell sexually oriented jokes, some keep suggestive pictures on the walls of the cubicles, and several men whistle at and make lurid comments to women employees in the lunch room. This is an example of what type of sexual harassment?
a) quid pro quo
b) hostile environment
c) harassment by a third party
d) none of these

Answer b   Page 746

46. Regarding sexual harassment, employers should realize that they:
a) can be held responsible for third-party sexual harassment.
b) are protected from liability if they are aware of a harassment problem, even if they don't take action.
c) are not liable for sexual harassment in the workplace if they have a formal policy against it.
d) are not liable if they didn't know it was taking place, even if one could reasonably expect them to know.

Answer a   Page 746

47. Which of the following is true about sexual harassment?
a) The best way to handle unwanted sexual attention is to ignore it.
b) If no one asks someone to stop making sexual comments, then sexual harassment has not taken place.
c) Employers can not be held liable for sexual harassment if they have a company policy against it.
d) The sexual harasser may be required to pay part of the settlement in a suit.

Answer d   Page 747

48. Regarding sexual harassment, employers should realize that they:
a) can be held responsible for third-party sexual harassment.
b) are protected from liability if they are aware of a harassment problem, even if they don't take action.
c) are not liable for sexual harassment in the workplace if they have a formal policy against it.
d) are not liable if they didn't know it was taking place, even if one could reasonably expect them to know.

Answer a   Page 748

49. In the recent Supreme Court ruling in Burlington Industries vs. Ellerth, the court held:
     a) employers were no longer liable for third-party sexual harassment.
     b) there does not have to be a superior-subordinate relationship for harassment to occur.
     c) complainants must prove intent to harass on the part of the harasser.
     d) employers are automatically liable if supervisors takes tangible employment action toward the person they are harassing.
Answer d   Page 748

50. If a manager is made aware of a sexual harassment problem, he/she should:
     a) immediately fire the person accused of the harassment.
     b) ask the complainant to approach the harasser and try to work it out.
     c) listen carefully and investigate quickly and thoroughly.
     d) make all and any findings public to protect all parties.
Answer c   Page 749

51. Experts estimate that ____ workers in the United States are subject to computer monitoring.
     a) 10 million
     b) 20 million
     c) 52 million
     d) 63 million
Answer b   Page 749

52. When it comes to monitoring electronic communication, especially e-mail:
     a) 80% of all organizations read employees' e-mail.
     b) supervisors may not read employees' e-mail without cause.
     c) only 15% of all companies have policies governing the use of e-mail.
     d) most employees don't know employers may read their e-mail without permission.
Answer d   Page 749

53. Businesses have which of the following responsibilities to their customers?
     a) The right of choosing the products they buy and use
     b) Properly managing a diverse workforce
     c) Reducing packaging, reusing material, and recycling when possible
     d) Earning a profit while being socially responsible
Answer a   Page 750

54. The Audi 5000 sedan was reported to have sudden, violent acceleration when the transmission was put into drive. Audi first blamed the condition on drivers who didn't know how to operate the transmission, but later was forced to recall the sedan and correct the transmission problem. Audi violated which area of responsibility businesses have to their customers?
     a) Dependable packaging
     b) Product safety and quality
     c) Truthful advertising
     d) Investor confidence
Answer b   Page 750

55. The advertisement and resulting product, "A psychically energized weight loss program," which turned out to be a book on how to achieve a positive mental attitude, violates which responsibility to the customer?
    a) The right to know
    b) The right to safety
    c) The right to be heard
    d) The right to choice

Answer a   Page 750

56. Small business has a number of social responsibilities to their investors including:
    a) selling a high-quality product at a reasonable price.
    b) observing all government requirements for product manufacture.
    c) earning the lowest profits at the highest cost of production.
    d) providing an attractive return on their investments.

Answer d   Page 751

57. E. F. Hutton and Co. was convicted of the violation of kiting laws. Check kiting is an illegal practice involving the writing checks against money that has not arrived at the bank on which the check is drawn. Doing this violated their business social responsibility in terms of:
    a) product quality.
    b) the consumer's right to know.
    c) their investors.
    d) the community

Answer c   Page 751

58. Citicorp was found guilty of violating parking laws. Parking involves complex shifts of funds between countries to avoid the payment of taxes. Citicorp maintained two sets of financial records for a parking scheme. These actions violate which area of business social responsibility?
    a) Investors
    b) Consumers
    c) Community
    d) Product quality

Answer a   Page 751

59. Barker Industries makes an annual donation of $100,000 to local charities, and allows its top managers leaves of absence to serve charities involved in community service. What area of social responsibility is Barker demonstrating?
    a) Customers
    b) Environment
    c) Employees
    d) Community

Answer d   Page 752

60. Leonard Stern, the chairman of Hartz Mountain, was concerned and outraged at the condition of New York City's homeless living in shelters and welfare hotels, and was determined to help them. Hartz Mountain backed loans for construction of clean, safe housing complexes, and helped create social programs to help homeless families. These efforts by Hartz Mountain are an example of a company's social responsibility to:

a) consumers.
b) investors.
c) employees.
d) the community.
Answer d   Page 752

True or False Questions

61. Polls show that increasingly the public is only holding companies accountable for the economic impact of their decisions, not the ethical implications.
Answer F   Page 723

62. In most situations, the ethical dilemma is clear-cut and obvious.
Answer F   Page 724

63. Stakeholders are the individuals and groups affected by a decision.
Answer T   Page 724

64. Ethics are the fundamental moral values and behavioral standards that form the foundation for the people of an organization as they make decisions and interact with stakeholders.
Answer T   Page 724

65. Small business owners seldom feel the pressure to violate ethical standards or to take shortcuts in their careers.
Answer F   Page 725

66. Fortunately, for businesses, it only takes a short time to build a reputation and it takes a long time to destroy it.
Answer T   Page 725

67. If a small business owner obeys the law, he/she can be certain that his/her actions are ethical.
Answer F   Page 726

68. In terms of ethical behavior, the law merely establishes the minimum standard of behavior.
Answer T   Page 726

69. The policies and procedures concerning ethical behavior in an organization serve as specific guidelines for people as they make daily decisions.
Answer T   Page 726

70. Brauer Software's problem with web marketing was over questions of the ethicality of marketing to children on the Internet.
Answer T   Page 727

71. The first step in developing an ethical framework is to identify the key stakeholders.
Answer F   Page 728

72. Since ethical decisions are based on absolute standards of conduct, it is unimportant to identify the stakeholders in any specific decision when determining the ethical thing to do.

Answer F   Page 728

73. The four-step process for developing an ethical framework is very similar to the process for problem-solving in business.
Answer T   Page 728

74. Although companies set standards for ethical behavior, the ultimate decision on whether to abide by ethical principles rests with the individual.
Answer T   Page 728

75. While corporate culture influences employees' ethical decisions, managers have little impact on those decisions.
Answer F   Page 728

76. If a manager is attempting to think through the public justification of an ethical decision the manager would need to answer questions such as, "Will I be able to explain to others why I've taken this action?"
Answer T   Page 729, Table 21.1

77. Nancy is thinking about an ethical situation and is asking herself, "Does this action meet my standards?", "What are my true motives?" etc. She is considering the ethical dimension of consequences and outcomes.
Answer F   Page 729, Table 21.1

78. A recent survey of senior managers, business school deans, and members of Congress supported the view that a business strengthens its competitive position by maintaining high ethical standards.
Answer T   Page 729

79. Immoral managers do not consider the impact that their decisions have on others.
Answer T   Page 730, Table 21.2

80. Amoral managers would not sacrifice their ethical standards just to earn a profit.
Answer F   Page 730, Table 21.2

81. If a manager says things like, "Everyone does it" or "I don't get paid to be ethical, I get paid to produce results," he/she is suffering from moral blindness.
Answer T   Page 731

82. The most effective way of diminishing moral blindness is through training.
Answer T   Page 731

83. Since ethical standards are constant from one culture to another, ethical decisions pose no special problems for companies engaged in international business.
Answer F   Page 732

84. The Golden Rule ethical test suggests choosing the option that produces the greatest good for the greatest number of people.
Answer F   Page 733

85. Kant's categorical imperative advises managers to take only those actions that a disinterested panel of professional colleagues would view as proper.
Answer F   Page 733

86. There is no universal answer for resolving ethical dilemmas.
Answer T   Page 733

87. If a company has a written code of ethics and provides clear instructions to employees, two-way communication is unimportant in maintaining ethical standards.
Answer F   Page 734

88. It is important that any ethical code is enforced fairly and consistently.
Answer T   Page 734

89. The best insurance against ethical violations is the hiring of people with strong moral principles.
Answer T   Page 735

90. To establish and maintain the highest level of ethical standards, the company's owner should hand down the company's ethical standards and require managers to enforce them.
Answer F   Page 735

91. Only about 35% of consumers would not buy products from companies that are not socially responsible.
Answer F   Page 736

92. Businesses have social responsibility to several constituencies: the environment, their employees, their shareholders, the community, and their customers.
Answer T   Page 736

93. Clean manufacturing systems stress recycling and reducing of materials.
Answer F   Page 737

94. When it comes to carrying out its social responsibility, one of the most important constituencies to the small business is its employees.
Answer T   Page 737

95. The increasing cultural diversity in the United States is hindering the entrepreneurial effort in the economy.
Answer F   Page 739

96. White, non-Hispanic males currently make up about 57% of the U.S. workforce.
Answer F   Page 739

97. Managing cultural diversity in the workforce is getting easier as society becomes more diverse.
Answer F   Page 740

98. The only way to achieve diversity in the small business is to let it take care of itself as society increases in diversity.

Answer F   Page 740

99. The starting point for managing diversity is learning your own biases and prejudices.
Answer F   Page 741

100. The management of diversity will require ongoing adjustments of your company to your workers.
Answer T   Page 741

101. One "break" small business gets over large companies is a significantly lower rate of substance abuse due to the "family-like" atmosphere that tends to prevail in small companies.
Answer F   Page 742

102. The majority of small companies realize they have as big a drug problem with their employees as larger companies do.
Answer F   Page 742

103. The use of random drug testing by small businesses is on the rise.
Answer T   Page 742

104. Effective drug prevention programs use random drug tests of employees and keep their drug policies unwritten for maximum flexibility.
Answer F   Page 743

105. Businesses with less than 50 employees are not subject to ADA and therefore may deal with HIV-positive and AIDS-infected employees without fear of government action.
Answer F   Page 743

106. AIDS is considered to be a "handicap," and AIDS-infected employees are protected against discrimination by the Americans with Disabilities Act.
Answer T   Page 743

107. The safest course of action for a small business to take with an employee who has AIDS is to fire him.
Answer F   Page 743

108. Circle Solution's response to an employee who tested positive for AIDS was not only legal and humane but prepared them when other employees became ill with AIDS.
Answer T   Page 744

109. Most small business owners know exactly what their legal obligations are to employees with AIDS.
Answer F   Page 745

110. Estimates on the number of women who have been sexually harassed on the job range from 80–90%.
Answer F   Page 745

111. An employer can be held liable for sexual harassment if he/she knew or should have known of the harassment and failed to take prompt action to stop it.

Answer T   Page 747

112. Employers can be held responsible for third-party sexual harassment if managers knew about it or should have known about it.

Answer T   Page 747

113. The best way to handle sexual harassment is to educate the employees and thereby prevent sexual harassment.

Answer T   Page 748

114. When a manager receives a complaint about sexual harassment, his/her first step should be to keep the complaint casual and urge the complainant to return to the alleged harasser her/himself and deal with the issue that way first.

Answer F   Page 749

115. When a sexual harassment complaint is made, the company should not inform the accused until the complaint has been thoroughly investigated.

Answer F   Page 749

116. A small business's responsibility to its customers includes the customers' right to honest communication and a right to choose among competing products.

Answer T   Page 750

117. In terms of social responsibility to the consumer, consumers have a right to be heard by the company.

Answer T   Page 750

118. Companies do not have an ethical obligation to inform consumers regarding their products.

Answer F   Page 751

119. Businesses have a responsibility to the communities in which they operate, according to your authors.

Answer T   Page 752

120. What managers and owners say is more important in determining employee ethical behavior than what they do.

Answer F   Page 753

Essay Questions

121. Define three key terms: ethics, stakeholders, and business ethics.

Pages 724–726

122. Describe the three levels of ethical standards. How do they impact the decision a person will make when facing an ethical dilemma?

Page 726

123. Your authors suggest a four-step process for developing an ethical framework. Identify and explain each of the four steps.

Page 728

124. What are the benefits of moral management?
Pages 728–730

125. What causes ethical lapses?
Pages 731–732

126. How can managers implement and maintain ethical principles into their companies?
Pages 733–734

127. What are a business's responsibilities to its employees? Briefly outline and explain each.
Pages 737–749

128. What can the small business owner do to develop an effective drug prevention program?
Page 743

129. What is the small business's responsibility to employees in terms of coping with AIDS in the
     workplace and having a legal and humane AIDS policy.
Pages 743–745

130. What is sexual harassment? What can a small business owner do to minimize the likelihood of
     sexual harassment?
Pages 745–748

131. What are the small business's responsibilities to its customers?
Pages 750–751

132. What are the small business owner's responsibilities to his/her investors and community?
Pages 751–752

Mini-Cases

Case 21-1: "What Do I Do Now?

Kara Loundes walked into Larry Bond's office and quietly but firmly said, "We have to talk." It was
after 6 p.m. and everyone else had left the small advertising agency for the day. Bond pushed aside the
project he was working on and motioned for Kara to sit down.

"What's up? What can I do for you?" he asked.

As she spoke, tears rolled down Kara's cheeks. "I don't know what else to do," she stammered. "Chuck
keeps making inappropriate comments and sexual advancements towards me. I tried to ignore them at
first, but they only got worse. Finally, I asked him firmly but politely to stop and told him that his
behavior was inappropriate and made it hard for me to work," she said. "He just laughed, stroked my
hair, and said, 'You know you want to go out with me, honey. I can help you in a lot of ways.'"

Larry could hardly believe what he was hearing. Although he hadn't worked closely with either Kara or Chuck recently, he knew them both very well ... at least he thought he did. As Kara finished telling her story, Larry sat and wondered what he should do.

Questions

1. What advice would you offer Larry? What should he do next?

2. What can business owners such as Larry do to avoid incidents of sexual harassment?

Case 21-2: To Close or Not To Close?

Maxi-Car had an older plant in a small community in Northern Wisconsin. The plant employs 50% of the community and provides about 20% of the tax base for the surrounding area. The models produced at the plant are not selling well. Updating the plant for the new round of models would cost as much as building a whole new plant. Sales in general for Maxi-Car have been on the decline for five years and they have significant excess production capacity.

Todd Jones is the Operations VP for Maxi-Car. After an extensive study, he recommends that they close the Northern Wisconsin plant and lay off the entire workforce, hourly and management. His report also shows that the impact on the community will be devastating. In all likelihood, it will turn the community into a "ghost town" and disrupt the economic base of the region for at least five years. The alternative, updating the plant, will eliminate Maxi-Car's dividend for the year and may well cause them to post a loss for the first time in ten years.

Questions

1. Who are the stakeholders in Maxi-Car's decision?

2. What are Maxi-Car's obligations to each of these stakeholder groups?

3. Does Maxi-Car owe a greater responsibility to any one stakeholder or set of stakeholders? Why?

Chapter 22 –
Business Law and Government Regulation

Multiple Choice Questions

1. After the United States the nation with the next highest total cost of civil lawsuits as a percentage of GDP is:
   a) Great Britain.
   b) Canada.
   c) France.
   d) Belgium.

Answer d   Page 759

2. _____ law governs the rights and the obligations between people and the parties they made promises to or agreements with.
   a) Agency
   b) Contract
   c) Freedom of contract
   d) UCC

Answer b   Page 760

3. A/An _____ is a promise or a set of promises for the breach of which the law gives a remedy, or the performance of which the law recognizes as a duty.
   a) agreement
   b) UCC
   c) warranty
   d) contract

Answer d   Page 760

4. To have an agreement, a contract must have:
   a) a promise by one party to do something in the future.
   b) the ability to contract.
   c) an intention to be bound by the contract.
   d) an offer and an acceptance.

Answer d   Page 760

5. To have a valid offer, there must be:
   a) an intention to be bound by the offer.
   b) a simple lack of disagreement by the offeree.
   c) a written communication of the offer.
   d) significant and substantial consideration.

Answer a   Page 761

6. Courts often supply missing terms in a contract when there is a reliable basis to do so. However, courts never specify or supply the ____ if it is missing.
   a) identity of the product
   b) time term
   c) quantity
   d) price term

Answer a   Page 761

7. On October 1, Althea writes Katherine a letter offering her a job at her travel agency. Katherine mails Althea a letter on October 2 accepting the offer. On October 3, before she receives Katherine's acceptance, Althea calls Katherine to rescind the offer. In terms of contract law:
   a) there is no contract since Althea calls to rescind the offer before she receives Katherine's acceptance.
   b) a contract is formed on October 2 when Katherine mails the letter of acceptance to Althea.
   c) no contract is formed since Katherine does not respond by the fastest means available—telephone.
   d) none of the these are correct.

Answer b   Page 761

8. Maria writes a letter offering to sell some office furniture to Lee. Lee, in a distant city, sends a telegram to Maria accepting the offer. Because of an error in the Western Union Office, the telegram never reaches Maria. What is the result?
   a) There is no contract since Lee responds by telegram instead of by mail.
   b) There is no contract since Maria never actually receives Lee's acceptance.
   c) A contract is formed as soon as Lee gave the telegram to the Western Union office.
   d) A contract is formed as soon as Maria writes the letter to Lee.

Answer c   Page 761

9. The courts use the presence or absence of a/an _____ to distinguish between serious promises and those that are not serious.
   a) consideration
   b) contractual capacity
   c) agreement
   d) written communication

Answer a   Page 761

10. John offers to buy steel from Tom in Cleveland for a specific price. Tom therefore plans to ship to John and does not sell the steel to another buyer. Before shipping Tom gets a phone call from John canceling the deal. Is John still bound by his contract with Tom?
    a) Yes, due to the principle of promissory estoppel.
    b) No, because Tom has not yet shipped the steel.
    c) No, because no consideration exchanged hands.
    d) Yes, because of the issue of legality.

Answer a   Page 762

11. In most cases dealing with the issue of consideration, courts:
    a) still consider a promise binding even if made without a consideration.
    b) do not evaluate the adequacy of the consideration.
    c) consider offers of "love and affection" to be valuable consideration.
    d) weigh the value of the consideration in ruling on the validity of the contract.

Answer b   Page 762

12. In terms of contractual capacity:

a) a minor can disaffirm and walk away from a contract even if already executed and the minor has benefited from it.
b) intoxicated individuals are generally always held liable for their contractual obligations, regardless of their condition upon execution of the contract.
c) an insane person can never have contractual capacity by definition.
d) if a minor benefits from a contract and then disaffirms it, he/she must fulfill the duty of restoration.
Answer d   Page 762

13. Al voluntarily becomes intoxicated at a local bar. While he is drunk, he still has a degree of reason and judgment. He sells his car for half of its value simply to irritate his wife. Later when sober, Al and his wife want the car back. This contract:
a) is void because of a lack of genuineness of assent.
b) is enforceable due to promissory estoppel.
c) is unenforceable due to duress and undue influence.
d) can be voided by Al or his wife.
Answer b   Page 763

14. Rupert, a very old man, suffers from bouts of senility. During a lucid moment, he contracts to buy a new freezer from a local appliance dealer. This contract is:
a) void.
b) voidable.
c) enforceable.
d) illegal.
Answer c   Page 763

15. Toni wants to buy software from Bill that she can modify in order to hack into her boyfriend's e-mail account to see if he's writing to another woman. When Bill discovers why Toni wants the software, he refuses to sell it to her. Toni sues Bill in small claims court. Is the contract valid?
a) Yes, because a verbal contract is binding.
b) No, because of the principle of legality.
c) Yes, because of promissory estoppel.
d) No, because Toni clearly crazy.
Answer b   Page 763

16. The owner of a small auto repair shop knowingly installs a used water pump in your car and tells you it is "brand new." This is:
a) fraud.
b) duress.
c) innocent misrepresentation.
d) breach of contract.
Answer a   Page 764

17. Sonny is buying a computer system for his college's administrative functions. The negotiated price of the system is $475, 000. He receives a contract for $375,000 with no explanation as to the change and gladly signs it and sends it back to the vendor. He receives a phone call from the vendor explaining that the secretary in typing the figures into the contract hit the 3 instead of the 4 on her keyboard. Sonny wants to hold the vendor to the contract. Is the contract legally binding on the contractor?
    a) Yes, because it constitutes a written offer.
    b) No, because of a lack of genuineness of assent on the part of the vendor.
    c) Yes, because of the law of agency covers the secretary as well as the salesperson.
    d) No, because this constitutes a mistake of fact that Sonny should have immediately recognized.
Answer d   Page 764

18. Gusti agrees to maintain Mrs. Poppendraius's yard, pulling weeds, cutting the grass weekly, and trimming the shrubbery once during the summer for $30 a month. Gusti makes a half-hearted attempt at pulling weeds, cuts the lawn once all summer and never touches the shrubbery. No damage is done except that Mrs. Poppendraius's yard appears neglected and unkempt. In terms of contract law:
    a) Gusti is not contractually obligated because he is a minor.
    b) Mrs. Poppendraius may collect compensatory damages.
    c) Gusti is in breach of contract.
    d) Mrs. Poppendraius may collect consequential damages.
Answer c   Page 765

19. The damages the parties to a contract specify in case of breach are called:
    a) compensatory damages.
    b) monetary damages.
    c) liquidated damages.
    d) consequential damages.
Answer a   Page 765

20. _____ is a remedy for breached contracts that deal with unique items and is designed to make the injured party "whole again."
    a) Consequential damage
    b) Specific performance
    c) Remedy at law
    d) Monetary damage
Answer b   Page 765

21. Which of the following contracts would be covered by the Uniform Commercial Code?
    a) The sale of accounting services
    b) The sale of real estate
    c) The sale of furniture
    d) All of the these
Answer a   Page 766

22. The Uniform Commercial Code:
    a) significantly revised Merchant Law.
    b) is based on case law and overturns much of the common law that merchant law was based on.
    c) makes minor changes to merchant law, largely making the law more uniform and consistent.

d) is the most significant revision of commercial law since the Napoleonic Code.

Answer c   Page 766

23. Ansel, a sugar manufacturer, agrees to sell Keith 10,000 pounds of sugar at the "usual price." A shortage forces the price of sugar up and Ansel charges Keith nearly 50% more for the sugar. In response, Keith disaffirms the contract. Which ruling is correct?
    a) The modification is enforceable because Ansel has the right to unilaterally modify the contract.
    b) The Code would confirm the contract and assign a price reasonable at the time of shipment.
    c) Keith would be permitted to void the contract since he has not agreed to the price increase.
    d) This contract is not covered by the Code, therefore, the common law applies and the modification is unenforceable.

Answer b   Page 767

24. The UCC requires that:
    a) the sale of all goods and services be warranted.
    b) only written contracts for the sales of goods over $1,500 are enforceable.
    c) verbal contracts are as enforceable as written contracts, regardless of the amount of the consideration.
    d) no new consideration need be offered if a contract is modified in good faith.

Answer d   Page 767

25. If a contract for the sale of goods omits the place for delivery, the Code states that delivery will take place at:
    a) the seller's place of business.
    b) the seller's residence.
    c) the buyer's place of business.
    d) the buyer's residence.

Answer a   Page 768

26. Under the UCC, when the innocent specifies their own damages for a potential breach of a sales contract and they are reasonable and not punitive, these damages are called:
    a) consequential damages.
    b) liquidation damages.
    c) compensatory damages.
    d) specific damages.

Answer b   Page 768

27. A/An _____ insures a buyer that the goods will be of average quality and that they are fit for the ordinary purposes for which such goods are used.
    a) implied warranty of merchantability
    b) implied warranty of fitness for a particular purpose
    c) express warranty
    d) warranty of title

Answer a   Page 769

28. The statute of limitations for a breach of contract suit is ____ years from the time the breach occurred.
    a) 2
    b) 3

c) 4
d) 7

Answer c   Page 769

29. A _____ is a promise or statement of fact by the seller about a product.
a) sales warranty
b) sales contract
c) copyright
d) contractual capacity

Answer a   Page 769

30. A/An _____ assures the buyer of a product that it will be of average quality, not the best and not the worst.
a) implied warranty
b) warranty of exclusivity
c) express warranty
d) warranty of merchantability

Answer d   Page 769

31. Which of the following phrases is sufficient to disclaim an implied sales warranty?
a) "No warranties"
b) "Seller makes no warranties on this product whatsoever"
c) "As is"
d) None of the above. A merchant cannot disclaim sales warranties.

Answer c   Page 770

32. Today, when it comes to product liability, the courts:
a) practice the *caveat emptor* rule.
b) rule that the scope of warranties include any person incurring personal or property loss due to a faulty product.
c) hold that the rule of *caveat venditor* is valid in all cases.
d) hold that only the parties directly involved in the execution of the contract are bound by the law of sales warranties.

Answer b   Page 770

33. Billy Bob's swamp racers are the fastest swamp mud racing machines in the country. Unfortunately drivers have to be careful because they are easily tipped over due to their high center of gravity. This is unfortunate because most swamp mud racers consider stability an important quality in their racers. Billy Bob has installed numerous decals in prominent places that state, "This sucker turns over easily but goes really fast." Still, Billy Bob could be sued for product liability under:
a) negligent manufacturing.
b) failure to warn.
c) implied warranty to perform.
d) negligent design.

Answer d   Page 770

34. When Fred Goodman sued Wendy's over his broken tooth due to bone fragments in his hamburger, he sued them on the basis of:
a) breach of implied warranty of merchantability.
b) negligent manufacturing.

c)   failure to warn and negligent design.
d)   implied warranty of fitness.
Answer a   Page 771

35. We Love Pets manufactures a pet carrier that is known to suddenly come apart if the pet shakes itself at the same time the owner picks the carrier up. It seems the combination of actions make the hinge pins fall out. WLP could be liable under:
a)   negligent manufacturing.
b)   failure to warn.
c)   implied warranty to perform.
d)   negligent design.
Answer b   Page 771

36. A _____ is a grant giving the inventor of a product the exclusive right to make, use, or sell it for a specific time.
a)   patent
b)   copyright
c)   trademark
d)   warranty
Answer a   Page 772

37. The first step in receiving a patent for the inventory is to:
a)   document the device.
b)   search existing patents.
c)   establish the invention's novelty.
d)   prove the origination of the idea.
Answer c   Page 773

38. A _____ is any distinctive work, symbol, name, logo, etc., that a company uses to identify the origin of a product or to distinguish it from other products.
a)   patent
b)   copyright
c)   trademark
d)   warranty
Answer c   Page 774

39. The duration of a _____ is indefinite but can be lost if it loses its unique character.
a)   patent
b)   copyright
c)   trademark
d)   warranty
Answer c   Page 775

40. The author of a hit song could apply for a _____ to protect that work from unauthorized use by others.
a)   patent
b)   trademark
c)   servicemark

d)   copyright

Answer d   Page 776

41.   An agent's duties when executing agency include:
a)   reimbursement of the principal for all expenses incurred in the execution of the agency.
b)   indemnification of the principal for any authorized payments or any loss incurred by the agency.
c)   performance of duties according to the principal's instruction and notification of the principal of all facts concerning the subject matter of the agency.
d)   all of the above.

Answer c   Page 777

42.   _____ is the most common type of bankruptcy, accounting for nearly 70% of all bankruptcies.
a)   Chapter 7
b)   Chapter 11
c)   Chapter 13
d)   Chapter 21

Answer a   Page 778

43.   In a Chapter 7 bankruptcy:
a)   a small firm gets a second chance by being protected from creditors while a reorganization plan is formulated.
b)   every piece of property the bankrupt debtor owns is subject to court attachment.
c)   loss is limited to $100,000 in unsecured debt and to $350,000 in secured debt.
d)   a debtor simply declares all of his firm's debts, and turns all assets over to a trustee who then sells and distributes them to settle both secured and unsecured debts.

Answer d   Page 778

44.   A _____ bankruptcy provides a small firm a second chance; it protects a firm from creditors while a reorganization plan is formulated.
a)   Chapter 7
b)   Chapter 11
c)   Chapter 13
d)   Chapter 21

Answer b   Page 779

45.   Chris is filing for bankruptcy. He is a sole proprietor and owes $50,000 on his credit cards and a bank note against his house for $150,000. He is going to start bankruptcy proceedings but he sees no way out and knows if he waits his creditors will force him into bankruptcy. Chris's simplest choice would be to file:
a)   Chapter 7.
b)   Chapter 11.
c)   Chapter 13.
d)   Chapter 21.

Answer c   Page 780

46.   The act that is the foundation on which antitrust policy in the United States is built is:
a)   the Clayton Act.
b)   the Sherman Anti-Trust Act.

    c) the Robinson-Patman Act.
    d) the Miller-Tydings Act.
Answer b   Page 780

47. The _____ forbids contracts that restrain trade or create monopolies.
    a) Clayton Act
    b) Sherman Anti-Trust Act
    c) Robinson-Patman Act
    d) Miller-Tydings Act
Answer b   Page 781

48. _____ states that a seller cannot require a buyer to purchase only his/her product to the exclusion of other competitive sellers' products.
    a) The Clayton Act
    b) The Sherman Act
    c) The Robinson-Patman Act
    d) The Miller-Tydings Act
Answer a   Page 782

49. The Clayton Act prohibits:
    a) fair trade agreements.
    b) sales contracts and warranties.
    c) any corporation purchasing the stock of another corporation.
    d) interlocking directorates.
Answer d   Page 782

50. This act was passed by Congress to supplement the Clayton Act, providing the power to prevent "unfair methods of competition in commerce or unfair or deceptive acts in commerce."
    a) The Federal Trade Commission Act
    b) The Sherman Act
    c) The Robinson-Patman Act
    d) The Miller-Tydings Act
Answer a   Page 782

51. _____ was passed to strengthen the Clayton Act, specifically to address price discrimination because many businesses were circumventing the original rules.
    a) The Federal Trade Commission Act
    b) The Sherman Act
    c) The Robinson-Patman Act
    d) The Miller-Tydings Act
Answer c   Page 782

52. The Robinson-Patman Act focuses on:
    a) price discrimination.
    b) product warranty.
    c) product liability.
    d) unsafe products.
Answer a   Page 782

53. _____ introduced an exception to the Sherman Anti-trust Act, permitting the use of fair trade agreements.
   a) The Federal Trade Commission Act
   b) The Clayton Act
   c) The Robinson-Patman Act
   d) The Miller-Tydings Act

Answer d   Page 783

54. In 1938, Congress passed the _____ creating an agency responsible for establishing standards for drugs, inspecting food and drug manufacturers, performing food-and drug-related research, etc.
   a) Miller-Tydings Act
   b) Consumer Product Safety Act
   c) Agricultural Marketing Act
   d) Food, Drug, and Cosmetics Act

Answer d   Page 783

55. The _____ requires lenders and sellers who extend credit to disclose fully the terms and conditions of credit arrangements to enable consumers to "shop around."
   a) Fair Credit Reporting Act
   b) Truth-In-Lending Act
   c) Consumer Product Safety Commission
   d) Equal Credit Opportunity Act

Answer b   Page 784

56. The Truth-In-Lending Act:
   a) applies to all installment contracts with more than two payments.
   b) prohibits discrimination in granting credit.
   c) requires a lender to disclose the total cost of credit or a loan.
   d) prohibits certain behavior on the part of a lender when trying to collect bad debts.

Answer c   Page 784

57. Under the Truth-In-Lending Act, the owner of a stolen credit card who notifies the credit card company of the theft before any unauthorized use of the card is liable for:
   a) none of the unauthorized charges.
   b) only $50 of any unauthorized charges.
   c) a total of $100.
   d) all of the charges. The owner has unlimited liability.

Answer b   Page 785

58. A credit card holder may withhold payment on a faulty product, providing a good faith effort was made to settle the dispute, under the:
   a) Truth-In-Lending Act.
   b) Equal Credit Opportunity Act.
   c) Fair Credit Billing Act.
   d) Fair Credit Reporting Act.

Answer c   Page 785

59. The _____ prohibits debt collectors from using intimidation to collect debts, calling on the debtor at inconvenient times, or contacting third parties about the debt.

a) Truth-In-Lending Act
b) Equal Credit Opportunity Act
c) Fair Credit Billing Act
d) Fair Credit Reporting Act

Answer d   Page 785

60. Passed in 1976 to deal with the disposal of solid waste, the _____ specifies how landfills should be managed and hazardous waste disposed of.
a) Resources Conservation and Recovery Act
b) Clean Water Act
c) Clean Air Act
d) Environmental Protection Act

Answer a   Page 786

True or False Questions

61. It is possible for a small business to win a lawsuit but still go out of business due to the costs of the suit.

Answer T   Page 759

62. A contract is simply a promise or set of promises regarding a duty and for which there is a remedy if the agreement is breached.

Answer T   Page 760

63. Courts judge a party's subjective, personal intentions to enter into a contract when a dispute about a contract's existence arises.

Answer F   Page 760

64. The more terms that are specified in a proposed offer, the more likely it is that an offer exists.

Answer T   Page 761

65. A missing quantity term in an offer usually defeats a contract.

Answer T   Page 761

66. Common law requires that an acceptance of an offer be made by the means specified by the offeror and it must reach the offeror in order to be effective.

Answer F   Page 761

67. Generally, the absence of consideration does not affect the obligation, i.e., the contract is still binding, even if there's no apparent consideration.

Answer F   Page 761

68. If two parties exchange promises to form a contract, valuable consideration exists.

Answer T   Page 761

69. Courts usually evaluate the value of the adequacy of consideration given for a promise.

Answer F   Page 761–762

70. A minor can avoid a contract at the minor's option but the adult cannot avoid a contract simply because it is with a minor.

Answer T   Page 762

71. The courts hold that a contract entered into by an intoxicated person or an insane person is always voidable.

Answer F   Page 763

72. For a contract to be enforceable, it must be legal.

Answer T   Page 763

73. Only mistakes of fact permit a contract to be voided.

Answer T   Page 764

74. Duress is the misrepresentation of a material fact with the intent to deceive which results in injury to an innocent party.

Answer F   Page 764

75. To be enforceable, a contract must be written.

Answer F   Page 765

76. Failure to perform as agreed in a contract constitutes breach.

Answer T   Page 765

77. In breach of contract, the injured party may only recover compensatory damages, moneys which place him/her in the same position he/she would have been had the contract been performed.

Answer F   Page 765

78. The Uniform Commercial Code has been adopted, at least in part, by all 50 states.

Answer T   Page 766

79. The Code does not cover contracts for the sale of services.

Answer T   Page 766

80. Under the UCC, a person is considered a professional merchant if he/she "deals in goods of the kind" and has a special knowledge of the business or of the goods, uses a merchant's agent to conduct business, or presents him/herself as a merchant.

Answer T   Page 766

81. Under the Code, as long as an offeree's response indicates a sincere willingness to accept, it will be an acceptance although the terms of the acceptance may be somewhat different.

Answer T   Page 767

82. Under the Code, a new consideration is required if an existing contract is modified.

Answer F   Page 767

83. Under the UCC, delivery of goods does not necessarily mean physical delivery, but simply making the goods available to the buyer.

Answer T   Page 768

84. The buyer must indicate acceptance of goods verbally or in writing for the acceptance to be binding.
Answer F   Page 768

85. The legal remedies for breach of contract are designed to put the nonbreaching party in the same position as if the contract had been carried out.
Answer T   Page 768

86. Today, the marketplace follows a policy of *caveat venditor*—"Let the seller beware."
Answer T   Page 769

87. An express warranty can be created by words or by actions.
Answer T   Page 769

88. Every seller who offers goods for sale implies a warranty to title for those goods.
Answer F   Page 769

89. A manufacturer of power saws who fails to place a safety guard on products would likely be liable for negligence if a customer is injured.
Answer T   Page 770

90. Patents are a grant from the federal government for the life of the inventor plus fifty years and cannot be renewed.
Answer F   Page 772

91. A device cannot be patented if it has been publicized in print anywhere in the world.
Answer T   Page 772

92. Filing for a patent is a simple process the small business owner can handle himself.
Answer F   Page 773

93. It took Robert Kearns 12 years to win his first suit for patent infringement on his intermittent windshield wipers from major car manufacturers.
Answer T   Page 774

94. Any distinctive word, phrase, symbol, design, name, logo, etc., may be a trademark.
Answer T   Page 774

95. Today, a company must establish its right to a trademark by actually using it.
Answer F   Page 775

96. A business can lose a trademark if it becomes generic.
Answer T   Page 775

97. A valid copyright lasts the lifetime of the author plus fifty years after death.
Answer T   Page 776

98. Once an entrepreneur acquires a patent, copyright, or trademark, his/her product or service is protected by the federal government, which will watch for and prosecute infringements.
Answer T   Page 776

99. Employees are agents of their employers when performing job-related activities.
Answer T   Page 777

100. Employees cannot bind a company to an agreement unless the owner intended for them to do so.
Answer F   Page 777

101. An agency remains valid until the principal and the agent mutually agree to dissolve it.
Answer F   Page 778

102. Liquidation bankruptcies are handled under Chapter 7 of the Bankruptcy Reform Act of 1978.
Answer F   Page 778

103. Bankruptcy proceedings can be filed by the owner or his/her creditors.
Answer T   Page 778

104. In a bankruptcy proceeding, all assets are subject to court attachment.
Answer F   Page 779

105. When a company files for Chapter 11 bankruptcy, every creditor must approve its plan for reorganization.
Answer F   Page 779

106. Chapter 13 bankruptcies protect a debtor from creditors' claims and permit the owner to file a plan for reorganization.
Answer F   Page 780

107. Individual debtors with unsecured debts of less than $100,000 or secured debts of less than $350,000 can file for bankruptcy under Chapter 13.
Answer T   Page 780

108. The regulations and restrictions the government imposes on businesses place a disproportionate burden on small companies.
Answer T   Page 780

109. In 1996, passage of the Small Business Regulatory Enforcement Fairness Act provided small businesses with some relief from government regulation.
Answer T   Page 780

110. The Sherman Anti-Trust Act outlaws the restraint of trade and any attempt to monopolize.
Answer T   Page 780

111. Currently, complying with government regulations is costing every individual in the United States nearly $6,700 per year.
Answer F   Page 781

112. The Clayton Act permits suppliers to charge customers different prices for the same product based on what the market will bear.
Answer F   Page 781

113. The Robinson-Patman Act focuses on preventing unfair labor practices.
Answer F   Page 782

114. The Miller-Tidings Act in 1937 introduced an exception to the Sherman Anti-Trust Act, permitting manufacturers to use fair trade agreements.
Answer T   Page 783

115. Recent consumer protection laws have reduced the required information on product labels to relieve the financial burden on small business.
Answer F   Page 783

116. The CPSC has the power to ban the production of any product it considers hazardous to consumers.
Answer T   Page 783

117. The owner of a stolen credit card is liable for all charges on the card even if he/she notifies the credit card company of the theft before any unauthorized use of the card is made.
Answer F   Page 784

118. Sam's Appliance Shop turns a past due account over to Jake's Collection Agency. Jake calls the customer at 4 a.m. every day and threatens him. This is illegal behavior on the part of Jake.
Answer T   Page 785

119. The Clean Air Act, passed in 1970, assigned the EPA the task of setting clean air standards.
Answer T   Page 785

120. The Clean Water Act, passed in 1972, has achieved its 1983 and 1985 goals for clean water, even though it was five years late in reaching them.
Answer F   Page 786

Essay Questions

121. What are the four key elements of a valid contract?
Page 760

122. What constitutes an agreement? What are the two key elements to agreement? Offer an example of each.
Pages 760–761

123. What is contractual capacity and who can not legally enter into a contract?
Pages 762–763

124. What is assent in a contract and what invalidates it?
Pages 764–765

125. Briefly explain the concept of breach of contract and the type of damages that can be collected for breach of contract.
Page 765

126. Outline and briefly explain the concepts of sales and sales contracts, breach of sales contract, sales warranties, and product liability as described in the Uniform Commercial Code.
Page 766–772

127. What part do patents, trademarks, and copyrights play in protecting intellectual property rights?
Pages 772–776

128. Explain the law of agency, who is an agent, what constitutes the relationship between an agent and a principal, and under what conditions can the relationship be terminated?
Pages 777–778

129. Describe the key features of bankruptcy proceedings under Chapter 7, Chapter 11, and Chapter 13.
Pages 778–780

130. Explain the basic prohibitions on trade practices of the Sheman Anti-Trust Act, the Clayton Act, and the Robinson-Patman Act. How is the Miller-Tydings Act related to these laws?
Pages 780–783

131. The government has created a number of laws and regulations in the area of consumer protection. Discuss.
Pages 783–784

132. Discuss government regulation in the area of consumer credit, identifying key legislation and what rights it grants consumers.
Pages 784–785

Mini-Cases

Case 22-1: Foreign Car Motors of Denver

Foreign Car Motors of Denver ran an ad in the local newspaper advertising a 1983 Mercedes-Benz 450 SEL. The newspaper erroneously stated the price as $30,950. Cal Smith (the owner of Foreign Car Motors of Denver) had instructed the newspaper to advertise the price at $37,950. Upon reading the advertisement in the morning paper, Ann Folger visited the car lot and told the salesman she would purchase the car. At first the salesman agreed, but upon learning of the advertising error, he refused to sell Ann the car.

Ann made her point clearly to Cal: "You advertised the car at this price ($30,950) and I accepted your offer. Here is my check and I expect you to sell me this car at the price I read in your ad."

Question

1. Is Cal obligated under law to sell the car to Ann for $30,950? Explain your answer in terms of contract law.

Case 22-2: New Age Textiles

Mick Stone had worked most of his life to make a success of New Age Textiles. "You feel awfully bad to see 23 years of sweat and tears fall apart in two and one-half years." The products which Mick's firm produces were hit by bad luck and hard economic times. The recession had caused a substantial decline in demand for New Age Textiles, and imports from the Far East flooded the market at prices below Mick's production cost.

"We knew we could shift into production of other products if we had the time," says Mick. "We owe our suppliers $300,000 and it doesn't look like we can pull that much cash together."

William Clark, a local banker, felt that Mick's company was basically sound if it could make the transition to the new products. Clark approached each of the three suppliers to see if some type of agreement could be reached.

Questions

1. What are Mick's options under bankruptcy law?

2. Mick decides he has to file for bankruptcy. Recommend which form of bankruptcy he should file under, explain what that form entails, and what the pros and cons are of that form of bankruptcy.